Tropical Plant Types

Tropical Plant Types

by

B. G. M. JAMIESON, B.Sc., Ph.D (Bristol)
University of Queensland, Australia

and

J. F. REYNOLDS, M.A. (Oxon)
Tabora School, Tanzania

PERGAMON PRESS

OXFORD · LONDON · EDINBURGH · NEW YORK
TORONTO · SYDNEY · PARIS · BRAUNSCHWEIG

PERGAMON PRESS LTD.,
Headington Hill Hall, Oxford
4 & 5 Fitzroy Square, London W.1
PERGAMON PRESS (SCOTLAND) LTD.,
2 & 3 Teviot Place, Edinburgh 1
PERGAMON PRESS INC.,
44–01 21st Street, Long Island City, New York 11101
PERGAMON OF CANADA, LTD.,
6 Adelaide Street East, Toronto, Ontario
PERGAMON PRESS (AUST.) PTY. LTD.,
20–22 Margaret Street, Sydney, New South Wales
PERGAMON PRESS S.A.R.L.,
24 rue des Écoles, Paris 5e
VIEWEG & SOHN GmbH,
Burgplatz 1, Braunschweig

Copyright © 1967 Pergamon Press Ltd.
First edition 1967
Library of Congress Catalog Card No. 66–30348

Printed in Great Britain by Dawson & Goodall Ltd., The Mendip Press, Parsonage Lane, Bath, Somerset.

(3060/67)

Contents

1399721

Preface

THE lack of advanced level biology textbooks using tropical animal and plant types as examples has necessitated the use in tropical schools and colleges of textbooks designed for temperate regions, with the result that the student's knowledge of the types described is usually "second hand" and local types tend to be ignored. This book of plant types, ranging from Bacteria to Flowering Plants, was written in the hope of providing a partial remedy to this situation. It is intended for use in conjunction with such texts prior to the publication of the remaining sections of a tropical biology.

Care has been taken to provide, as far as practicable, examples which occur throughout the tropics. Alternatively, an attempt is made to give sufficient examples to enable students in most parts of the tropics to obtain information on locally available types. Non-tropical types are included only where their omission would lessen the usefulness of the book or where corresponding tropical types are too diverse for adequate coverage, and exotic types are readily accessible from biological supply houses.

The book is intended for pupils in the final 2 years of their secondary education, and for first-year university students in tropical countries, but will also be of use in the sub-tropics. It is particularly designed to meet the requirements of the Cambridge Overseas Advanced Level Biology Examination, to which both authors have taught in Africa for many years, and equivalent local examinations.

It is a great pleasure to acknowledge our debt to our artist, Miss P. Fawcett, for her incomparable illustrations. Miss V. Jackman, Mr. V. S. Ratnakumar and Miss M. Grierson are also thanked for providing illustrations. Miss Grierson has rendered invaluable aid by making available material in the collections of the Royal Botanic Gardens, Kew, with the kind permission of the Director, Sir George Taylor. Special thanks are due to Mr. K. Vanamala Naidu and Mr. Ratnakumar for freely devoting a great deal of their time to preparation of species lists and illustrations of Indian material; and to Professor G. K. Berrie, University of Lagos, for his helpful comments on the manuscript. We wish also to acknowledge permission to redraw or reproduce illustrations from the following sources: James, *Plant Physiology*, Oxford; Irvine, *West African Botany*, Oxford; Smith, *Cryptogamic Botany*, McGraw-Hill Book Co.; McLean & Cook, *Textbook of Theoretical Botany*, Longmans, Green & Co. Ltd.; and Brown, *The Plant Kingdom*, Ginn & Co. (Blaisdell Publishing Co.).

Lastly, we thank our publishers for the consideration they have shown us.

We hope that readers will send in suggestions for improvement of the book so that it may be made more useful for the students for whom it is intended.

CHAPTER 1

Bacteria and Viruses

THE simpler plants are unicellular or consist of a thallus. A thallus is a relatively undifferentiated multicellular body with no vascular system and therefore no true stem, roots or leaves. They were once placed in the phylum Thallophyta. This included the Algae, Fungi, Lichens, Bacteria and, in some schemes, the Viruses. That this grouping was a natural one, that is, one which contained only relatively closely related forms, has for a long time been doubted. Advances in knowledge of the physiology of these organisms and of their structure under the electron microscope have led to new schemes of classification. In one scheme living organisms are divided into those which lack cellular organization, i.e. the viruses, and those with cellular organization. The latter are divided into: (1) procaryotic forms, in which there is no nuclear membrane and organelles bounded by membranes, such as mitochondria and chloroplasts, are absent, i.e. bacteria and blue–green algae (Cyanophyta); and (2) eucaryotic forms, in which there is a true nucleus and membrane-bound organelles occur; this group consists of the remaining animals and plants, including fungi.

On the basis of this scheme and other considerations some workers have gone so far as to recognize five kingdoms of living organisms: Viruses, Bacteria, Fungi, Plants and Animals, in place of the plant and animal kingdoms into which living organisms are conventionally divided.

The five kingdoms are recognized because their peculiar characters suggest that they have originated independently from the first living organisms which, it is now considered, were probably heterotrophic (see p. 32).

That these groups are so distinct is questioned by many authorities, however. Some hold that the fungi and algae are closely related, the most common view being that the algae are ancestral; some bacteria appear to be related to blue–green algae which are retained in the plant kingdom and others to protozoa; and the view that viruses are virtually isolated genes of organisms which have degenerated to the extent of losing their cytoplasm has some followers. Lichens are compound organisms, consisting of algal and fungal components in symbiosis and were formerly included in the Thallophyta as a separate class. The alga can usually exist independently of the fungus but the latter cannot live without its algal partner. Lichens are, therefore, to be regarded as examples of mutualism and not as a valid taxonomic grouping; they are classified according to their fungal component which belongs to one or other of two great divisions of the fungi (p. 78).

Nutrition

Nutrition involves obtaining three main commodities: energy for the characteristic activities of the organism; carbon, whose properties have been exploited by, and are essential for, life as we know it; and nitrogen, which is an essential constituent of proteins upon which the structure and reactions of protoplasm depend.

Two main and several subsidiary classes of organisms are recognized according to the way in which they obtain these commodities. The two main classes are known as autotrophes and heterotrophes. These are sometimes defined merely in relation to their energy sources so that any organism deriving its energy from inorganic sources, such as sunlight, is termed an autotrophe. The terms are better defined with relation to all three of the commodities mentioned above, however.

Autotrophes

An autotrophe is *an organism which can live without an external supply of organic substances, being capable of both derivation of energy, and the syntheses characteristic of its metabolism, from inorganic sources.*

Heterotrophes

Heterotrophes are *organisms which cannot base their syntheses solely on inorganic substances and almost always derive their energy from organic, already elaborated, sources.*

As inferred at the end of the last sentence, a very few organisms which are heterotrophes, in that they require some organic food materials, resemble autotrophes, in being able to utilize inorganic energy sources. These constitute borderline cases between autotrophes and heterotrophes, as so often occur between man-made classes. Examples are some euglenas which derive their energy from sunlight and their organic carbon from carbon dioxide (i.e. can photosynthesize) but rely on amino acids or more complex nitrogenous compounds for their nitrogen supply; and probably *Chilomonas*, a flagellate protozoon, which is discussed below. (See also the bacteria *Chlorobium* and *Chromatium*, below.)

Types of Autotrophes

Autotrophes which use the energy of light are termed photoautotrophes while others which use the energy released by inorganic reactions are termed chemoautotrophes.

Photoautotrophes

All of these fix the energy of light by means of a pigment, of which the chief is chlorophyll, and use this energy to bring about the chemical reduction of carbon dioxide to produce, ultimately, carbohydrates, the bonds of which store the energy for when it is needed. This process is termed photosynthesis. The most important examples are the higher green plants. In these the pigment is chlorophyll, with other constituents, and the nitrogen source is nitrate or possibly ammonia and nitrite. Inorganic salts are taken up in solution and no external organic substances are required. This type of photoautotrophic nutrition is known as holophytic nutrition.

Photoautotrophic bacteria carry out photosynthesis with specialized bacterial pigments. For instance, the sulphur bacteria, *Chromatium* and *Chlorobium*, photosynthesize by means of a green chlorophyll-like pigment. *Chlorobium* is green but *Chromatium* is rendered purple by the presence, in addition to its chlorophyll, of a red pigment. They obtain hydrogen for reduction of carbon dioxide (the carbon source) not from water but from hydrogen sulphide:

$$n\,CO_2 + 2n\,H_2S + \text{light energy} \rightarrow n\,(CH_2O) + n\,H_2O + 2n\,S$$
$$\text{(carbohydrate)}$$

Under some conditions the oxidation proceeds as far as sulphate. Neither uses molecular oxygen (O_2) in respiration. Such respiration is termed anaerobic respiration. Some normally anaerobic organisms are capable of an alternative type of respiration, termed aerobic respiration, in which free, molecular oxygen is used. Such an organism is referred to as a facultative anaerobe. *Chlorobium* and *Chromatium* are not capable of using molecular oxygen and are therefore termed obligate anaerobes.

Both genera are important in reducing the amount of sulphides, the chief causes of pollution, in natural waters. When the bacteria are unusually abundant they cause a conspicuous green or red coloration of water and are sometimes responsible for "red seas". A further interesting feature of their biology is that they are capable of using organic substances, and in fact grow better if these are supplied. As they have an alternative to their normally autotrophic nutrition, they are said to be facultative autotrophes.

These coloured sulphur bacteria are thus intermediate between bacteria and green plants in possessing photosynthetic pigments which are similar to those of the latter and also represent a "half-way house" between autotrophes and heterotrophes.

Chemoautotrophes

Chemoautotrophes derive their energy from inorganic oxidations. They are limited to bacteria and perhaps a few protozoa. They get their carbon from carbon dioxide and their nitrogen usually from ammonia. The energy which they obtain from inorganic reactions is, like that derived from light by photoautotrophes, used to bring about the reduction of carbon dioxide.

Examples of chemoautotrophes are:

The sulphur bacterium Beggiatoa. This is an unusually large bacterium, from $50\,\mu$ to 1 cm long, which oxidizes sulphides aerobically in two stages, first to sulphur and then to sulphate. As long as sulphide is available, the cell contains globules of free sulphur but, if the supply fails, energy is obtained by oxidizing the sulphur to sulphate, considerable quantities of sulphuric acid being formed. Taking, as an example, the oxidation of sodium sulphide, the reaction is:

$$2Na_2S + O_2 + 2H_2O \rightarrow 2S + 4NaOH + \text{energy}$$

The hydroxide, in combination with carbon dioxide, which is always present, gives a mixture of carbonate and bicarbonate.

The sulphur bacteria of the genus Thiobacillus. The thiobacilli are obligate anaerobes with the exception of *Thiobacillus denitrificans*. This obtains the energy for its vital activities by oxidizing sulphur or one of its derivatives, the oxygen used being either molecular (aerobic respiration) or combined (anaerobic respiration). The combined oxygen which is used is that located in nitrate molecules which the bacterium therefore reduces. Taking thiosulphate as a starting point, the reaction would be:

$$5\ Na_2S_2O_3 + 8KNO_3 + 2NaHCO_3 \rightarrow 6Na_2SO_4 + 4K_2SO_4 + 4N_2$$

| Sodium thiosulphate | Potassium nitrate | Sodium bicarbonate | Sodium sulphate | Potassium sulphate |

$$+ 2Co_2 + H_2O + energy$$

Note that it is a denitrifying bacterium, doing the dis-service of converting available nitrogen of nitrate to molecular nitrogen, which very few organisms can utilize.

Thiobacillus thio-oxidans is, again, an obligate chemoautotrophe which derives its energy from the oxidation of sulphur or its derivatives. This oxidation is always aerobic. Taking sulphur as a starting point:

$$2S + 3O_2 + 2H_2O \rightarrow 2H_2SO_4 + energy$$

The remarkable bacterium *Th. thiocyanoxidans* grows on thiocyanates. Given these and aerated water and certain trace elements this microbe can synthesize all its cellular requirements.

The participation of sulphur bacteria in the "sulphur cycle" is discussed on p. 22.

The nitrifying bacteria Nitrosomonas *and* Nitrobacter. These useful bacteria obtain their energy by oxidation of ammonium (carbonate) to nitrite (*Nitrosomonas*) and nitrite to nitrate (*Nitrobacter*).

$$\textit{Nitrosomonas: } NH_3 + 3O \rightarrow HNO_2 + H_2O + energy$$

$$\textit{Nitrobacter: } HNO_2 + O \rightarrow HNO_3 + energy$$

The efficiency of energy utilization by *Nitrosomonas* has been investigated experimentally. It has been found that for every gram of carbon assimilated as carbohydrate, 35 g of nitrogen are oxidized. Oxidation of 35 g of nitrogen releases 166 cal of energy but only 9·85 cal are needed to convert 1 g of carbon of carbon dioxide to carbohydrate. Thus 9·85/166, or about 6% of the calories released, are actually used in synthesis. It has been shown experimentally that heat production accounts for the other 94% of released energy.

The iron bacterium Hydrogenomonas. The activities of this chemo-autotrophe are inimical to man's interests. It oxidizes ferrous compounds to ferric compounds:

$$4FeCO_3 + 6H_2O + O_2 \rightarrow 4Fe(OH)_3 + 4CO_2 + energy$$

Reactions such as this taking place inside water-pipes can cause considerable trouble by clogging the pipes and causing discoloration of the water. Bad tastes and smells also result from the decomposition of the dead bacteria after a population "crash".

The methane bacterium Methanosomonas. This bacterium oxidizes methane to obtain energy for the incorporation of carbon dioxide into organic compounds:

$$CH_4 + 2O_2 \rightarrow CO_2 + 2H_2O + energy$$

Because methane is an organic compound, *Methanosomonas* is often regarded as being on the borderline between autotrophes and heterotrophes, but as methane probably existed in the primaeval atmosphere, and was not, presumably, derived from living organisms, it is legitimate to consider *Methanosomonas* to be a chemoautotrophe.

The flagellate protozoon Chilomonas paramecium. *Chilomonas* is a colourless flagellate which is said to be able to live in the dark in a medium of magnesium sulphate, ammonium chloride, potassium acid phosphate and sodium acetate, deriving its carbon solely from carbon dioxide. It obtains its energy by oxidation of the acetate:

$$CH_3COOH + 2O_2 \rightarrow 2CO_2 + 2H_2O + energy$$

The acetate is, of course, organic and the animal is therefore a heterotrophe, but it is said that acetate can be excluded if silica is present as a catalyst. The experimental techniques used were, however, dubious and the vitamin thiamine is needed for optimum growth.

Types of Heterotrophes
Saprozoic and saprophytic organisms

Saprophagous animals (such as *Astasia*) and saprophytes (colourless plants such as *Psalliota*, the mushroom and many bacteria) typically obtain their energy, carbon and nitrogen from external liquid organic substances which are absorbed, with or without predigestion and mobilization by the organism, through the integument. However, both the energy and carbon sources can be inorganic as in some euglenas. The essential feature of this type of nutrition is that some elaborated, organic materials are required and that these are taken up by absorption through the integument. Heterotrophic bacteria are discussed on p. 12.

Parasites

Parasitism is an intimate association between individuals of two species which results in one, called the parasite, living at the expense of the other, the host. It should be noted that those parasites which take up their food by absorption through the integument, e.g. *Plasmodium*, *Trypanosoma* and *Taenia*, are saprozoic organisms whose habitat is the interior of other organisms, although the term saprozoic is not usually applied to them.

Holozoic organisms

Holozoic organisms (all free-living vertebrates and most other animals) obtain their energy, carbon and nitrogen from external organic substances which they take into a mouth or food vacuole. Usually, at least some of the food is in solid form. Taking food into a mouth or food vacuole is termed ingestion and is peculiar to this group. They require varying amounts of accessory factors called vitamins.

BACTERIA

The bacteria are a group of extremely small organisms which, for convenience, are usually regarded as plants. There is no particular reason for regarding the group as monophyletic (i.e. of a single origin); some bacteria (e.g. *Treponema pallidum*, the causative agent of syphilis) are not sharply distinct from the protozoa, while others have obvious affinities with the Cyanophyta (blue–green algae).

Anthony van Leeuwenhoek, an amateur Dutch scientist of the seventeenth century, was the first person to see bacteria though he considered them to be small animals ("animalcules"); by 1683 he had described and figured the three main morphological groups of bacteria. Little further progress was made until the studies of Pasteur and Kock nearly 200 years later; since then progress has been continuous, and a vast amount of knowledge of this important group has accumulated.

Size and form

Bacteria appear as little more than specks in the field of view even under the highest powers of the light microscope. *Escherichia coli,* a common inhabitant of the human intestines, measures 2·0 × 0·5 μ while many species are considerably smaller than this. One consequence of this small size is that bacteria are subject to surface forces which keep them constantly in motion. Such passive motion is termed Brownian movement and is characteristic also of the dispersed particles of a substance in the colloidal state and of other small particles. Another effect of their small size is that the ratio of surface area to volume (or weight) is very large so that the area of contact between a bacterium and its surroundings is relatively great.

Most bacteria have a characteristic shape (Fig. 1.) that may be that of a straight rod (bacillus), a curved rod (spirillum), or a sphere (coccus). These descriptive names are often incorporated into the scientific names of bacterial species. A few bacteria have a filamentous form.

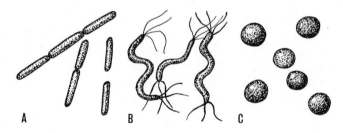

A   B   C

FIG. 1. Types of bacteria. A, bacilli. B, Spirillum. C, cocci.

Structure

The small size of bacteria makes the study of bacterial structure very difficult as many structural features are at, or beyond, the limit of resolution of the light microscope. For this reason most of the observations on bacterial structure have been interpreted by analogy with the known structures of larger plant and animal cells; more recent studies using the electron microscope and other techniques indicate that, by and large, this approach has been a valid one.

Bacteria are essentially unicellular (or non-cellular) organisms; sometimes the individuals cells form chains or clusters. Chemically the protoplasm of bacteria seems to have much the same composition as that of other organisms. It is generally agreed that the cytoplasm is bounded by a membrane which, by analogy with other cells, is thought to consist of lipoprotein. Exterior to the membrane is a thin but fairly rigid cell wall which in many species appears to contain cellulose or hemicellulose and possibly chitin. Typically the cell wall is surrounded by a slime layer composed of a polysaccharide gum such as galactan, levulan, or dextran. In some bacteria the slime layer is conspicuous and is then called a capsule. Capsules are particularly characteristic of pathogenic bacteria.

The large amount of work that has been devoted to establishing the nature of the nucleus in bacterial cells has produced no convincing demonstration of a definite nucleus separated from the cytoplasm by a nuclear membrane. DNA is certainly present and has been shown to be located on simple rod-like chromosomes which are said to form the nuclear apparatus or "nuclear equivalent" (Fig. 2).

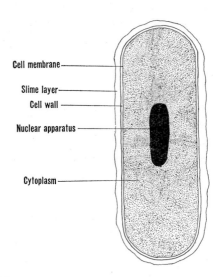

Cell membrane

Slime layer
Cell wall

Nuclear apparatus

Cytoplasm

FIG. 2. Diagram to show the structure of a generalized bacterium.

The only other organelles that are certainly known to occur in bacteria are flagella. These are found in all the curved bacteria and in many of the bacilli but are absent from most cocci. Flagella may be several times longer than the cell from which they originate. They appear to arise in the peripheral cytoplasm, passing to the exterior through the membrane, cell wall and slime layer.

Reproduction

Reproduction in bacteria is entirely by asexual binary fission. As far as can be seen the membrane grows inwards from all sides, gradually dividing the cell into two halves. When the ingrowing edges of the membrane meet, the new dividing membrane splits, allowing the two daughter cells to separate and complete the process by forming a new cell wall on the outer surface of the split membrane. Under favourable conditions fission may take place once every 20 or 30 min. It is obvious that if a few bacteria reach a suitable medium very large numbers can be produced in a short time. After a time, however, the cells cease dividing and the majority die. This population "crash" is thought to be brought about mainly by an accumulation of toxic excretory products and also by exhaustion of the food supplies.

Some workers claim to have seen mitosis during fission, but this is not accepted by the majority of workers. This is not surprising in view of the controversial nature of the bacterial nucleus, though on theoretical grounds it would seem likely that there is some process for duplicating the genetical material prior to fission.

Conjugation

While there is no evidence for any kind of sexual reproduction there is now abundant evidence that a type of conjugation takes place that results in an exchange of genes between conjugants. The frequency of such exchanges under natural conditions is not known.

Spores

Most bacilli, but few cocci or spirilla, have the ability to produce highly resistant resting bodies called endospores or, for the sake of brevity, spores. Spore formation usually takes place when food supplies have been exhausted or when other environmental factors are unsuitable. Each cell forms one spore only, so that spore formation is not a method of asexual reproduction as in many fungi. Spores appear denser than the normal vegetative cells and also differ from the latter in a number of chemical features. They contain less potassium and phosphorus but more nucleoproteins, lipoids, calcium and manganese than the vegetative cells; the significance of these differences is not clear. The spore wall has two layers known as intine and exine.

Spores can remain dormant, but viable, for many years (in some cases forty or more years) and can also withstand many environmental influences that rapidly kill vegetative cells. When spores land on a suitable medium they rapidly germinate to produce vegetative cells.

The Physiology of Bacteria

Many groups of animals or plants are of interest on account of the adaptive variations that they show on a certain basic structural plan. In such cases the basic plan affords the necessary criteria for a definition of a major classificatory group such as a phylum, while the modifications on this plan afford means of distinguishing other categories such as classes, orders and so on. Bacteria are of interest, not on account of their structural diversity, but on account of the great variety of biochemical reactions that they can bring about. It is necessary, therefore, to include a discussion of their physiology in the present account. This versatility means, of course, that bacteria have an extremely varied "armament" of enzyme systems. As knowledge of these systems grows it is increasingly used in the classification of bacteria; this, however, is a topic that is beyond the scope of the present work.

The most striking difference between the general physiology of bacteria and that of higher organisms lies in the remarkable ability of bacteria to use "unlikely" materials as substrates for the provision of energy. Nevertheless, in many, perhaps in all, bacteria the energy released by the aerobic or anaerobic breakdown of these substrates appears in the high-energy phosphate bonds of adenosine triphosphate ATP, as in most higher organisms.

In addition to obtaining energy from materials not usable by higher organisms bacteria can synthesize their own organic components from a much wider variety of substances than can higher plants. Some bacteria are completely autotrophic (i.e. are able to make all their organic compounds from simple inorganic materials) but the majority are heterotrophic to a greater or lesser extent. The distinction between the two groups is not quite so sharp as might be thought, as some heterotrophic bacteria require only minute traces of preformed organic material in order to thrive. Since most bacteria are heterotrophic but cannot ingest food it follows that most are either saprophytic or parasitic. Saprophytic bacteria are vitally important in the economy of nature as they are largely responsible for maintaining a flow of nutrients essential for the growth of higher plants by decomposing the complex organic materials of dead organisms into simpler materials. Parasitic bacteria are responsible for a great number of diseases; to many people the term bacteria is synonomous with "disease-producing organisms". Such people see only one facet of bacterial action, forgetting that without saprophytic bacteria life, as we know it, could not continue to exist.

At this point it should perhaps be emphasized that while bacteria as a group have these extraordinarily diverse biochemical abilities, any one bacterium is limited to a certain number. Thus the distribution of a particular bacterium might be limited by the availability of a certain chemical in its surroundings in much the same way that an insect's distribution is limited by the availability of food plants suitable for its larvae.

Illustrations of the biochemical abilities of bacteria will now be given by describing some of the activities of various autotrophic and heterotrophic bacteria.

Autotrophic bacteria

Autotrophic bacteria have been discussed above and are also dealt with under the nitrogen and sulphur cycles in the present chapter. It will suffice here to remind the student that they are divisible into two groups: those which obtain their energy from the oxidation of inorganic compounds, the chemosynthetic autotrophes (chemoautotrophes) and those which possess chlorophyll-like pigments which enable them to transform radiant solar energy into chemical energy in an analogous manner to that which occurs in the photosynthesis of higher plants, the photosynthetic autotrophes (photo autotrophes).

Examples of chemoautotrophic bacteria are the nitrifying bacteria *Nitrosomonas*, *Nitrosococcus* and *Nitrobacter* (p. 5); the sulphur bacterium *Thiobacillus* (p. 4); the iron bacterium *Hydrogenomonas* and the methane bacterium *Methanosomonas* (p. 6).

Photoautotrophic bacteria are exemplified by *Chloratium* and *Chlorobium* (p. 3). As far as is known, all photoautotrophes are anaerobic.

Heterotrophic bacteria

The nutritional requirements of heterotrophic bacteria are so varied that few worthwhile generalizations can be made. Nevertheless, three main groups of heterotrophes can be recognized on the basis of their physiological requirements. These groups are:

(a) Non-exacting chemosynthetic heterotrophes. These derive their carbon from organic sources and their nitrogen from inorganic sources, usually ammonia.

(b) Semi-exacting chemosynthetic heterotrophes. These derive their carbon from organic sources and are unable to assimilate all their nitrogen from inorganic sources—a few specific amino acids being needed.

(c) Exacting heterotrophes. Carbon is assimilated from organic sources as in the two previous groups. Several different amino acids have to be present in addition to a number of vitamins. Most parasitic bacteria belong to this group.

As has already been mentioned, bacteria are able to utilize a wide variety of substrates for the provision of energy; furthermore, many different pathways exist for the degradation of complex molecules into simpler ones with consequent liberation of energy. It seems likely that the majority of heterotrophic bacteria are aerobic and that a fair number of these maintain their supplies of ATP by metabolic pathways very similar to, if not identical with those of higher plant and animal tissues. Many bacteria are facultative anaerobes and a few are obligate anaerobes. It is among these that the methods of degradation are so varied that different bacteria starting with the same substrate may produce very different end products. For no bacterium are the end products absolutely fixed as these are affected by many factors including concentration of substrate, pH, temperature, and oxygen concentration. Breakdowns that take place under anaerobic conditions are usually called fermentations in microbiology, this term is also applied to aerobic breakdowns that do not proceed to completion. For example, *Acetobacter* (an organism responsible for the spoilage of wines) uses oxygen to convert ethyl alcohol to acetic acid (vinegar), but, as the process does not result in the complete oxidation of the alcohol to carbon dioxide and water, it is called a fermentation.

Sugars of one sort or another are the commonest starting points for most bacterial fermentations. As already indicated, the fermentation products depend not only on the organism but on various environmental factors. The commonest fermentation products resulting from the breakdown of sugars by bacteria are: acetic acid, acetone, acetylmethyl-carbinol, butyric acid, carbon dioxide, hydrogen, formic acid, methane, lactic acid, propionic acid, pyruvic acid, succinic acid, ethyl alcohol, propyl alcohol, isopropyl alcohol, and butyl alcohol. Consideration of the metabolic pathways by which these products are formed is beyond the scope of this work except to point out that the formation of such products as pyruvic acid, lactic acid, and ethyl alcohol seems to involve the same enzyme systems as in higher organisms. The important point to remember about bacteria is that they possess many enzyme systems not possessed by higher organisms.

Although comparatively few bacteria can ferment unchanged proteins, the dead bodies of animals provide an excellent environment for many bacteria, as proteolytic enzymes released from the lyosomes of the dead cells convert many of the dead animal's proteins to polypeptides that can be utilized by these bacteria. Peptones, in particular, can be absorbed. Once absorbed the peptones undergo complete hydrolysis into amino acids the greater part of which are fermented to release energy. Since many of the known fermentation pathways for amino acids produce extremely unpleasant smelling compounds, protein fermentation is usually called putrefaction. Characteristic of such compounds are the amines, produced by decarboxylation under anaerobic conditions, e.g.

$$CH_2NH_2COOH \rightarrow CH_3NH_2 + CO_2$$
$$\text{Glycine} \qquad \text{Methylamine}$$

The higher amines, called ptomaines, are toxic substances that can prove fatal if introduced into the blood stream. This can happen during dissection of a decaying body if the dissector accidentally cuts himself or has scratches on his hands.

Bacteria and the Circulation of Elements

Bacteria play an indispensable part in the circulation of chemical elements in nature and without their activity the earth would cease to support the higher forms of life. It is therefore desirable to discuss the carbon, nitrogen and sulphur cycles here. First, however, a little must be said about the breakdown of dead plant and animal materials to yield humus, which is an essential step in the recirculation of these elements.

The elementary student tends to think of soil as lifeless except for a few annelids and other easily seen invertebrates. In fact the soil is teeming with microscopic organisms—bacteria, protozoa, algae, nematodes, etc. The abundance of these organisms is best indicated, not by counts (e.g. 5000 million bacteria per gram of soil), but by estimates of total weight; thus, some soils have been estimated to contain over 4 tons of bacteria per acre. When the other organisms are also included, estimates of 8–10 tons of living matter per acre are obtained.

Formation of humus

The cellulose of dead plants is broken down into simpler carbohydrates by extracellular cellulases secreted by fungi and some bacteria, e.g. *Cytophaga*. The sugars produced by these hydrolyses provide nourishment for a great number of bacteria whose respiratory metabolism gradually restores the carbon of the cellulose to the atmosphere as carbon dioxide. Pectins, lignins and waxes are slowly decomposed and gradually accumulate as the brownish-black complex known as humus. It is difficult to overemphasize the importance of humus in soil fertility as it not only provides a medium from which nutrients are slowly released, but also improves the physical condition of the soil, especially its crumb-structure and water holding capacity. A soil rich in humus is far more resistant to soil erosion than one poor in humus. It is unfortunate that several common human practices, e.g. the starting of bush fires at the start of the dry season in tropical countries, destroy humus and make the soil very liable to erosion.

The carbon cycle

It was shown on p. 2 that nutrition involves the acquisition, amongst other things of three all-important commodities, carbon, nitrogen and energy. The initial source of the carbon of living organisms is molecular carbon dioxide, in the atmosphere or dissolved in natural waters, which is photosynthetically or chemosynthetically fixed by autotrophic organisms. Removal of carbon dioxide from the source is counteracted by its return to the atmosphere by processes which are discussed below. These opposing processes represent a circulation of carbon which is conveniently termed the carbon cycle. This is diagrammatically summarized in Fig. 3.

The concentration of carbon dioxide in the atmosphere of the primaeval earth was probably many times the 0.03 per cent which it at present represents. The primary, igneous, rocks were composed mainly of silicates of basic elements, an example of them being Feldspar, $K_2O,Al_2O_3,6SiO_2$; carbon-containing rocks would have been rare. As the igneous rocks cooled, carbon dioxide and water in the atmosphere would have decomposed these silicates with the formation of quartz, aluminosilicates (clay) and alkali carbonates and bicarbonates, a process which is still occurring. As carbonates of sodium and potassium and all bicarbonates are soluble, some of them would have been dissolved in rainwater and carried to the sea. Carbonic acid formed by solution of carbon dioxide in rainwater is also constantly converting insoluble carbonates, including magnesium and calcium carbonates, to soluble bicarbonates. A large proportion of the calcium and magnesium bicarbonates were utilized by shell-forming animals, including forms similar to the present day foraminiferan protozoon *Globigerina*, which converted the bicarbonates to carbonates thus releasing half the carbon as carbon dioxide. On the death of these shelled animals, some of the carbonates would have been converted to soluble bicarbonates again, but much remained fixed in the shells which participated, as fossils, in production of the sedimentary rocks of the world, often after great alteration. Even today, vast areas of the ocean floor are being covered by a deep "ooze" composed of the shells of dead Foraminifera. It has been estimated that the carbon dioxide contained in rocks is 30,000 times that in the atmosphere.

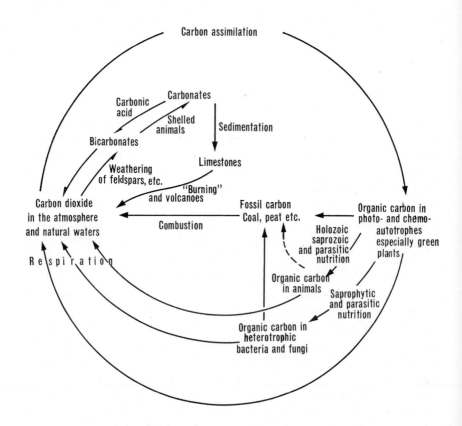

FIG. 3. The carbon cycle.

Another process removing carbon dioxide from circulation, at least for long periods, is the formation of "fossil fuels" such as coal, peat and petroleum, and the incorporation of organic matter in the earth's crust in other ways, which have occurred where decomposition of dead organisms is incomplete.

The carbon fixed by autotrophes, of which the chief are green plants, passes to organisms which feed on these, i.e. holozoic and parasitic animals and parasitic (pathogenic) bacteria and fungi, or to animals which feed on their dead remains, i.e. saprozoic animals and saprophytic plants. All these organisms restore carbon dioxide to its free form by respiration. Bacterial decay of organic matter, which releases carbon dioxide, is, of course, part of the respiratory processes of the bacteria concerned. Other natural processes which add carbon dioxide to the atmosphere are volcanic activity and the decomposition of carbonic acid and bicarbonates in natural waters. The sea acts as a "buffer" which prevents sudden fluctuations in the concentration of atmospheric carbon dioxide.

If these natural processes alone were at work, it is probable that the removal of carbon dioxide as sedimentary rocks and fossil organic carbon would ultimately exhaust the free carbon dioxide in the soil, in natural waters and in the atmosphere. Nevertheless, there is evidence that at present the concentration of carbon dioxide in the atmosphere is gradually increasing and this increase seems to be due to human activities: the burning of limestones to produce quicklime, with release of carbon dioxide, and the combustion of fossil fuels, particularly coal and petroleum. The burning off of vast areas of "bush" must, alone, contribute enormous quantities of carbon dioxide to the atmosphere, but this (like the combustion of any newly produced organic matter) can have only a very short-term effect as regrowth of the plants reverses the process.

The nitrogen cycle

We have seen that most of the nitrogen which is taken up from the soil by green plants is absorbed as nitrate, although absorption of nitrite and ammonia also occurs. These compounds constitute the "available nitrogen" source of the plant which is incorporated in amino compounds, particularly proteins, in the plant. Two pathways for replenishment of the soil nitrogen exist: firstly, the return of organic nitrogen of plants, and of animals feeding directly or indirectly on them, as a result of death and decay, and secondly, the conversion of atmospheric nitrogen to an available form. The production of soil nitrate from organic nitrogen involves two processes: ammonification in which ammonia is formed by bacteria of decay from proteins and other organic nitrogenous compounds, and nitrification, in which bacteria convert ammonia to nitrite and then nitrate. The conversion of atmospheric nitrogen to an available form is termed nitrogen fixation. This term covers the production of nitrate by the effect of lightning on nitrogen and oxygen in the atmosphere (electrical fixation) and the production of organic nitrogen from molecular nitrogen by nitrogen-fixing micro-organisms which is ultimately converted to nitrate by ammonifying and nitrifying bacteria. Acting against these agents, which increase available soil nitrogen, are denitrifying bacteria which convert nitrate to ammonia and nitrogen (inorganic denitrification) and putrefying bacteria which oxidize, i.e. decompose, organic nitrogen and release some molecular nitrogen (organic denitrification).

The transformation of nitrogen and its compounds which we have outlined contributes to a circulation of nitrogen, known as the nitrogen cycle of which a schematic representation is given in Fig. 4. We may now deal in greater detail with the stages in the cycle.

Ammonification. The decay of complex organic nitrogenous compounds is brought about by numerous species of bacteria, and by actinomycetes and filamentous fungi. It results in the formation of simpler nitrogen-containing compounds and ultimately of ammonia. The bacteria concerned in decay are termed putrefying bacteria. The end products of protein putrefaction depend to a large extent on the pH of the medium and also on the degree of aeration. Alkaline and neutral conditions favour reactions which release ammonia whilst amines are produced under more acid conditions. Where oxygen is present and the pH rises, *Pseudomonas* rapidly oxidizes amines to ammonia. Bacteria which produce ammonia are termed ammonifying bacteria. Several species of these are often collectively referred to as *Bacterium mycoides*. These bacteria are anaerobic saprophytes which derive their energy from the oxidative breakdown of organic compounds. If sugars are abundant relative to proteins, they do not release ammonia but instead take up soluble nitrogen compounds from the soil while oxidizing the sugars. If proteins are abundant, they utilize these both as an energy source and as a source of nitrogen and carbon. Their action on proteins produces ammonia in greater quantities than can be utilized and it is therefore liberated into the soil.

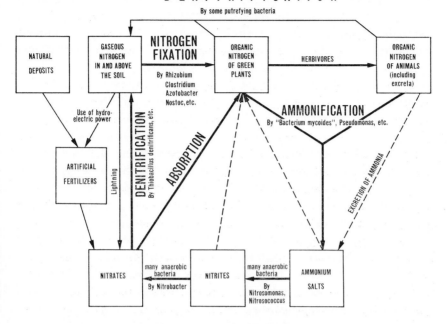

FIG. 4. The nitrogen cycle.

Nitrification. The nitrifying bacteria are aerobic chemosynthetic organisms deriving energy for carbon assimilation from the oxidation of inorganic nitrogen compounds. They include *Nitrosomonas* and *Nitrosococcus*, which oxidize ammonia to nitrite, and *Nitrobacter*, which oxidizes nitrite to nitrate (for equations and further information see p. 5). Nitrification is favoured by an alkaline pH, the absence of large amounts of carbohydrates in the soil, and good aeration. It is fortunate that the ammonia oxidizers and the nitrite oxidizers always occur together as otherwise nitrites, which are rather toxic, would accumulate in the soil.

Nitrogen fixation. Nitrogen fixation includes electrical fixation by lightning. The latter causes nitrogen to combine with oxygen to give nitric acid which enters the soil in rainwater. Some ammonia is formed in this manner by combination of nitrogen with traces of hydrogen in the upper atmosphere. At the Rothamsted Experimental Station in England measurements made over a period of 5 years showed that 4·4 lb of available nitrogen entered each acre of soil per year by these means.

This balanced loss of nitrogen by leaching. The amount of available nitrogen contributed to the soil by rainwater is, however, small compared with that fixed by soil micro-organisms. Nitrogen fixation is brought about by the free-living bacteria *Azotobacter* and *Clostridium* and by two types of organisms which live in symbiotic association with higher plants. The latter are species of bacteria of the genus *Rhizobium* which occur in nodules on the roots of leguminous plants, and certain fungi which live in the cortex of plant roots which are known as fungi of mycorrhiza. Recent research has cast doubt on the nitrogen-fixing abilities and symbiotic nature of mycorrhizal fungi, however. Some blue–green algae, including *Nostoc*, also fix nitrogen. Very little is known about the chemistry of nitrogen fixation but it has been suggested that the primary products are hydroxylamine and ammonia. It is likely that more than one mechanism exists as some nitrogen fixers are aerobic and others anaerobic.

Azotobacter is a genus of coccus-like, aerobic, saprophytic bacteria. *Azotobacter chroococcum*, and to a lesser extent *Azotobacter agilis*, are widely distributed in soil and water. They obtain carbon and energy for their syntheses by breaking down carbohydrates in the soil; they obtain nitrogen from the air, combining it with organic compounds. If nitrates are abundant, however, they absorb nitrogen in this form and nitrogen fixation ceases. *Azotobacter* is usually absent from soils more acid than pH 5 and flourishes best if there is ample humus and good aeration. Its nitrogen fixing activities are enhanced by the presence of other bacteria.

Clostridium is a genus of rod-shaped, anaerobic, saprophytic bacteria which also fixes atmospheric nitrogen while obtaining energy and carbon from breakdown of soil carbohydrates. When cultured in isolation from other organisms they fix nitrogen only in anaerobic conditions, but if certain other bacteria which utilize molecular oxygen are present (e.g. *Azotobacter*), they fix nitrogen aerobically, as is the case in the soil.

It has been estimated that saprophytic nitrogen-fixing bacteria add about 6 lb of combined nitrogen to each acre of soil in a year.

Rhizobium includes a number of species of rod-shaped symbiotic, heterotrophic bacteria each of which infects only certain species of leguminous plants. Some of them were once collectively known as *Bacillus radicicola*. In the soil, *Rhizobium* is usually found as a sphere or coccus which may develop cilia and move about. If it comes into contact with a root hair it multiplies, and the cell wall of the root hair is softened, thus allowing entry of the bacteria. They then penetrate the cortex until they reach the pericycle (p. 150) which they stimulate to proliferate.

This proliferation results in the formation of a warty protuberance or nodule which is externally visible. Many nodules are usually produced each of which houses many bacteria within its cells. In this situation the bacteria become transversely striped and often branch to become Y- or X-shaped. When the nodule forms, the vascular system of the host extends to surround the infected cells and an exchange of soluble materials is therefore possible between the host and the bacteria. *Rhizobium* utilizes host sugars as a source of energy and of carbon and combines molecular nitrogen from the soil atmosphere in organic compounds. Most of the organic nitrogen fixed by the bacteria passes from the nodules into the host tissues where it is used for protein synthesis. In the soya bean about 90% of the nitrogen is used by the host. The actual enrichment of the soil in nitrogen is less direct, however. It enters the soil by death of the host, by death of the nodules which occurs as old roots or the cortex of functioning roots die off, or by diffusion from the nodules into the soil. The former two are of greater importance than the latter. The total addition of nitrogen to the soil by symbiotic bacteria far exceeds that by saprophytic bacteria, and has been estimated at between 100 and 200 lb of nitrogen per acre per year, as an average. Nitrogen fixation by the symbionts is depressed if inorganic nitrogen compounds are abundant in the soil, but, even then, the amount fixed by the bacteria commonly exceeds that absorbed from the soil by the roots. It is somewhat surprising that *Rhizobium* has never been found to fix nitrogen when cultured outside the nodules, being, then, dependent on inorganic compounds for its nitrogen.

Denitrification of inorganic compounds. Many bacteria which are obligate and facultative anaerobes reduce nitrate to nitrite and ammonia but comparatively few liberate nitrogen or nitrous oxide from nitrate. Examples of the latter are *Micrococcus denitrificans*, *Psuedomonas aeruginosa* and *Thiobacillus denitrificans*. This denitrification does not usually occur in cultivated soils as these are kept well aerated. *Th. denitrificans* uses nitrate as a hydrogen acceptor in anaerobic conditions, thereby reducing the nitrate and releasing free nitrogen (p. 5).

Denitrification of organic compounds. Loss of combined nitrogen to the atmosphere as molecular nitrogen is also brought about by some decay bacteria which oxidize organic matter in the soil with the release of free nitrogen. Their denitrifying activity is favoured by poor aeration and is again of little importance in well cultivated soils.

Where animals and plants are allowed to decompose in the soil which supported them, the processes of nitrogen enrichment (ammonification, nitrification, and nitrogen fixation) balance the processes of nitrogen depletion, (denitrification, leaching) and the available nitrogen content of the soil remains roughly constant. Where, however, crops, wool, meat and other protein-containing products are removed from the land which produced them, a depletion of the available nitrogen occurs. To a certain extent this can be counteracted by control of natural processes, particularly by growing leguminous plants and ploughing them into the soil (an important part of many crop rotation cycles), but usually in agriculture it is necessary to fertilize the soil by bringing in natural manures or artificial fertilizers. Even natural soils in the tropics often require enrichment in available nitrogen because of excessive leaching, absence of the appropriate bacteria owing to high acidity, and other factors, before they will give a satisfactory yield of crops.

The sulphur cycle

Sulphur is an important constituent of many proteins in animals and plants. As an example, it is an indispensable constituent of three essential amino acids, methionine, cysteine and cystine. It is responsible for the toughness of keratinized tissues, including hair. It is constantly being transformed, mainly by the activities of living organisms, from inorganic to organic forms and such transformations result in a circulation of sulphur which may be termed the sulphur cycle. This is represented diagrammatically and in a much simplified form in Fig. 5.

Sulphur is taken up as sulphates by higher plants and most microorganisms and is incorporated by reductive processes in organic compounds, mainly sulphur-containing amino acids or their residues in proteins. Higher animals obtain their organic sulphur by feeding directly or indirectly on plants. This organic sulphur returns to an inorganic form, mainly sulphide, by the action of putrefying bacteria on the dead remains of organisms or on excrement. Some bacteria "short-circuit" this process by reducing sulphate to sulphide. These sulphate-reducing bacteria belong to an important but heterogeneous assemblage of sulphur bacteria, others of which oxidize sulphide to sulphur or sulphur to sulphate.

We may now deal briefly with the bacterially promoted stages in this cyclic process.

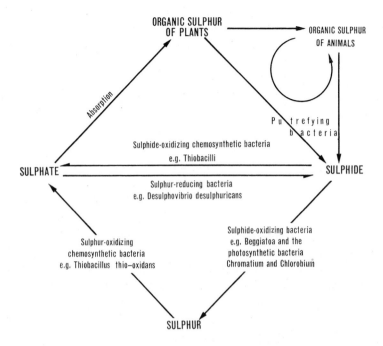

FIG. 5. The sulphur cycle.

Oxidation of sulphur to sulphates. A well known genus of bacteria which converts sulphur or its derivatives to sulphate is *Thiobacillus*. Its species are chemoautotrophes some of which have been discussed on p. 4.

Thiobacillus thio-oxidans is an immobile rod-like bacterium which is normally found in the vicinity of a sulphur granule. It can produce and survives normal, or stronger, solutions of sulphuric acid. This acid causes severe damage to stone buildings in industrial cities, where sulphur compounds are readily available in the atmosphere. Other thiobacilli oxidize sulphides, thiosulphates (p. 5), and polythionates.

Oxidation of sulphides to sulphur. Although several thiobacilli can oxidize sulphides to sulphur, they are intolerant of high concentrations of the former compounds. The chief sulphide-oxidizing organisms are certain colourless sulphur bacteria, including *Beggiatoa* and coloured ones, including *Chromatium* and *Chlorobium*. These three genera have been discussed on pp. 3 and 4.

Reduction of sulphate to sulphide. The most important agents bringing about reduction of sulphates to sulphides are the sulphate-reducing bacteria of which *Desulphovibrio desulphuricans* is a well known example. They are economically very important because they pollute natural waters by their production of sulphides, which are poisonous to most organisms. They are heterotrophic, living on decaying organic matter, and are obligate anaerobes, being intolerant of molecular oxygen. The conversion of sulphate to sulphide which they bring about provides the oxygen which they require for their respiration ($SO_4'' \rightarrow S'' + 4O$). Although anaerobic, they use cytochromes in respiration. The sulphides which they produce off the coast of West Africa periodically cause the death of such huge numbers of fish that the dead bodies of the latter are thrown up feet deep along miles of the coast and the hydrogen sulphide released into the atmosphere tarnishes metal and blackens paint in towns in the area.

Under some conditions *Desulphovibrio* shows autotrophic nutrition as it can derive respiratory energy from the oxidation of free hydrogen (with the oxygen from sulphates) instead of oxidizing organic compounds. It then obtains its carbon from carbonates. This type of respiration has serious economic implications because, by a mass action effect, it facilitates the rusting of iron which, crudely, is represented by the equation:

$$Fe + 2H_2O \rightarrow Fe(OH)_2 + \boxed{H_2 \text{ (Removed by } Desulphovibrio\text{)}}$$

On the credit side, sulphate-reducing bacteria were probably responsible for the formation of deposits of sulphur in Texas which provide over 90 per cent of the world's sulphur, an element without which industry could not survive. These deposits occupy the site of a former arm of the Mexican Gulf, the evaporating waters of which supplied the sulphates for oxidation by bacteria. Sulphate-reducing bacteria are also believed to have contributed to the formation of petroleum deposits.

Conversion of organic sulphur to inorganic sulphur. The sulphur in proteins and other organic substances in dead organisms is converted to inorganic sulphide by putrefying bacteria. The unpleasant smell of decaying organic matter is largely due to the release of these sulphides, notably the gaseous hydrogen sulphide. Bacteria of putrefaction are not sulphur bacteria in the strict sense as the production of sulphide by them is incidental to their normal metabolism.

The phosphorus cycle

Considerations of space do not permit a detailed discussion of the circulation of phosphorus. The following section is therefore restricted to a consideration of the role of bacteria in releasing soluble phosphates.

Although phosphorus is the twelfth most abundant element it is very unevenly distributed so that in many regions its low concentration acts as a limiting factor in plant growth. Since most mineral phosphates are insoluble it is clear that any bacterial activities that result in the formation of phosphate ions will be of great importance. The reactions involved are not specific and many different species of bacteria play a part in maintaining a circulation of "available" phosphorus. The phosphorus of organic compounds becomes available as a result of the wide variety of fermentations to which the compounds of dead plants and animals are subjected. Amongst the bacteria that are important in forming phosphate ions from mineral phosphates are the sulphur bacteria. The sulphuric acid that these bacteria produce by oxidizing sulphur reacts with mineral phosphates forming phosphoric acid (which ionizes to release phosphate ions) and the corresponding sulphate, e.g.

$$Ca_3(PO_4)_2 + 3H_2SO_4 \rightarrow 2H_3PO_4 + 3CaSO_4$$
$$\downarrow$$

Bacteria in Industry

Much of the early work on bacteria was devoted to isolating the species that cause diseases. While the disease-producing bacteria are still being intensively studied, more and more attention is being given to finding out how some bacterial activities can be used to benefit man. Industrial microbiology deals not only with bacteria but also with yeasts and moulds. Yeasts are used in the production of ethyl alcohol which, quite apart from its use in alcoholic drinks, is extensively used in industrial chemistry (e.g. 500 million gallons a year were used industrially in the U.S.A. during the Second World War); moulds, such as *Penicillium*, provide the antibiotics which have proved so valuable in the fight against bacterial diseases.

To use bacteria successfully in industry it is necessary to be able to identify the different species accurately, to maintain them in pure culture, and to know just how their activities are affected by changes in substrate concentration, oxygen concentration, pH, temperature and so on. Furthermore, the industrial bacteriologist is always searching for mutant strains with rather different fermentation properties than the parent strain that may be better adapted to perform the tasks desired.

The following examples illustrate some of the ways in which the known properties of bacteria have been exploited by man.

1. The dairy industry

Milk contains proteins, lactose, fats, vitamins, and salts. The first three ingredients provide suitable substrates for a number of different bacteria which are responsible for the changes that take place in milk that is allowed to stand at room temperature. Souring is caused by the so-called homofermentative bacteria (e.g. *Streptococcus lactis* and *Lactobacillus bulgaricus*) that ferment sugars to lactic acid. Eventually, enough lactic acid is produced to cause curdling.

In cheese making, curds are usually produced by the combined action of rennet (an extract of rennin and some pepsin obtained from calves' stomachs) and lactic acid bacteria. Hard cheeses (e.g. Cheddar, Cheshire, Edam and various Swiss cheeses) are prepared by separating the curds from the watery whey under pressure so that most of the free water is removed. The curd is then allowed to "ripen" for a period of between several months and 2 years, the exact time depending on the type of cheese being prepared. The final flavour and smell result from the products of bacterial action on the various food materials present in the curd. The methods employed in the making of Swiss cheeses result in a replacement of lactic acid bacteria by propionic acid bacteria (e.g. *Propionibacterium freudenreichii* and *P. shermanii*) which ferment lactose and lactic acid to produce acetic acid, propionic acid, and carbon dioxide. The latter product is responsible for the holes that are characteristic of this type of cheese. Soft cheeses (e.g. Camembert) are prepared by allowing the whey to drain off from the curd. During the fairly short ripening period conditions are adjusted to favour the growth of certain putrefactive bacteria whose products impart the flavours characteristic of this type of cheese.

Long before bacteria were discovered "rule of thumb" methods had been developed for making cheeses. Particularly in the dirtier dairies and farms, spoilage through the activities of undesirable bacteria and fungi was frequent. Modern cheese making starts with milk freed from bacteria by pasteurization and uses pure cultures under carefully controlled hygienic conditions to bring about the desired changes. With such methods spoilage is greatly reduced and there is far less risk of pathogens being transmitted.

Butter is manufactured by inoculating pasteurized cream with a mixture of *Streptococcus lactis*, *S. cremoris*, *Leuconostoc citrovorum*, and *L. dextranicum*. The streptococci produce lactic acid while the other species produce acetic acid, acetylmethylcarbinol, and diacetyl; the concentrations of these substances influence the taste of the butter. Once the cream has been soured it is churned, thereby separating out the butterfat which is washed and salted before being packed or tinned. The fairly high salt content (2·5 per cent) inhibits further bacterial growth so that butter usually "keeps" well.

2. *The retting of flax*

Flax, *Linum usitatissimum*, is a plant that is grown extensively in temperate and subtropical countries to obtain fibres from which linen, canvas, and similar fabrics are made; in addition, linseed oil is obtained from its seeds. The valuable fibres are those of the phloem (p. 145). The phloem fibres occur in groups and are held together and to surrounding tissues by pectic substances. The process of separating groups of phloem fibres from the other tissues is called retting. There are several methods of retting but the one that yields the most satisfactory fibres is to immerse the flax stems in water and allow the soil bacterium, *Clostridium butyricum*, to ferment the plant tissues, including the pectic substances that bind the cells together. It is important to stop the process when the pectin holding groups of fibres to other cells has been fermented but before the pectin holding individual fibres together has been attacked. In very few countries are pure cultures and controlled conditions employed in retting; the success of the primitive method depends on the commonness of *C. butyricum* in the soil, and the skill of the retters in deciding when to stop the process.

3. *The preparation of organic compounds*

A number of organic compounds are obtained more easily by the use of bacteria than by chemical methods. In contrast to retting, many of these processes involve the use of carefully standardized conditions, including the use of pure cultures.

(a) *Lactic acid.* Lactic acid is used in the preparation of plastics and of various pharmaceutical products. There are several species of lactic acid bacteria that can be used to ferment sugars to lactic acid. *Lactobacillus debruckii* is the one normally used since it is slightly thermophilic and can thus be used at temperatures that are inhibitory to most other bacteria. This means that far fewer precautions have to be taken to prevent contamination with other bacteria whose activities would produce unwanted fermentation products.

During fermentation calcium carbonate is added to the fermentation mixture to neutralize the acid which would otherwise inhibit further activity of the bacteria. When the fermentation is complete, the calcium lactate is crystallized out and treated with sulphuric acid when the calcium is precipitated as calcium sulphate. The remaining lactic acid can then be further purified by suitable chemical methods. Yields of lactic acid equivalent to 85–90 per cent of the sugar consumed are regularly obtained.

(b) *Butyl alcohol.* This alcohol is used in the manufacture of lacquers. It is obtained, together with acetone, various acids, carbon dioxide, hydrogen, and riboflavin, when starch or sugar are fermented by *Clostridium butylicum* and *C. acetobutylicum.* The fermentation is a particularly complex one and the greatest care has to be taken to maintain the appropriate conditions and to prevent contamination with other organisms.

(c) *Acetic acid (vinegar).* This is usually produced by allowing species of *Acetobacter* to grow on the surface of wine in large, partly filled casks. The ethyl alcohol of the wine is partly converted to acetic acid from which it is separated by distillation:

$$CH_3CH_2OH + O_2 \rightarrow CH_3COOH + H_2O$$

(d) *Antibiotics and vitamins.* Most antibiotics are produced from fungi, but the valuable streptomycin which is active against a number of bacteria not affected by penicillin is produced by *Streptomyces griseus.* Aureomycin and oxytetracycline are produced by *S. aureofaciens* and *S. rimosus.* The fermentation requirements for the bacterial production of these antibiotics are kept as trade secrets.

A number of bacterial fermentations produce vitamins of the B complex, e.g. butyl alcohol fermentation, and can be used for the commercial preparation of these substances.

4. *As insecticides*

As yet very few bacteria have been used to kill plants or animals whose activities are inimical to man. This is mainly because the bacterial diseases of animals other than man and some of his domestic animals have not been intensively studied until comparatively recently. It will also be appreciated that before attacking the insect pests of food crops with pathogenic bacteria it is most important to make sure that the bacteria concerned do not harm man, or, better still, vertebrates in general.

Bacillus thuringiensis has been found to kill many harmful caterpillars. The pathogen is marketed in a wettable powder containing 3000 million live spores per gram of powder; this is applied at dosages of between $\frac{1}{2}$ and 6 lb per acre.

As the long-term effects of most chemical insecticides are now the subject of grave concern it is to be hoped that more attention will be paid to biological methods of pest control.

VIRUSES

If nothing else, the viruses illustrate the impossibility of drawing rigid lines between different phenomena. Prior to the discovery of viruses most biologists had a fairly clear idea of what they meant by a living organism; now it is impossible to construct a satisfactory definition of "life" as viruses exhibit features normally associated with both living things and inanimate matter.

Viruses were discovered when it was found impossible to establish any connection between certain diseases and bacteria. In 1892 fluid extracted from tobacco plants infected with mosaic disease was passed through bacteria-retaining filters. The filtrate was then injected into healthy plants which developed the symptoms of the disease. During the next 20 years more diseases of both plants and animals were shown to be caused by filtrable agents which became known as viruses. A major advance occurred in 1935 when a "protein" carefully crystallized from the juice of mosaic-infected plants was found to retain its infectivity after repeated crystallizations. Since then many more viruses have been chemically examined and all have been found to consist of nucleoproteins. The "protein" crystallized in 1935 presumably had the same constitution.

The electron microscope has enabled the shape, size, and structure of viruses to be studied. Most viruses appear to be roughly spherical in shape though the most recent techniques indicate that many "spherical" viruses are polyhedral in shape, the twenty-sided icosahedron being one of the commonest forms. There is a considerable size range; the largest viruses (e.g. the vaccinia of cowpox) with diameters a little over 200 mμ are little smaller than the smallest bacteria whilst the smallest viruses such as tobacco mosaic virus have diameters of about 10 mμ. Chemical analysis has shown that all viruses consist predominately of nucleoproteins. Various techniques have established that nucleic acid (RNA in the case of most plant viruses, DNA in most animal viruses) forms the core of the virus particle. This core is enclosed by a shell of protein known as the capsid. Since it is considered that there is insufficient nucleic acid to provide "codes" for many different proteins it is thought that the individual units (capsomeres) that make up the capsid consist of numbers of identical protein molecules arranged in such a way as to give the particle its characteristic shape. Many of the larger viruses have a shape more complex than that of a polyhedron; this may reflect the possession of a greater variety of protein "building bricks". Whilst the smaller viruses appear to consist of nucleoprotein, only the larger ones appear to contain lipoids, carbohydrates, water, and a number of enzymes and co-enzymes. Whether or not such forms are metabolic in the normal sense of the word is difficult to say as no virus will multiply outside a living cell.

All viruses are obligate parasites, and, in fact, make their presence apparent only by their effects on their hosts. Most viruses are more or less confined to one host species and, in that host, to particular tissues or cells. The viruses that attack bacteria are known as bacteriophages or, more commonly now, phages. Most phages have a complex structure and are differentiated into a "head" and "tail".

Many of our ideas about the effects of viruses on cells have been derived from studies of phages. When a phage (Fig. 6) comes into contact

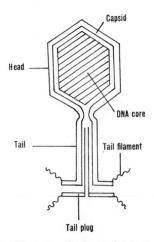

FIG. 6. Diagram of a bacteriophage virus.

with a bacterium the DNA core is somehow injected into the cell, the capsid being left on the outside. Once inside the cell it seems likely that the viral DNA becomes attached to a chromosome where it in some way suppresses the normal "instructions" of the genes of the host cell. In this way the only "instructions" received by the bacterium's synthetic machinery are ones "issued" by the viral DNA. The result is that the normal syntheses of the cell cease and are replaced by syntheses of viral nucleic acid and protein. These associate together to form more virus particles and the host cell finally disintegrates to release the virus particles, consisting of nucleic acid with a surrounding "infective protein" capsid, that it has manufactured. While there are obviously many details to be filled in before this concept of viral activity is complete, it is generally accepted that viruses do multiply by taking over the synthetic machinery of the host cell so that this produces new viral components from the substances present in the cell's "metabolic pool". All other parasites use host material as food and convert it into their own protoplasm by the activities of their own enzyme systems.

We may conclude this brief introduction to the viruses by attempting to define the group. Viruses are ultramicroscopic, filtrable agents, composed primarily of nucleoprotein that are obligate parasites inside plant or animal cells whose metabolism is altered in such a way that the cell produces more particles of the virus.

CHAPTER 2

Algae

ALGAE are unicellular or multicellular organisms which usually have chlorophyll and which rarely have multicellular sex organs. If chlorophyll is lacking, the general characteristics of the organism indicate its affinities with chlorophyll-containing forms. Where sex organs are multicellular, all their cells form gametes, there being no sterile jacket cells, unlike more advanced forms. They are aquatic plants or live in damp habitats and familiar examples are the sea-weeds, the green scum on ponds, and the green stain on shaded walls or tree trunks.

Fossil algae are known from the oldest rocks which contain remains of living organisms. This fact, taken with the great simplicity of form of many algae, which ranks them with the protozoa, and distinguishes them from mosses, ferns and seed plants, suggests that they represent a truly primitive form of life and that they still retain much of the organization of the first chlorophyll-containing plants. Nevertheless, evolution within the algae has resulted in some forms, particularly among the brown algae, which approach flowering plants in the complexity of their structure.

There is considerable variation in the algae in photosynthetic pigments, in the reserve products of photosynthesis (the photosynthate), and in the chemical nature of the cell wall, where one is present. These biochemical variations correspond to different morphological types and have led to the division of the algae by taxonomists into several "classes". Each class has its own evolutionary characteristics and in some cases at least these are sufficiently distinctive to suggest that the classes have taken origin separately from a primaeval photosynthetic stock or even from the heterotrophic precursors of these which have been postulated*. Certainly, the separate "classes" of algae differ more than do the classes of, say,

*It has been suggested by some workers that the first living organisms were heterotrophes originating from and sustained by organic molecules produced from the primaeval atmosphere by inanimate factors such as lightning.

32

the Craniata (fishes, amphibia, reptiles, birds and mammals). The elevation of these classes of algae to the rank of separate phyla or divisions by modern taxonomists seems justified and is accepted in the present work. It will, therefore, be understood that the term "algae" is a general term covering a number of phyla and no longer belongs to any recognized taxonomic category. It remains useful, however, to denote those plants which have the characteristics defined above.

The divisions of the algae are set out in Table 1. The table lists also the photosynthetic pigments; the photosynthate; cell wall constituents; and other characteristics of each division. We will study members of only three of the divisions: the Chlorophyta, Euglenophyta and Phaeophyta.

EUGLENOPHYTA
Euglena
Habitat and form

Euglena is a genus of green flagellates which commonly occur in fresh water containing nitrogenous matter. Among the commoner species are *E. viridis*, the rod-like chloroplasts of which radiate from a common centre, like the rays of a star; *E. geniculata* which has two such groups of chloroplasts (Fig. 7); and *E. gracilis*, in which the chloroplasts are scattered, just below the external surface.

It consists of a single spindle-shaped protoplast (Fig. 7) which is usually pointed at the posterior end. There is no cell wall, the organism being bounded by a spirally striated, elastic pellicle. At the anterior end opens a flask-shaped cytopharynx which in holozoic relatives is used for ingestion. From the posterior wall of the cytopharynx a flagellum arises by two roots, each of which is attached to a basal granule or blepharoplast. On one side of the cytopharynx is a red pigment-spot or stigma, and on one root of the flagellum is a light sensitive swelling, the photoreceptor. Orientation to light occurs in response to shading of the photoreceptor by the stigma.

A large contractile vacuole discharges into the base of the cytopharynx. After discharge the vacuole is succeeded by a new vacuole which develops from small vesicles which form around the former vacuole before its collapse. There is no continuity between successive vacuoles. The contractile vacuole is an osmoregulatory organelle. It seems unlikely that it is significantly concerned with excretion, which occurs over the general body surface.

In *Euglena viridis* and *E. geniculata*, a proteinaceous body, the pyrenoid, which is responsible for the formation of reserve carbohydrate, is present

TABLE 1

SUMMARY OF ALGAL DIVISIONS AND THEIR NOTEWORTHY ATTRIBUTES (From BOLD, *The Plant Kingdom*, PRENTICE HALL.)

Division	Common name	Pigments	Stored photo-synthate	Cell wall	Flagellar number and insertion[3]	Habitat
Chlorophyta	Green algae	Chloro.[1]a,b	Starch	Cellulose	2–8, equal, apical	f.w., b.w., s.w.[2]
Charophyta	Stoneworts	Chloro.a,b	Starch	Cellulose plus pectin	2, equal, apical	f.w., b.w.
Euglenophyta	Euglenoids	Chloro.a,b	Paramylon	Absent	1–3, apical sub-apical	f.w., b.w., s.w.
Chrysophyta	Golden algae (including diatoms)	Chloro.a, some have c; e, in some	Oil, leucosin	Pectin plus silicon dioxide	1–2, unequal or equal, apical	f.w., b.w., s.w.
Phaeophyta	Brown algae	Chloro.a,c	Mannitol, laminarin	Cellulose plus algin	2, unequal, lateral	f.w. (rare) b.w., s.w.
Pyrrophyta	Dinoflagel-lates, in part	Chloro.a,c	Starch	Cellulose or absent	2, 1 trailing, 1 girdling	f.w., b.w., s.w.
Rhodophyta	Red algae	Chloro.a,d Phycocyanin, Phycoery-thrin	Floridean starch	Cellulose	Absent	f.w. (some), b.w., s.w. (most)
Cyanophyta	Blue–green algae	Chloro.a, Phycocyanin, Phycoery-thrin	Cyanophycean starch	Cellulose plus pectin	Absent	f.w., b.w., s.w.

[1]Chloro. = Chlorophyll.
[3]In motile cells, when these are produced.
[2]f.w. = fresh water; b.w. = brackish water; s.w. = salt water.

at the point from which the chloroplasts radiate. Around each pyrenoid are granules of the carbohydrate which is termed paramylum (or paramylon) and is allied to starch. These granules also occur in the general cytoplasm. In *E. gracilis* there is a pyrenoid within each chloroplast but pyrenoids are absent from the cytoplasm.

The position of the nucleus varies in different species. In *E. viridis* it lies posteriorly, behind the chloroplasts. It contains an endosome, a body which pulls in two and acts as a spindle during fission (asexual division) (Fig. 8) and around which chromosomes appear.

Locomotion

Locomotion is by rhythmic contractile creeping movements, (euglenoid movement), permitted by flexibility of the pellicle; and by swimming. In swimming the flagellum is trailed obliquely backwards. Along the flagellum pass waves which increase in velocity and amplitude from base to tip and impart a spiral forward movement to the organism.

Nutrition

Euglena, although possessing a cytopharynx, takes no solid food and is almost holophytic (see p. 3). Investigations indicate that all euglenas require some organic materials in the external medium and are, therefore, partly saprophytic (if looked upon as plants) or saprozoic (if regarded as animals).

Excretion

Excretion, like gaseous exchange, occurs by diffusion through the pellicle.

Reproduction

Reproduction is asexual, by longitudinal binary fission (division into two). Prior to division, the organism usually comes to rest and secretes a mucilaginous envelope or a thick-walled cyst. Palmella stages in which several individuals are produced and remain in association may occur. In fission the flagellum is withdrawn, and division of the nucleus and chloroplasts is followed by longitudinal division of the cytoplasm, initiated by division of the cytopharynx. Details of the division process are given in Fig. 8.

Relationships (see p. 42).

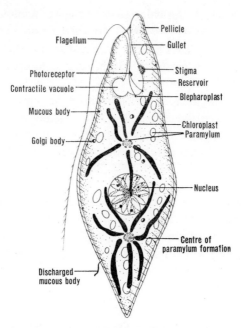

FIG. 7. *Euglena geniculata*, a species with two groups of chloroplasts, each group having a stellate arrangement, and mucous bodies below the pellicle which can be discharged through minute pores. The mucus is used in the formation of a cyst or of a palmelloid stage. Redrawn from Hollande in Grassé.

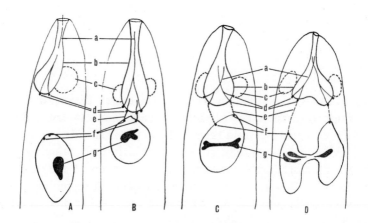

FIG. 8. Reproduction by longitudinal fission in a species of *Euglena*. Adapted from Ratcliffe.

CHLOROPHYTA

As examples of the Chlorophyta we will take *Chlamydomonas* and *Volvox*, in the order Volvocales, and *Spirogyra*, in the order Conjugales, but first some introduction to this instructive group is necessary.

The chlorophyll, the photosynthate, and the cell wall constituent in the Chlorophyta are of the same nature as in higher plants, being respectively chlorophyll a and b, starch and cellulose. The pigments are contained in chloroplasts the shape of which varies greatly in different genera.

The Chlorophyta are particularly interesting in their range of form and types of reproduction.

Range of form

The lower members, e.g. *Chlamydomonas*, are unicellular but these unicellular forms have given rise to colonial, usually motile forms, on the one hand, e.g. *Volvox* (Fig. 14), and filamentous forms on the other, e.g. *Spirogyra* (Fig. 22) and *Ulothrix* (Ulotrichales). *Spirogyra* has virtually no morphological differentiation of the cells relative to each other, and can therefore be regarded as a colony; whereas in *Ulothrix* reproduction is by means of motile gametes and involves only part of the filament, which can be considered to represent a stage beyond the colonial. The way in which filamentous forms may have arisen from unicellular forms by the formation of chains of individuals forming a colony is exemplified by *Pleurococcus*, which normally exists as single cells, or aggregates of single cells, but not infrequently forms branched filaments (Fig. 9). In another evolutionary line a flat thallus has been produced in which the cells divide in more than one plane. In *Ulva*, the sea lettuce, there are two tiers of cells in the thallus.

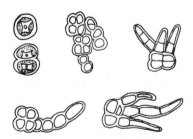

FIG. 9. *Pleurococcus naegelii*. Redrawn from Fritsch.

A complexity of external form approaching that of higher plants is reached in the order Siphonales, although the thallus is a single multi-nucleate cell or coenocyte. In *Caulerpa* the thallus, which consists of interwoven filaments or hyphae, may be as much as 10 cm high, and in appearance simulates stem, root and leaves.

Reproduction

The diversity of structure in the Chlorophyta is paralleled by great variation of methods of reproduction. In most members both sexual and asexual reproduction occur. Sexual reproduction may involve union of similar gametes (isogamy) or of dissimilar gametes (anisogamy), and in some, one gamete is small and motile, and is termed the male gamete (if flagellated, the antherozoid), whereas the other is large and passive, and is therefore termed the female gamete or ovum. Fertilization of a passive ovum by a motile male gamete is known as oogamy. Asexual reproduction is usually by the production of minute flagellated bodies known as zoospores.

Some Chlorophyta display alternation of generations, that is, alternation of a haploid gamete-producing plant, the gametophyte, with a diploid plant which produces spores by meiosis, and is termed the sporophyte. This phenomenon is discussed in Chapter 6, and it will suffice here to mention that in the Chlorophyta the gametophyte and sporophyte generations are not usually referred to as such, but are called the haplophase and diplophase, respectively. These terms refer to their chromosome complements rather than the types of reproductive cells that they produce, and are applicable to all animals and plants.

Alternation of generations is found throughout the Phaeophyta, although obscured in *Fucus* and some other genera, and is common in the Rhodophyta. Regular alternation of gametophyte and sporophyte constitutes the basic pattern of the life history in all green plants, from the mosses and liverworts to the seed plants inclusively (see Chapter 6).

Chlamydomonas

Habitat and form

Species of this genus are common in fresh water, sometimes colouring large areas green. The organism (Fig. 10) is unicellular, and is enclosed in a thin cellulose membrane or cell wall. In form it is ellipsoidal with the end which is forward in locomotion, i.e. the anterior end, often produced into a papilla or beak. From the anterior end, usually from the sides of the apical papilla, project two flagella. At the base of each flagellum there lies a basal granule, or blepharoplast, near each end of which is a contractile vacuole.

Most of the protoplast is occupied by a single chloroplast which is deeply cup-shaped with the open end facing anteriorly. It is separated by a thin outer layer of cytoplasm from the cell wall. In the thickened posterior end of the chloroplast is situated a single large pyrenoid, a body

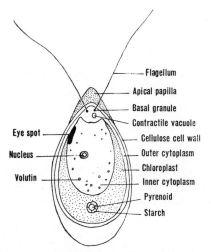

FIG. 10. *Chlamydomonas*. Vegetative cell. Redrawn from Cook and Mclean, after Pascher.

around which develop starch grains. Adjacent to the forward edge of the chloroplast is a minute red carotinoid body, which is sensitive to light, the stigma or eye-spot. The stigma is said to be overlain by a minute lens lying in the thickness of the cellulose cell wall. Lying in the inner cytoplasm, enclosed by the chloroplast and near its base, is the single nucleus.

Locomotion

Accounts as to the method of locomotion conflict, but the view that each flagellum is held extended, and that its tip describes a circle, so that the flagella act as tractor propellors which pull the organism forward, is probably erroneous. The normal movement is probably a sideways lash consisting of an effective, propellant back-stroke with the flagellum held extended, followed by a relaxed forward recovery stroke of the strongly curved flagellum. Forward movement of the organism is accompanied by rotation about its long axis. It is possible, however, that other modes of action of the flagella exist. As in other flagellates, activity of the flagellum is intrinsic in the flagellum itself, provided that it is in connection with the basal granule or blepharoplast; it is not comparable with the action of a whip.

Physiology

All species of *Chlamydomonas* are green, and their nutrition is holophytic. As a result of the sensitivity of the stigma, the organisms collect in regions of adequate illumination but avoid intense illumination which, from comparison with higher plants, would presumably destroy the chlorophyll.

Exchange of oxygen, carbon dioxide and other substances occurs by diffusion in solution through the cell wall.

Reproduction

When the organism has reached a certain size, reproduction usually occurs. In asexual reproduction (Fig. 11) the individual comes to rest, the flagella are withdrawn, and division of the nucleus and chloroplast

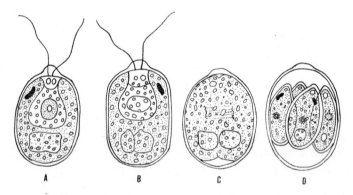

A   B   C   D

Fig. 11. *Chlamydomonas*. Asexual reproduction. Redrawn from Dill.

is followed by division of the cytoplasm. If further divisions occur they may appear to be mutually at right-angles, owing to rotation of the dividing organism through 90° between divisions, but each division is, in fact, longitudinal. Two to sixteen individuals are thus formed. Each of these becomes a small replica of the parent, developing flagella and its own cell wall, and is released by rupture or dissolution of the parent cell wall. Growth then continues until the adult size is reached. Sometimes the daughter individuals do not develop flagella, and are retained within the parent cell wall which gradually becomes mucilaginous. The daughter cells may repeat this process, their walls in turn becoming mucilaginous, until large numbers of non-motile individuals are embedded in mucilage. This constitutes a palmella stage (Fig. 12). Reversion to the motile condition readily occurs.

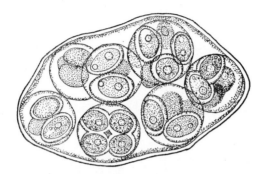

FIG. 12. *Chlamydomonas braunii.*   Palmella   stage.   Redrawn   from
Goroschankin.

In sexual reproduction (Fig. 13), division results in the formation of sixteen, thirty-two or sixty-four individuals which resemble the parent except in lacking the cell wall. These are gametes (sex cells), for on liberation, by rupture of the parent cell wall, they fuse in pairs. Usually gametes from different parents unite so that, although there is morphological isogamy (i.e. union of morphologically similar gametes or isogametes) there is physiological heterogamy. (Heterogamy is the union of morphologically similar but physiologically different gametes.) In some species the uniting gametes are dissimilar in size, according to the number of divisions producing them, so that there is the beginning of anisogamy (union of gametes of unequal size). *Chlamydomonas braunii* is wholly anisogamous, and produces macrogametes and microgametes which are unusual in possessing cell walls. In the latter species the macrogametes soon come to rest and, at least sometimes, lose their flagella. Each passive macrogamete is fertilized by a motile male gamete, the contents of which pass into the macrogamete. This condition approaches oogamy, the motile gamete being equivalent to a motile male gamete or antherozoid, and the macrogamete to a passive female gamete or ovum.

The zygote produced by union of gametes contains reddish oil drops. It secretes a thick wall, and is resistant to desiccation. In favourable conditions the contents of the zygote divide to give several individuals which are freed by rupture of its wall. These individuals, which are often termed zoospores, are produced by reduction division of the zygote and are, therefore, comparable with the spores produced by the sporophytes

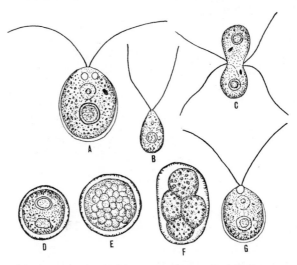

FIG. 13. *Chlamydomonas reinhardi.* Sexual reproduction. A, mature individual. B, gamete. C, gametes fusing. D, young zygote. E, mature zygote. F, zoospores produced by division of zygote. G, a zoospore. Redrawn from Goroschankin.

of multicellular plants with alternation of generations. It must not be thought, however, that alternation of generations occurs in *Chlamydomonas.* The zygote is the only diploid stage in the life cycle (diplophase) and does not undergo any vegetative development to produce a diploid plant. Alternation of generations can be said to occur only where mitotic division occurs in the diplophase and a diploid plant is therefore included in the life cycle in addition to a haploid plant. Alternation of generations does occur in some Chlorophyta, however, and is discussed in Chapter 6.

Relationships of green flagellates

It is highly probable that green flagellates, including *Euglena* and *Chlamydomonas,* and colourless flagellates are closely related, as the two groups show many points of morphological similarity, and green forms change to colourless saprophytic forms (or even, according to some workers, holozoic forms) if kept in the dark. Within the Euglenophyta are placed genera containing chlorophyll, and with red eye-spots, of which the commonest are *Euglena, Phacus* and *Leptocinclis*; and also colourless genera which are mostly holozoic, common examples of which are *Astasia*, with one flagellum; *Peranema*, with a pharyngeal rod supporting the cytopharynx, and two flagella, one of which is fixed to the pellicle; and *Entosiphon, Heteronema* and *Anisonema* with two flagella, one of which is extended, and the other trailed posteriorly. Examples of colourless unicellular flagellates which are morphologically very similar to *Chlamydomonas*, and are therefore placed with it in the Chlorophyta, are *Polytoma* and *Polytomella*.

These colourless, and green, unicellular algae are inseparable from the Protozoa and are usually included in that phylum by protozoologists. This is supported by the existence of graded series between flagellates and rhizopod protozoa, which include *Amoeba* and the existence of flagellate stages in the life cycles of many protozoa. The issue as to whether *Chlamydomonas* and *Euglena* should be placed in the animal kingdom as Protozoa is avoided by placing all unicellular or acellular organisms in a group called the Protista.

The terminology which is used is unimportant so long as the evolutionary implications of the combination of typical animal and typical plant characteristics in the green flagellates (see Table 2) and the obvious close relationship of green and colourless forms are understood. The implications are that such flagellates were ancestral to the plant and animal kingdoms, and that present day forms such as *Euglena* and *Chlamydomonas* are survivors of this ancestral stock. This is not to say that these two genera have themselves ever been in the direct line of evolution of the two kingdoms.

As Table 2 shows, *Euglena* is less plant-like than *Chlamydomonas*, and the Euglenophyta are probably an offshoot from the ancestral flagellates which has arisen independently of the Chlorophyta. The possibility exists that the first flagellates were colourless, heterotrophic organisms.

There seems little reason to doubt that *Chlamydomonas* is a descendant of the ancestral stock of the multicellular green plants. Evidence of this is the similarity of chlorophyll, of the photosynthate (starch) and the composition of the cell wall (cellulose) (Table 1). The motility of *Chlamydomonas* may be regarded as the retention of a primitive character.

TABLE 2

ANIMAL AND PLANT CHARACTERISTICS OF EUGLENA AND CHLAMYDOMONAS

	Euglena	*Chlamydomonas*	Remarks
Plant characters	Possession of chlorophyll and holophytic nutrition		Unknown in animals
	Storage of paramylum, allied to starch of higher plants	Storage of starch	Animals store carbohydrates as glycogen, as do fungi
	—	Cellulose cell wall	Animal cells lack cell walls and though they may secrete external matrix this is never cellulose
Animal characters	Absence of cell wall	—	Naked reproductive bodies occur from Thallophyta to gymnosperms. Myxomycete fungi lack cell walls
	Presence of contractile vacuoles		Occur in some true plants, e.g. *Spirogyra* in conjugation
	Centrioles formed during nuclear division		Centrioles are rare above the lower Thallophyta
	Flagellation and motility		Naked motile reproductive bodies, i.e. Zoospores and/or antherozoids occur from Thallophyta to g y m n o s p e r m s. Some have eye-spots, e.g. antherozoids of *Fucus*
	Presence of an eye-spot		
	Absence of vacuole containing cell sap		Vacuole present in plant cells above the lowest Thallophyta, but also in some animal cells

Motility is characteristic of animals, but should not be glibly labelled as an "animal characteristic" as though it were exclusive to animals. Motile, flagellate stages occur in the life history of the majority of plant as well as animal divisions.

Chlamydomonas is thus undoubtedly a plant, and appears to be a little changed representative of the ancestral stock of the multicellular green plants. The order to which it belongs, the Volvocales, appear to be a side-line in evolution from this stock. Evolution in this order has proceeded as far as the development of colonial forms, such as *Volvox*, in which there is almost sufficient integration and division of labour between individuals of the colony to merit regarding it as multicellular. But it is doubtful that multicellular plants are, in fact, descended from such forms (see p. 48).

Volvox

Habitat and form

The largest and most complex colonial member of the Volvocales is *Volvox* which is common in still, fresh water. A single colony or coenobium (Greek "common-life") consists of up to 60,000 individuals arranged as the periphery of a hollow sphere (Fig. 14). Each individual cell bears a

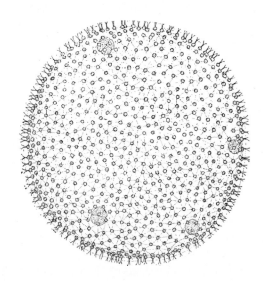

Fig. 14. *Volvox aureus*. Coenobium in the vegetative condition. From Smith.

closer resemblance to *Sphaerella* (=*Haematococcus*) than to *Chlamydomonas* in that the cell wall is mucilaginous and is traversed by long cytoplasmic processes or fibrils. In *Volvox* the fibrils of adjacent cells are in contact. The chloroplast (Fig. 15) is globose, ovoid, cupped or stellate and contains one or more pyrenoids. Associated with the chloroplast is a stigma or eye-spot. Each cell has usually several contractile vacuoles. In many

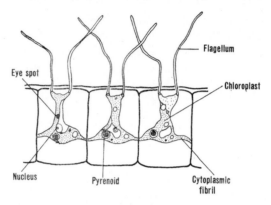

FIG. 15. *Volvox* sp. Vegetative cells. Redrawn from Cook and Mclean, after Rich.

species the middle lamellae bounding the mucilaginous cell walls are distinctly visible and form a reticulate pattern of polygons over the surface of the colony.

The colony moves and rotates slowly with the same aspect always forward so that the colony has a definite polarity. This differentiation into anterior and posterior "poles" is associated with considerable morphological and physiological differentiation. Thus certain large cells at the posterior pole lack the two flagella of each of the other cells, and are set aside for reproduction, and the stigmata of the anterior cells are larger than those of the more posterior cells.

Reproduction

Asexual reproduction is brought about by the repeated division of large posterior cells known as parthenogonidia each of which produces many individuals grouped in such a way as to form the walls of a sphere (Fig. 16A–D). At first the individuals of the new colony lack flagella and the anterior end of each constituent cell faces towards the centre, but shortly before development of flagella the young colony everts by means of a small pore on one side of the colony and takes up the mature orientation with the flagella external (Fig. 16 E–G). On rupture of the walls of the parthenogonidia the daughter colonies are released into the cavity of the parent colony, which they may fill, and are finally released by dissolution and death of the latter. They may themselves give rise to daughter colonies before their release.

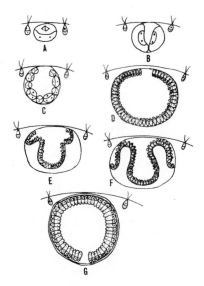

FIG. 16. *Volvox aureus*. Stages in the development of an asexual daughter colony. A and B, a parthenogonidium dividing. C and D, production of a colony, the cells of which face inwards. E–G, eversion of the daughter colony so that the constituent cells face outwards. Redrawn from Cook and Mclean, after Zimmermann.

Sexual reproduction is oogamous. The male gametes (Fig. 17A) are biflagellate spindle-shaped antherozoids with pale green chloroplasts. They adhere in circular plates or antheridia each of which is formed by repeated fission of a special enlarged cell of which there may be several in the colony.

The non-motile female gametes or oospheres develop singly in special cells which resemble parthenogonidia but are larger (Fig. 17B). After fertilization each secretes a thick wall which in some species is spiny (Fig. 17B). This oospore is released by dissolution of the parent and can resist desiccation. On germination it releases a single haploid zoospore which by division produces a new coenobium.

Both types of gametes and parthenogonidia may be produced in the same colony but usually sexual reproduction occurs only at the end of a period favourable for growth and asexual reproduction. It appears that union of gametes from the same coenobium, in cases where the latter produces both types of gametes, does not occur.

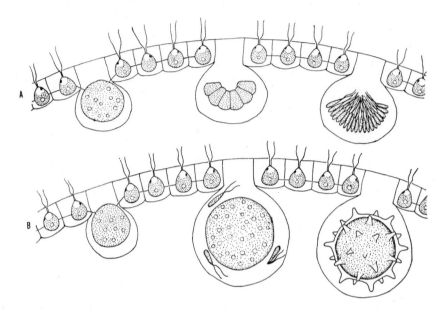

FIG. 17. *Volvox* sp. Sexual reproduction. A, stages in the production of antherozoids, the male gametes. B, stages in the development of a female gamete or oosphere and its fertilization to give a zygote or oospore. Redrawn after Smith.

Relationships

Volvox has many of the characteristics of a multicellular plant rather than of a colony. Thus only a few cells participate in reproduction and the individual cells act in co-ordination, their protoplasts being, as in higher plants, in continuity by cytoplasmic fibrillae. This division of labour between vegetative and reproductive cells is associated with both physiological and morphological differentiation as has been shown above. *Volvox* differs strikingly from multicellular plants, however, in its motility and it would appear most unlikely that multicellular plants evolved from *Volvox*-like organisms (see p. 116).

Although evolution from *Volvox*-like forms to higher plants is in doubt, the evolution of *Volvox* from unicellular plants is well supported by a remarkably perfect series of extant forms increasing in numbers of individuals and in morphological and physiological differentiation, i.e. in division of labour. This series is presented by *Gonium, Pandorina, Eudorina, Pleodorina* and *Volvox* and can be considered to have originated from a unicellular form similar to *Chlamydomonas* or *Sphaerella*. In recognizing this series there is no suggestion that the simpler genera were directly ancestral to the more complex.

Gonium (Fig. 18) consists of a flat square of four to sixteen *Chlamydomonas*-like individuals among which there is no morphological differentiation (although, as in all the coenobial Volvocales, there is polarity) and

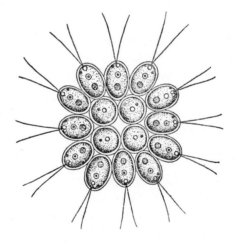

FIG. 18. *Gonium pectorale*. From Brown after Stein and Schussing.

no continuity of cytoplasm. All the cells can produce daughter colonies in asexual reproduction and each can act as an isogamete or produce isogametes by fission.

Pandorina (Fig. 19) consists of a sphere of sixteen cells tightly packed in a mucilaginous matrix. There is no cytoplasmic continuity between cells and each cell is capable of forming daughter colonies and of sexual reproduction. The latter is usually isogamous but in some species is slightly anisogamous.

Eudorina (Fig. 20) consists of thirty-two cells on the surface of a jelly sphere. Reproduction is a property of any cell of the colony but there is

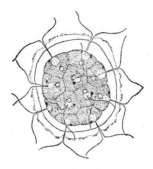

FIG. 19. *Pandorina morum*. From Smith, *Cryptogamic Botany*, McGraw
Hill Book Co. Used by permission.

physiological differentiation in the definite antero-posterior polarity and
morphological differentiation in that the anterior cells have larger eye-
spots. The colonies are mainly dioecious and sexual reproduction is
anisogamous and reaches oogamy in some species. The cells are in communication by cytoplasmic fibrillae.

In *Pleodorina* (Fig. 21) there are up to 128 cells on the surface of a
hollow jelly sphere and the coenobium shows greater division of labour
in that the anterior individuals have the largest eye-spots, are incapable
of reproduction and may be smaller than the posterior. Sexual reproduction
is oogamous.

Volvox (Fig. 14), as we have seen, reaches a peak in numbers of individuals (up to 60,000); in diameter (often greater than 2 mm); in division
of labour (the anterior cells being incapable of reproduction and having
larger light organelles); in having obligate oogamy and in the cytoplasmic
continuity of the constituent cells.

Spirogyra
Habitat and form

Spirogyra is a green, filamentous, unbranched alga which is common
as green masses floating, or entangled in weeds, in temperate and tropical
fresh water which is not excessively disturbed. The filaments may rarely
be found attached to the substrate by branched colourless terminal
holdfasts but usually each breaks away from its holdfast early in development.

Each filament consists of a row of morphologically, and, at least in the
metabolic condition, physiologically indistinguishable cylindrical cells
joined end to end (Fig. 22). The wall of each cell is of polysaccharide

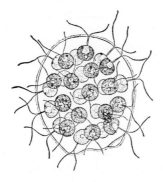

FIG. 20. *Eudorina unicocca.* From Smith, *Cryptogamic Botany*, McGraw-Hill Book Co. Used by permission.

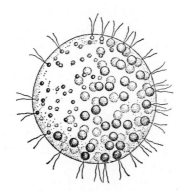

FIG. 21. *Pleodorina californica.* From Brown.

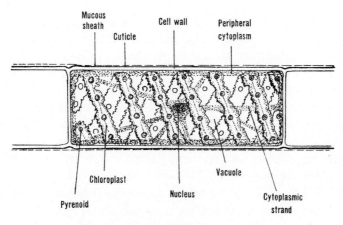

FIG. 22. A cell of *Spirogyra,* × 400.

and the entire filament is ensheathed by a thin cuticle, and, outside this, a mucous sheath. The cytoplasm of each cell consists of a thin layer lining the walls and surrounding a large, fluid-filled vacuole, and delicate cytoplasmic threads running from the peripheral layer to a central mass of cytoplasm which is suspended in the vacuole and encloses the single nucleus. In addition, slender cytoplasmic strands connect the inner flange of the chloroplast, which is T-shaped in cross-section, with the nuclear mass.

The chloroplast consists of a green band running in a spiral through the length of the cell in the peripheral cytoplasm. There may be one or two or several chloroplasts in a cell. The chloroplast shows periodic expansions in each of which is situated a rounded colourless body, the pyrenoid, around which starch produced as a result of photosynthesis is stored. There is no continuity between chloroplasts of consecutive cells.

Growth is intercalary, that is to say it occurs at any point along the length of the filament, as opposed to the primarily apical growth of higher plants. In contrast, also, with higher plants the nucleus begins to divide after the rest of the protoplast has begun to divide and the two divisions are completed simultaneously. Division of the protoplast occurs by ingrowth of a ring from the lateral walls of the cell so that ultimately a partition divides the cell transversely. The position of this partition is determined by the position of the metabolic nucleus and, at completion, it lies half-way between the daughter nuclei.

Reproduction

It is frequently said that *Spirogyra*, and the Conjugales as a whole, lack asexual reproduction. The filament reproduces, both by sexual means and vegetatively by fragmentation at predetermined positions, where the cell walls are specialized, and gives single cells each of which subsequently grows and divides to form a filament. There seems no reason why this vegetative reproduction should not be regarded as true asexual reproduction as, owing to the lack of morphological differentiation and of interdependence of the constituent cells of the filament, the filament is usually regarded as a colony and therefore each cell as an individual.

Sexual reproduction (Fig. 23) usually occurs at the end of periods favourable for growth and asexual reproduction. Filaments come together in pairs, probably owing to surface tension changes, and become invested in a common mucous sheath. Protuberances then grow out from opposite cells, one from each. These are in contact from their formation and their growth pushes the filaments apart. The wall separating the lumina of the protuberances then breaks down so that a continuous conjugation canal joins the cavities of the two cells and the two protoplasts come into contact. The entire protoplast of one cell of each opposed pair then rounds off and, because of the pumping of water by contractile vacuoles

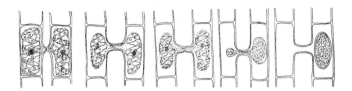

Fig. 23. Stages in conjugation and zygote formation in *Spirogyra*.

in its periphery into the cell, is forced into the conjugation canal. By this stage the contents of the partner cell have rounded off. The latter gamete then retreats into its cell and draws the other gamete with it. Union is then completed and the zygote secretes a thick wall, and secretes oil drops, thus becoming a zygospore. The motile gamete is termed the male gamete and the relatively stationary gamete the female gamete. This type of sexual reproduction is known as conjugation because each cell acts as a hologamete, that is to say, participates wholly in the sexual union. The old cell walls soon disintegrate and release the resistant zygospores which germinate on return of favourable conditions.

In some species the male gametes are formed in one filament and all the zygospores in the other and one filament may be considered male and the other female. This is morphological isogamy and physiological heterogamy and the species are dioecious. In other species, zygospores are formed in both filaments owing to passage of male gametes in both directions. These species are monoecious.

Conjugation between filaments as described above is known as ladder or scalariform conjugation. In some species a conjugation canal develops between adjacent cells of the same filament, a phenomenon known as chain conjugation.

On germination (Fig. 24), the three-layered wall of the zygospore ruptures and four nuclei are produced from the single zygote nucleus by reduction division (meiosis). Three of these abort but the other survives. The contents of the zygospore then divide into a colourless rhizoidal

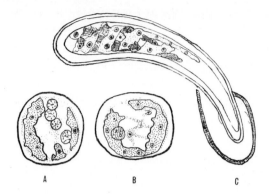

A   B   C

FIG. 24. *Spirogyra*. Germination of the zygospore. A, four nuclei produced by meiotic division of the zygote nucleus. B, three of these degenerate. C, vegetative filament growing out of ruptured zygospore wall. Redrawn from Cook and Mclean.

holdfast and a typical vegetative cell which undergoes repeated divisions to form a filament. This filament is haploid and the zygote marks the only diploid phase of the life history. Alternation of generations cannot be said to occur because there are no mitotic divisions of the zygote and therefore the latter does not undergo vegetative development.

PHAEOPHYTA

The Phaeophyta or brown algae are so called because the green colour of the chlorophyll is masked by the xanthophyll pigment fucoxanthin which imparts a brown colour to the plants. In *Fucus*, the pigments found in the plastids (phaeoplasts) are chlorophyll a, chlorophyll c (in place of chlorophyll b of higher plants), β-carotene and fucoxanthin.

Unicellular forms occur and connect the group with the flagellata, and some genera are filamentous, but most have a highly differentiated thallus which in some, in which vascular elements are developed, approaches a flowering plant in its complexity.

The Phaeophyta is the first group of plants in our study in which alternation of generations is general (see p. 38). It is perhaps unfortunate, therefore, that the example used in elementary studies, *Fucus*, has no apparent alternation. Where alternation occurs in the Phaeophyta the gametophyte and sporophyte may be morphologically similar or, as in the kelp, *Laminaria*, dissimilar. In the latter genus the sporophyte is large and conspicuous while the gametophyte is small and filamentous. In other genera, however, the gametophyte is the conspicuous generation.

We will see in the higher plants that, within each division, one generation, either the gametophyte or the sporophyte, is always more conspicuous than the other and that a graded series exists in reduction of the gametophyte and emphasis of the sporophyte.

Sexual reproduction in the Phaeophyta is isogamous in the lower forms and isogamous or oogamous in the higher forms. Asexual reproduction is by the production of peculiar pear-shaped zoospores each of which has a pair of lateral flagella.

As an example of the Phaeophyta we will take *Fucus*. Although it is restricted to temperate regions it is chosen because its biology is better known than that of other brown algae. The tropical genus *Sargassum* (Fig. 25A) is similar in many respects.

Fucus

Habitat and form

The three most common species of *Fucus* are the monoecious *F. spiralis* which is identifiable by its twisted frond, absence of bladders, entire margin and winged reproductive apices; *F. vesiculosus* with paired, buoyant bladders and *F. serratus* with serrate margins which, like *F. vesiculosus*, is dioecious. The three species occur, in the order given, in downshore sequence in the intertidal zone of the rocky shores of Great Britain.

The thallus of *Fucus* (Fig. 25B–F) is anchored to the substrate by a tough, branched, non-absorptive holdfast (hapteron). From the hapteron arises a stem-like stipe which bears terminally the dichotomously branched fronds. This dichotomy or paired branching is not, however, symmetrical, only the first pair of laterals being commonly equal in development. The branched region of the thallus is flattened in one plane but each frond is supported by a much-thickened midrib which is continuous with the stipe.

Scattered over the thallus are minute pores which open into small cavities called cryptostomata, or cryptoblasts, the walls of which are lined with small hairs or filaments some of which project through the pores.

Reproduction

When the plant is mature, reproductive branches develop. These branches differ from the vegetative branches on which they are borne by their regular dichotomous branching at short intervals. The tips of these branches, which form the periphery of a fan, become swollen and filled with mucilage. These swollen regions are called receptacles (Fig. 25).

They lack midribs. The receptacles have a punctate appearance owing to the presence of the pores in cavities which are homologous with the sterile cryptostomata but contain the reproductive organs. The cavities are termed conceptacles and their pores ostioles.

Owing to growth and division of neighbouring cells, the walls of the conceptacle (Fig. 26), which are produced from a single cell, assume the form of a flask sunk below the surface of the thallus but in communication with the outside world by the ostiole. Those hairs which project through

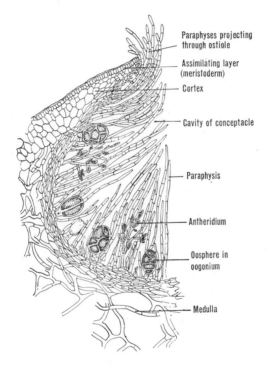

Paraphyses projecting through ostiole

Assimilating layer (meristoderm)

Cortex

Cavity of conceptacle

Paraphysis

Antheridium

Oosphere in oogonium

Medulla

Fig. 26. *Fucus spiralis*. Longitudinal section through a mature conceptacle. Highly magnified.

Fig. 25. Sporophytes of brown algae. A, *Sargassum bacciferum* (redrawn from Kerner). B, *Fucus vesiculosus*, $\times \frac{1}{5}$. C, *F. spiralis*, $\times \frac{1}{6}$ (both redrawn from Carola Dickinson). D–F, *F. serratus* (original): D, entire plant, $\times \frac{1}{12}$; E, vegetative frond showing dichotomously branched midrib, $\times \frac{1}{3}$; F, reproductive fronds with terminal receptacles lacking midribs and perforated by many ostioles which open into conceptacles, $\times \frac{1}{3}$.

the ostiole are colourless but the hairs lining the basal part of the chamber contain pigmented plastids and are perhaps concerned with the secretion of mucus.

There is complete anisogamy (i.e. oogamy), the female gametes being passive oospheres or eggs borne in oogonia (Fig. 27) and the male gametes biflagellate motile antherozoids, or "spermatozoa", produced in antheridia (Fig. 27). In *F. spiralis* both types of gametes are produced in the same conceptacle but *F. vesiculosus* and *F. serratus* are dioecious.

The oogonia are produced on the walls of the conceptacle whereas the antheridia arise on branched filaments and projecting from the walls and are rarely borne directly on the latter. Each oogonium arises from a superficial cell in the wall of the conceptacle. This divides to form a single basal cell or stalk cell and a cell which constitutes the oogonium. The oogonium enlarges and its diploid nucleus undergoes reduction division to produce eight haploid nuclei. Each of these appropriates a portion of the cytoplasm so that eight female gametes or oospheres are produced. The oogonium wall has three layers: an outer exochiton, a middle mesochiton and an inner mucilaginous endochiton. On rupture of the exochiton the eight oospheres are released as a group enclosed in the mesochiton. This egg mass is forced out through the ostiole when the thallus contracts because of drying at low tide. When the tide again covers the plant the mesochiton ruptures and on dissolution of the endochiton the individual oospheres are released. Each oosphere is a passive spherical body coloured brownish by many plastids.

In the formation of antheridia, superficial cells of the conceptacle wall divide so as to form much-branched filaments. Some of the branches are sterile and may be termed paraphyses but others constitute the antheridia. Each antheridium has a two-layered wall. Its single diploid nucleus divides meiotically to give sixty-four antherozoids, each with a haploid nucleus. Each antherozoid is pear-shaped and has an orange eye-spot and two lateral flagella (Fig. 27). One flagellum is directed forward and is a little longer than the sperm; it is surrounded by a highly mobile funnel-shaped membrane which is believed to function in attaching the sperm to the egg. The other flagellum is directed posteriorly and is about three times the length of the sperm. Each flagellum is made up of eleven strands and bears minute hairs. When the outer wall of the antheridium ruptures, the orange mass of antherozoids is released from the antheridium while still enclosed in the inner wall. Pressure on the conceptacle owing to drying at low tide then forces the sperm masses out of the ostiole. When the plants are lapped by the returning tide, the coat enclosing the sperm becomes gelatinous and the sperm escape into the water and swim actively to the eggs. A single antherozoid effects fertilization. Its nucleus fuses with the female nucleus and the zygote, thus produced, immediately secretes a membrane, which prevents the entry of other sperm, and thereby becomes an oospore. The oospore in *Fucus* is not a resistant stage and it commences to germinate immediately provided it is in water. An account of development from the zygote will help to elucidate the complex structure of the thallus.

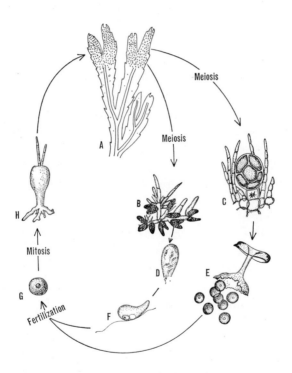

FIG. 27. Life cycle of *Fucus*. A, fertile portion of mature sporophyte. B, antheridia on branched filaments within a conceptacle. C, an oogonium containing ova and surrounded by sterile paraphyses within a conceptacle. D, antherozoids escaping from the exuded sac formed by the inner wall of the antheridium. E, ova being released from the exuded sac formed by the two inner layers of the oogonium. F, a biflagellate antherozoid. G, zygote. H, young sporophyte. (A, original, the rest after Thuret.)

Embryonic development and growth

The nucleus of the zygote divides first and then a wall is laid down in a plane at right-angles to the incident light. The lower cell contains few plastids and from it develop elongated attachment cells known as rhizoids. The plant attaches to rock surfaces by the rhizoids and from them the holdfast later develops. The upper cell divides to form a club-shaped thallus which bears apically a funnel-shaped depression from which arises a tuft of hairs or filaments (Fig. 27). Each of these filaments has a basal region of active cell division. Growth of the thallus proceeds, however, from a single apical cell lying in the floor of the depression. Because growth in *Fucus* is from an apical cell, the genus has been contrasted with filamentous forms but, in fact, the apical cell is merely the persistent basal cell of one of the terminal filaments and the structure of *Fucus*, although complex, is essentially filamentous.

The apical cell has the form at first of a three-sided and later of a four-sided pyramid with its apex outward. This cell cuts off cells by walls laid down parallel to its four sides and to its base. The cells cut off in one plane are thinner than those cut off in the plane at right-angles so that the thallus soon assumes a flattened form. When the apical cell divides longitudinally, and each new apical cell proceeds to divide in the way already described, a forking or dichotomous branching of the thallus is produced. The first branches are equally developed but subsequent dichotomy is not symmetrical, one branch always showing a greater potential of elongation than the other. This difference in potential is related to difference in size of the two cells produced by longitudinal division of the initial apical cell. The superior growth potential alternates rhythmically from one side of the plant to the other so that, although individual dichotomies are asymmetrical, the thallus as a whole remains roughly symmetrical.

As a result of the divisions on all sides of the apical cells, a mass of similar, thin-walled cells, with dense contents and numerous phaeoplasts, is produced behind the apex. As new cells are cut off this mass of cells comes to lie progressively further behind the apex and differentiation into the constituent tissues of the thallus commences. These layers are shown in Fig. 26. The outermost of the cells change very little in form and constitute the outermost layer of the thallus. The layer is rich in phaeoplasts and because of its importance in photosynthesis is termed the assimilating layer or, because its cells are capable of division, the meristoderm. Increase in size of the vacuoles of the underlying cells produces a tissue known as the cortex. The cortical cells contain numerous plastids and are concerned with carbohydrate manufacture and storage. They, too, are capable of division and the cortex therefore increases in thickness towards the base of the plant. The innermost of the cells produced at the apex develop into a central tissue or medulla composed of elongated branched filaments, the constituent cells of which have few plastids. The large spaces between the filaments are filled with mucilage. Ramifying amongst the medullary filaments are thick-walled hyphae or fibres produced from the inner cells of the cortex. These fibres form the bulk of the stipe and holdfast. In the midrib the medulla is thicker than elsewhere and the medullary filaments are conspicuous, running longitudinally. These longitudinal filaments probably serve to convey food materials in solution.

Thus division of labour in *Fucus* is more pronounced than in most "thallophytes": distinct tissues are concerned with absorption and photosynthesis (meristoderm); conduction (medullary filaments); storage of carbohydrates (cortex); strengthening (cortical hyphae or fibres); attachment (fibres of the holdfast); and reproduction (cells lining the conceptacles) to mention the more important ones.

Reduction of alternation of generations in Fucus

We have already seen (p. 54) that other Phaeophyta show a strict alternation of generations and that this involves, as it does in chlorophyll-containing plants above the thallophytes, alternation of a diploid asexual spore-producing plant, the sporophyte, with a haploid sexual gamete-producing plant, the gametophyte. The fact that other genera of the Phaeophyta show alternation has aroused the suspicion that the diploid *Fucus* plant which gives rise to gametes is in fact homologous with a sporophyte and the hypothesis has been put forward that the undivided antheridia and oogonia are really sporangia. It is considered that the gametophyte has been reduced to gametes only. The existence of traces of septation in the oogonia and antheridia which is never found in normal sporangia of Phaeophyta is explained by considering the septa to be the remains of cellularization of the gametophyte. The complexity of the walls of the antheridia and oogonia further suggests that they might be sporangia containing precociously developed, but much reduced, gametophytes.

Indirect evidence that such a reduction of the gametophyte could occur is seen in the related genus *Laminaria* in which the gametophyte is a minute filament on which the gametangia are borne; by the occasional precocious germination of zoospores to form gametophytes while still in the sporangia in some Phaeophyta which show alternation of generations; and by the series of reduction in the gametophyte which exists in higher plants and culminates in the angiosperms in which the gametophyte consists of little more than gametes (see p. 218). This reduction in the gametophyte in *Fucus* must, however, be regarded as an independent development which has not led to the production of higher forms, and the fact that the life history of *Fucus* resembles that of an animal in that only the gametes are haploid, though worthy of note, of course suggests no affinity between the two kingdoms.

CHAPTER 3

Fungi

THE Fungi are unicellular or basically filamentous plants which are devoid of chlorophyll and are therefore either saprophytic or parasitic. They show many resemblances to the Algae and are considered by some authorities to be algae which have become heterotrophic and have, perhaps as a result of parasitism, emphasized asexual reproduction often at the expense of sexual reproduction. The latter is progressively simplified and obscured as the higher forms are approached. The many points of morphological similarity of the fungi and algae make it impossible to categorically rule out derivation of the fungi from the algae.

One reason for considering fungi, with their morphological resemblance to algae, to succeed the latter group was the belief that the heterotrophic mode of nutrition must necessarily have been derived from the autotrophic, photosynthetic, nutrition of the algae. The hypothesis has been advanced, however, that fungi may constitute a separate kingdom which existed before the plant and animal kingdoms and that its members were saprophytic upon organic substances formed without the intervention of biological systems. It has even been suggested that fungi gave rise to the plant and animal kingdoms and that this explains their close resemblances to the lowest plants, the algae, and the lowest animals, the protozoa. Morphological resemblances to the algae are many and the presence, in some fungi, of a cellulose cell wall is a plant feature. On the other hand, forms like the Myxomycetes or slime moulds, which can engulf and apparently digest bacteria, and are amoeboid in form and movement, perhaps connect them with the rhizopod protozoa. The storage of glycogen and the common occurrence of chitin, in the cell walls, are animal features. In short, it has been suggested that the heterotrophic precursors of the animal kingdom and of chlorophyll-containing plants, which we have previously mentioned, were fungi.

The fossil record is so scanty as to be almost valueless in enabling us to choose between these views, and even the most profound research into the comparative morphology and physiology of existing types cannot establish with certainty the affinities of these ancient groups.

Whatever their phylogenetic position, fungi comprise a very large and important group of saprophytes and plant (and sometimes animal) parasites. Organic substances, of which the main are carbohydrates and amino acids, are absorbed from the substrate and inorganic substances, including nitrates, ammonia, phosphates and sulphates, are also absorbed. Their requirements of metallic elements appear to differ from those of higher plants.

Except in the simplest forms, the thallus consists of a mycelium or network of filaments known as hyphae. In the lower forms these are coenocytic with few or no cross walls. Hyphae of higher forms are septate and may be aggregated, as in the fructification of the mushroom, into pseudo-tissues.

The fungi are divided into the following groups according to the method of spore production.

1. Archimycetes

These have no mycelium, the body of the organism being a naked mass of protoplasm, the plasmodium, which forms one or more sporangia. The spores give rise to motile flagellated swarm cells which function as gametes. Examples are the free-living amoeboid slime moulds and *Plasmodiophora* which causes swellings of the roots known as club root in cabbage and other Brassicae.

2. Phycomycetes

The thallus in these is unicellular or is composed of filaments known as hyphae. The hyphae are frequently coenocytic and septa are commonly restricted to the older parts or to the reproductive branches of the thallus. Reproduction is asexual by the production of zoospores or of non-motile spores and sexual by production of motile isogametes or by oogamy. Only rarely, in a few of the aquatic forms, is the antherozoid released from the antheridium.

The group is largely aquatic but it contains terrestrial saprophytes of which we will study *Mucor* (Fig. 29) and parasites of higher plants including *Pythium*, *Cystopus* and *Peronospora* which will be dealt with in a separate volume.

3. Ascomycetes

The typical spores in these are ascospores which are produced in elongated sacs called asci, usually eight spores to an ascus. The asci are borne on ascogenous hyphae which may develop from oogonia known as ascogonia after union with antheridia. Commonly, however, sex organs are not distinguishable and the nuclei which unite in the production of asci from ascogenous hyphae are produced from vegetative hyphae. Asexual reproduction is by the production of non-motile spores called conidia or conidiospores, which may be cut off in chains and produce new mycelia on germination. The asci are commonly produced in fruiting bodies composed of a pseudo-parenchyma of compacted hyphae. These fruiting bodies may be flask-shaped perithecia or cup-like apothecia.

Among the simplest of the Ascomycetes is *Penicillium* (Fig. 28) from which the antibiotic Penicillin is obtained. Some Ascomycetes form attractive, small, often highly coloured club-like fruiting bodies on soil and many are serious plant parasites. We will study a somewhat aberrant Ascomycete of great economic importance, *Saccharomyces cerevisiae*, brewers' yeast.

4. Basidiomycetes

This group lies apart from the rest of the fungi and is believed by some to be of separate origin. Basidiomycetes are characterized by great complexity of the fruiting bodies and by the production of basidia, which are club-shaped bodies each of which typically bears four spores (basidiospores) on projections known as sterigmata. The basidia may be scattered over the entire fructification or grouped in definite regions.

The mycelium, which develops from a basidiospore, is composed of uninucleate cells, but secondary mycelia, with binucleate cells, commonly develop by confluence of two mycelia and give rise to the fructifications, nuclear union occurring in the production of each basidium. Asexual reproduction when present is by the production of conidiospores.

Basidiomycetes of immense economic importance are the two orders of plant parasites the Uredinales or rusts, of which the grain rust, *Puccinia graminins*, will be dealt with in a further volume, and the Ustilaginales or smuts. We will study in this chapter a saprophytic member, *Psalliota*, the mushroom, which belongs to the large order Agaricales.

5. Fungi Imperfecti

This is a group in which only asexual stages, which are often referable to the Ascomycetes, are known. They are plant parasites.

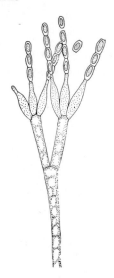

Fig. 28. *Penicillium.* Conidia borne on branched conidiophore.

PHYCOMYCETES
Mucor
Habitat and form

Mucor is a genus of some forty to eighty species (the number recognized depending on the importance attached to certain criteria in classification), saprophytic on decaying organic material in soil and on other sources of organic substances including human foodstuffs. It is one of the first fungi to appear on fresh horse dung and may be cultured in the laboratory by keeping the dung moist under a bell jar. A similar treatment of moist bread may yield *Mucor* but commonly produces *Rhizopus*, another of the Mucorales.

The thallus consists of a weft or mycelium of branching and interwoven hyphae (Fig. 29), the cytoplasm of which contains many small nuclei. Septa are produced only in the older parts of the mycelium and in the reproductive hyphae. The mycelium is therefore coenocytic. The walls of the hyphae are said to consist of a substance allied to animal chitin but there is indirect evidence for the presence of cellulose. The hyphae ramify both over and within the substrate from which the following nutrients must be absorbed for healthy growth: carbohydrate, e.g. glucose; a suitable nitrogen source, e.g. inorganic ammonium salts and more complex nitrogenous substances such as amino acids; certain mineral elements, particularly potassium, sodium, iron, magnesium, sulphur and phosphorus; and, for some species, an external source of vitamin B_1 (thiamin). Where the nutrient materials exist in nondiffusible forms, for instance, carbohydrates as starch and amino acids in the combined form as protein, digestive ferments are exuded from the hyphae into the substrate and the substances are absorbed after breakdown to diffusible forms.

Reproduction

Within a few days of the development of the mycelium from a spore asexual reproduction commences (Fig. 29). Certain hyphae are produced which grow vertically (according to some authorities because they are negatively hydrotropic, according to others because they are positively phototropic) and the tip of each hypha enlarges to form a spherical vesicle containing many nuclei. In some species the hypha is branched and a vesicle develops at the tip of each branch. Cleavage of the cytoplasm then occurs and each nucleus appropriates a small amount of cytoplasm so that many elliptical, or in some species spherical, spores (sporangiospores) are produced. The contents of the sporangium as the vesicle is called, are meanwhile isolated from the contents of the supporting hypha or sporangiophore by the development of a dome-shaped septum, the columella. The size of the sporangiospores ranges from slightly less than 3·0 µ in diameter in *Mucor buntingii*, in which they are spherical, to 28 × 10·5 µ in *M. irbutensis* which has elliptical spores.

The wall of the sporangium darkens with age and in most species is dark brown or black at maturity though in a few it is olive-green or even rose-coloured. In some species, including *M. mucedo*, the common bread mould, and *M. spinosus*, the sporangium wall becomes coated with crystals of calcium oxalate which in the latter species gives it a spiny appearance. The sporangiospores are shed by dissolution of the wall of the sporangium owing to deliquescence, the sporangium becoming enveloped in a drop of liquid, as in *M. mucedo*; or by fragmentation of the dry wall as in *M. racemosus*. The columella remains intact and the ruptured sporangium wall persists as a small ragged collar or collarette at its base. The spores adhere to the columella but, as they dry, are wafted away by air currents or removed passively by insects. In suitable conditions each sporangiospore germinates by protrusion of hyphae which grow and branch to form a mycelium.

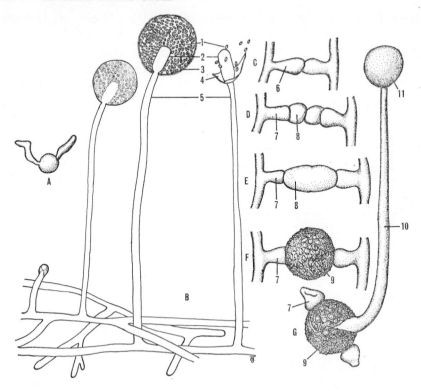

FIG. 29. *Mucor*. Stages in development. A, germinating sporangiospore. B, mycelium bearing sporangia: 1, sporangiospore; 2, columella; 3, wall of sporangium; 4, collarette; 5, sporangiophore. C–F, conjugation and zygospore formation: 6, progametangium; 7, suspensor; 8, gametangium; 9, zygospore. G, germinating zygospore: 10, promycelial hypha; 11, sporangium.

An additional form of asexual reproduction occurs in some species. Portions of the cytoplasm become enclosed in thick spherical or elliptical walls, thus forming chlamydospores, which are released on dissolution of the hypha. The subsequent development of chlamydospores resembles that of sporangiospores. Both types of spores are capable of resisting unfavourable conditions, including desiccation, for long periods.

Reproduction in *Mucor* is mainly asexual but sexual reproduction also occurs under certain conditions. In sexual reproduction (Fig. 29) two hyphae come into contact and each develops a lateral swelling at the point of contact. These swellings are termed progametangia and their growth pushes the hyphae apart. The protoplasm in each progametangium contains many nuclei. Development of a transverse septum near the tip of each progametangium divides the latter into a proximal suspensor and a distal (apical) gametangium. Subsequently the adpressed walls of the gametangia break down and the protoplasts of the two gametangia mingle. The single protoplast thus formed secretes a thick wall of several layers, the outermost of which is dark and bears many low pyramidal excrescences, and constitutes the zygospore. The old gametangial walls rupture because of the growth of the zygospore and flake off. On the death of the suspensors the zygospore is freed. The zygospores resemble the asexually produced spores in being resistant to adverse conditions but, unlike the latter, they do not germinate in favourable conditions until a dormant period of about 4 months has elapsed. Germination produces a promycelial hypha at the tip of which a sporangium is formed and the subsequently liberated sporangiospores give rise to new mycelia. It is said that the zygospores sometimes give rise directly to mycelia.

The nuclear events in formation of the zygospore are not fully understood, partly because of the opacity of the walls of the zygospore and partly because of the small size of the nuclei. According to Cutter (1942), whose observations confirm and extend those of several other workers, the zygote of *M. genevensis* initially contains about fifty nuclei as a result of mitotic divisions. These nuclei begin to fuse in pairs, union being completed in about 4 days. By the sixth day, however, the large fusion nuclei are replaced by twice their number of smaller nuclei, presumably as a result of reduction divisions or meiosis. The nuclei of the promycelial hypha produced by germination of the zygospore would thus be haploid as would be the sporangiospores and the subsequent mycelia.

Other workers state, however, that only two nuclei unite in the formation of the zygote and the fusion nucleus is said by some to give four nuclei by reduction division prior to germination, rather as in *Spirogyra*. Another view is that meiosis occurs in the promycelial hypha. These conflicting opinions may be valid conclusions from observations of different species. What does emerge from the confused picture is that the normal mycelium is haploid and that the diploid phase is limited to the zygospore and possibly the promycelial hypha.

The relative rarity of sexual reproduction as compared with asexual reproduction was explained in 1904 by Blakeslee's discovery of heterothallism in the Mucorales, a phenomenon which was later found to occur throughout the fungi. Blakeslee found that members of the Mucorales, including several species of *Mucor*, did not reproduce sexually unless mycelia derived from separate spores were mixed. The two conjugating mycelia were morphologically identical but physiologically distinct and were distinguished as + and − strains. No sex could be attributed to these strains. The existence, within a species, of strains which in reproduction could be shown to be physiologically distinct but were otherwise indistinguishable was termed heterothallism. In some species, however, sexual reproduction was found to occur by conjugation in a mycelium derived from a single spore. Such species were said to be homothallic.

In some homothallic species morphological differences between conjugating gametangia are observable, however. Such species are said to be heterogamic and homothallic and one example is *Absidia spinosa* in which the gametangia differ greatly in size. The smaller gametangium is said to be the male and the other the female. In hybridization of *A. spinosa* with *Mucor hiemalis*, a species in which both gametangia are alike, i.e. is homogamic, but which is heterothallic, it was found that male gametangia of *Absidia spinosa* united with the gametangia of the + strain of *Mucor hiemalis* and the female gametangium with the − strain gametangia of *M. hiemalis*. Thus it may be said that although *M. hiemalis* is homogamic, its − strain gametangia are physiologically male and its + strain gametangia are physiologically female.

In the genus *Mucor* a single promycelial sporangium gives rise to either + or − strain spores, never to both, a condition which differs from most other fungi.

ASCOMYCETES
SACCHAROMYCETALES
A Yeast, Saccharomyces
Form and habitat

Saccharomyces cerevisiae is an organism of great economic importance known, because it is used to ferment malt in the production of beer, as brewer's yeast. It is a unicellular plant which exists in two forms of which it is believed that one is diploid and the other haploid. These two forms are, in their behaviour, similar respectively to the sporophytic and gametophytic phases in plants which show alternation of generations. We shall see below, however, that alternation is not obligate and that either phase is capable of reproducing asexually by budding for long periods. Also the gametophytic stage is commonly omitted.

The diploid cells (Fig. 30C) are either spherical or slightly ovoid and are about 10 μ in diameter. The cell wall is delicate and appears to be a compound of two polysaccharides (glycogen and mannan) with phosphoric acid. There is no cellulose. The cytoplasm contains a large vacuole which is often considered to form part of the nuclear apparatus. According to the latter view the nucleus is represented by a nucleolus-like body and the vacuole, then known as the nuclear vacuole, and a system of threads (believed to be chromatin) and granules on the surface of the vacuole. Other authoritative accounts describe the nucleus as a well defined structure and consider the vacuole and associated structures to be distinct. The performance of the nucleus in cell division (asexual reproduction) is equally uncertain. Some authorities claim that division is entirely amitotic while others state that it is by simple mitosis (involving, according to some, two chromosomes).

In addition to the large vacuole there exist in the cytoplasm smaller vacuoles, in which are stored glycogen, and others in which volutin, a substance closely allied to if not identical with ribonucleic acid, occurs. Oil globules are also reported.

Reproduction

Asexual reproduction by budding (Fig. 30A, B) occurs abundantly in aqueous conditions with sufficient food materials. An alternative form of reproduction, which is also asexual, occurs in unfavourable conditions, particularly shortage of water. It involves the formation in the yeast cell, presumably by reduction division (meiosis), of four spores (Fig. 30D) which are generally considered to be ascospores, though it is by no means certain that *Saccharomyces* is truly an ascomycete. In true ascomycetes, ascopore formation follows nuclear fusion and it has been shown in *Saccharomyces* that, although a long period of asexual budding may precede formation of these spores, there is at some period before their formation a union of two cells and of their nuclei. The asexual budding has, however, become very important in *Saccharomyces* and in some species of the genus it is the only type of reproduction known.

In budding a protrusion of the cell wall develops and grows until it constitutes a second cell attached to the first by a narrow neck. Each cell contains a single nucleus derived by division of the original nucleus. That the nuclear division is mitotic is, as we have seen above, not certainly established. If the connecting neck breaks, the two cells separate but frequently proliferation by budding is more rapid than separation and masses of interconnected cells develop. In *Saccharomyces ludwigii* these masses in certain nutritional conditions resemble hyphae.

Sexual reproduction is brought about by union of ascospores in pairs after rupture of the cell wall (ascus) which encloses them. If conditions are favourable the zygotes thus produced immediately commence asexual budding of the type already described. If, however, the ascospores fail

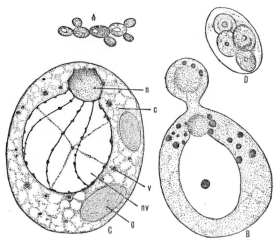

FIG. 30. *Saccharomyces*. A, cells budding and forming chains. B, single cell forming bud. C, a single cell: c, cytoplasm; g, glycogen; n, nucleolus; nv, nuclear vacuole; v, volutin. D, ascospore formation. Adapted from James.

to conjugate, each may reproduce asexually by budding. The individuals produced in absence of conjugation are much smaller than the individuals which gave rise to ascospores and are believed to be haploid because they arise from ascospores. The haploid individuals never form ascospores but they eventually conjugate in pairs, and the resultant zygotes, like those produced by direct conjugation of the ascospores, give rise to large, presumably diploid, cells by budding.

The life history of *Saccharomyces cerevisiae* may be summarized as follows (Fig. 31). *Saccharomyces cerevisiae* is normally encountered as a diploid form which reproduces asexually by budding. This is to be regarded as a sporophytic stage as it gives rise to spores (ascospores), presumably by reduction division. These may produce smaller, gametophytic, individuals. The latter individuals give rise to gametes, i.e. conjugating individuals, after a period of asexual (or vegetative) budding.

There is a tendency to reduction of the gametophyte, however. The reproductive cells of the sporophyte generation which would, if alternation were normal, act as asexual spores, in certain circumstances act as gametes. The gametophytic stage is then missed out and the life history is spent, with the exception of the "gametes" (ascospores), solely in the diploid condition.

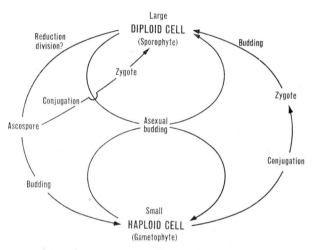

FIG. 31. Life cycle of *Saccharomyces*.

In another member of the family Saccharomycetaceae, *Schizosaccharomyces octosporus* (Fig. 32), no alternation of generations can be made out as the cells are exclusively haploid and the zygote, which is produced in certain circumstances by conjugation, is the only diploid phase. The zygote immediately gives rise (it is believed by reduction division) to eight spores. The spores are considered to be ascospores and the zygote wall thus constitutes an ascus. The life history of *Schizosaccharomyces* thus closely resembles that of a true ascomycete and suggests that the life history of *Saccharomyces cerevisiae* has developed by the interpolation of a period of asexual budding of the zygote, termed by analogy with higher plants the sporophytic stage, and reduction of the haploid stage in which the life history of fungi is normally spent. This haploid phase is called by analogy the gametophytic stage.

It will be seen that where the gametophytic stage of the life history of *Saccharomyces* is omitted, the life history resembles that of *Fucus* in which the sporophyte also gives rise to individuals which fuse in pairs. It must,

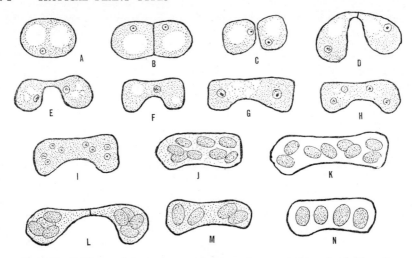

FIG. 32. *Schizosaccharomyces octosporus*. A, vegetative, haploid cell. B, cell division. C–F, stages in conjugation. G–K, stages in formation of ascospores. L–N, parthenogenetic formation of ascospores. From Smith.

however, be remembered that in *Saccharomyces* the conjugating units (ascospores) would seem to be spores acting as gametes, while in *Fucus* the uniting organisms are typical gametes produced from an extremely reduced and almost unrecognizable gametophyte borne within the sporangia of the sporophyte. Also in *Fucus* reduction of the gametophyte is invariable and there is no asexual reproduction.

BASIDIOMYCETES

Psalliota

Form and habitat

Psalliota (Agaricaceae) is a large genus of gill-bearing fungi (Agaricales), the fructifications of which are welcome additions to the diet of people of temperate and tropical regions. Its members are known colloquially as mushrooms; a term extended in some parts of the world to include other genera and even poisonous Agaricaceae. The three British species are *Psalliota campestris*, the field mushroom (Fig. 33E); *P. arvensis*, the horse mushroom; and *P. hortensis*, the cultivated mushroom. The latter is cultivated in many parts of the world.

The mushroom is a saprophyte on organic materials in soil, though some accounts claim that it can also subsist on grass roots. It is particularly common in well manured open grassland. The mycelium is septate, like that of all basidiomycetes, but it differs from the mycelia of most agarics in that the cells, instead of being binucleate, are multinucleate. *In vitro* the mycelium has been shown to grow well in a solution containing glucose; urea as a nitrogen source; sulphate and phosphate of potassium, magnesium and calcium; and traces of iron, manganese, zinc and copper.

Reproduction

Most agarics are heterothallic in that fruiting bodies are not produced unless two mycelia unite. On union of the two mycelia a nucleus from one mycelium migrates into the nearest cell of the other mycelium so that the latter cell, which is initially uninucleate, becomes binucleate. Subsequent septation of the hypha then occurs by formation of "clamp connections" which ensure that each new cell receives a nucleus derived from each of the uniting mycelia by mitotic division. *Psalliota* is exceptional, however, in being homothallic, i.e. a mycelium derived from a single spore is capable of giving rise to fruiting bodies. Furthermore, it differs from most agarics in its multinucleate cells and in lacking clamp connections. Although it is homothallic, anastomoses between distinct mycelia frequently occur and anastomoses within the mycelium create a three-dimensional network. Certain of the hyphae are compacted into white string-like growths known as rhizomorphs which facilitate spreading of the fungus. These rhizomorphs are not so highly developed nor as effective in spreading the fungus as are those of, for instance, *Armillaria mellea*, the honey agaric, a parasite of trees, in which the rhizomorphs are composed of a compact pseudo-tissue and may run for many yards.

The development of a fructification (sporophore) is shown in Fig. 33A–D. It arises as a knob on the mycelium. This knob consists of closely compacted hyphae which, by their growth, enlarges and assumes the form of an ovoid constricted at its equator. The lower portion constitutes the stipe or stalk of the sporophore and the upper portion becomes transformed into the cap or pileus with its ventral gills or lamellae; the velum or veil, which protects the gills in development; and the upper part of the stipe. The transformation of this upper portion proceeds as follows. At first a ring-shaped or annular cavity develops towards its lower surface concentric with the developing stipe. The lower wall of this cavity constitutes the velum and the upper wall the pileus. From the developing pileus hyphae grow down into the cavity in such a way that they form

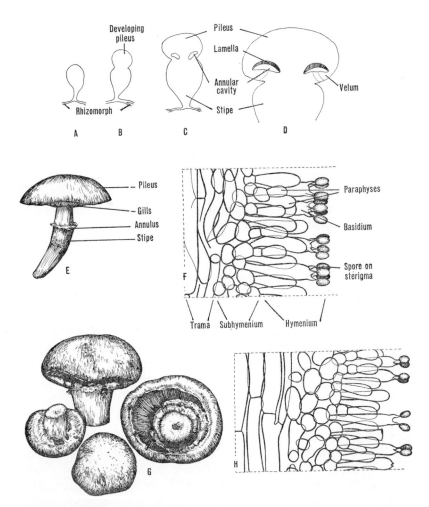

FIG. 33. *Psalliota*. A–D, stages in the development of the sporophore. E, *Psalliota campestris*, the field mushroom, × ½. F, section of a gill of the same, highly magnified. G, *P. hortensis*, cultivated mushroom, × ½; note that the velum is beginning to split in the specimen on the left. H, section of gill of same, highly magnified, showing sterigmata reduced to two per basidium (E, F and H redrawn from Buller).

radiating vertical lamellae, the gills, which become differentiated as described below. The gills do not actually join the stipe, being separate from the latter by a small distance, a characteristic of the genus. Because the gills converge towards the stipe there is more room between adjacent gills peripherally than centrally, and it is found that the space between adjacent full-length gills (primary gills) is occupied peripherally by half-length gills (secondary gills), and intercalated between half-length and full-length gills are quarter-length gills (tertiary gills). The arrangement is not, however, perfectly regular. These gills are exposed when, through growth of the stipe, the velum breaks. The velum is thereafter represented by a slight fringe on the circumference of the pileus and a conspicuous ragged annulus around the top of the stipe. Such a velum is known as a partial veil as opposed to the universal veil of some agarics which extends, before rupture, from the pileus to the base of the stipe and ruptures in two places, leaving an upper annulus and a basal volva. In some agarics there is no veil and the gills are exposed throughout their development. The top of the pileus, which is at first convex, becomes concave as the mushroom ages.

Each gill is made up of closely compacted hyphae which constitute three pseudo-tissues. Seen in vertical section (Fig. 33F) these pseudo-tissues are a central trama, the innermost hyphae of which run vertically downwards and the lateral hyphae obliquely outwards; a subhymenium consisting of two layers of rounded cells; and an outermost single-celled layer, the hymenium, consisting of the tips of the hyphae, which if sterile are termed paraphyses and if spore-bearing are called basidia. The basidia are longer than the paraphyses and each bears on its outermost surface four projections known as sterigmata. In the mature basidium, the tip of each sterigma bears a single basidiospore.

Although the cells of the general mycelium of *Psalliota* are unusual in possessing several nuclei, the number of nuclei per cell is less in the sporophore and is successively reduced as the subhymenium is approached until each cell of the subhymenium and hymenium possesses only two nuclei as in other Basidiomycetes. In each basidium these nuclei unite to form a diploid nucleus with eighteen chromosomes. This then gives rise to four nuclei by reduction division. Typically in Basidiomycetes four sterigmata then grow out from the tip of the club-shaped basidium and the tip of each sterigma swells. A single nucleus then migrates into each swelling, thus forming a basidiospore. Migration of each nucleus is said to be due to the action of a protoplasmic fibril, equivalent to an astral ray of an animal cell, which extends from each nucleus to a centriole which has come to lie at the base of each sterigma. The four centrioles arise during the reduction divisions. (Centrioles are typical of dividing animal cells and in plants occur only in the lower forms, chiefly those with flagella). Also, increasing vacuolation of the basidium, which is observable, probably forces the nucleus and associated cytoplasm into the sterigma. The nucleus of each basidiospore divides once before the spore is shed. *Psalliota hortensis*, the cultivated mushroom, is unusual in that only two sterigmata are borne on each basidium (Fig. 33F, H). Each spore receives two nuclei and on their division, before discharge, becomes quadrinucleate.

The spores are colourless at first but gradually turn to a purplish brown. This and the darkening of a pinkish cell sap in the hyphae of the gills gives the mature gills their characteristic dark brown coloration.

Each spore has a projection or hilum near its attachment to the sterigma and, just before discharge of the spore from the sterigma, this projection exudes a drop of water. The mechanism of discharge is not clear but the spore is shot out horizontally to a distance of about 0·1 mm and then falls under gravity. By the time it emerges below the lamellae its volume has decreased because of drying and it is easily wafted away by air currents. The almost constant distance between opposing gill surfaces of 0·5–0·7 mm ensures that spores do not stick to opposing gills as does the great sensitivity of the sporophore to gravity. The gills grow vertically in response to gravity and the stipe maintains them in a vertical position owing to its negative geotropism.

It has been estimated that a mushroom about 3 in. in diameter produces about 800 million spores and the fact that a single mycelium may last for several years, and may produce several fructifications each year, indicates the small chances of successful propagation by the spores. It is known that in water a small proportion of the spores will germinate in laboratory conditions after a week or ten days. Germination is facilitated by the proximity of a mycelium.

Lichens

A lichen is a symbiotic association between an alga and a fungus. The fungus forms the body or thallus of the compound organism. It obtains oxygen during the day and photosynthetic products from the alga, while the alga obtains from the fungus anchorage, carbon dioxide, water and protection from desiccation. The fungus is almost always an Ascomycete while the alga is usually a unicellular member of the Chlorophyta or less commonly of the Cyanophyta. Occasionally the alga is filamentous and in some tropical lichens the fungus is a Basidiomycete. The algal component can, and often does, grow alone (an example is *Pleurococcus*) but the fungus dies without its symbiotic partner.

Although the lichen thallus is composed mainly of fungal hyphae, its form is distinctive and unlike that of any "pure" fungus. Three main forms of thalli occur among the known "species". These are the encrusting (crustose) form; the flattened, somewhat leaf-like (foliose) form; and the shrub-like, upright or pendant (fruticose) form.

In the more complex lichens, the following layers can be distinguished.

1. An upper cortex of closely compacted hyphae.
2. A layer containing the algal cells or gonidia, the gonidial layer.
3. A less compact layer, the medulla.
4. A lower cortex (often absent).
5. A hypothallus, a thin sheet of hyphae which is more easily seen at the margins than elsewhere.

Any of these layers may be absent as a distinct stratum but, by definition, algal and fungal components are always present. The structure of a species of *Physcia* is shown in Fig. 34.

Reproduction

Asexual reproduction occurs by the formation of small rounded bodies termed soredia which are dispersed by wind. Each soredium consists of one or more algal cells surrounded by fungal hyphae. Soredia are usually recognizable as a greyish powder on the thallus.

In sexual reproduction the fungus reproduces in the way characteristic of the order to which it belongs. If, as is usual, it is an Ascomycete it produces cup-shaped fruiting bodies termed apothecia (Fig. 34) or flask-shaped ones termed perithecia on the walls of which develop asci. Each ascus typically contains eight ascospores. Although these may germinate on a suitable surface, the hyphae they produce will not survive unless they come into contact with the appropriate alga.

Ecology

Lichens have a wider distribution on the earth's surface than any other plants, occurring from the arctic and above the tree-line on mountains, to hot desert regions, and are pioneer organisms on uncolonized rocks,

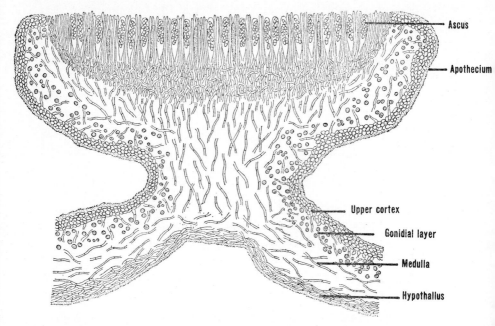

FIG. 34. Semi-diagrammatic vertical section of a species of the lichen *Physcia*, passing through an apothecium. Adapted from Smith.

a versatility which they apparently owe to their compound nature. The biological characteristics of the fungus are more radically changed than are those of the algal partner as the following list shows.

Fungi	*Lichens*
Best developed in warm countries	Best developed in cold countries
Mostly of delicate texture	Mostly of tough texture
Prefer shade	Prefer sun
Require much moisture	Can tolerate severe drought
Thrive in bad air	Require pure air
Grow rapidly	Grow slowly
Develop secondarily	Usually pioneers

CHAPTER 4

Bryophyta—Liverworts and Mosses

THE phylum Bryophyta contains three classes:
1. Hepaticae or liverworts.
2. Musci or mosses.
3. Anthocerotae, a group sometimes classed with the liverworts.

All are inconspicuous plants except when massed. They show alternation of generations which has been defined on p. 38 and is discussed in detail in Chapter 6. The plant which is recognized as a liverwort or as a moss is a gametophyte, that is to say, a haploid plant which gives rise to gametes whose union produces the zygote and hence the sporophyte.

Archegonium

The Bryophyta differ from the algae, but resemble the ferns (Pteridophyta) and certain seed plants (Gymnospermae), in having the female gamete enclosed in a flask-like multicellular structure termed the archegonium which is embedded in the tissues of the gametophyte. The archegonium (Fig. 43B) consists of a rounded basal portion, the venter, and a more slender terminal portion, the neck. The wall or jacket of the archegonium (including the neck) surrounds an axial column of cells arranged in single file which consist of a variable number of neck canal cells, a ventral canal cell and a large basal egg cell (oosphere). In all plants with archegonia (collectively termed the Archegoniatae) the male gametes are motile and usually require external water in which to reach the archegonium. Within the archegonium fertilization and development of the embryo sporophyte occur.

Sporophyte

In bryophytes, the sporophyte is throughout the whole of its life nutritionally dependent on the gametophyte. This contrasts with the Pteridophyta (e.g. ferns) where the sporophyte becomes the dominant generation

81

and is only dependent as an embryo on the gametophyte, and with the Spermatophyta where the female gametophyte has come to be wholly dependent on the sporophyte for its nutrition. The sporophyte of a bryophyte is insignificant in size and appearance relative to the gametophyte but the degree of nutritional dependence of the mature sporophyte on the gametophyte varies. In the mosses, and also many liverworts, the sporophyte is capable of photosynthesis and that of *Anthoceros* can, in some circumstances, become nutritionally independent. The significance of these trends is discussed in a review of alternation of generations in Chapter 6.

The sporophyte of most bryophytes consists of a foot, by which nutrients are obtained from the gametophyte throughout life and which is variously modified for this function, a seta (stalk) and a terminal spore-containing capsule. Branching does not occur and lateral appendages, e.g. leaves, are lacking. In liverworts the wall of the capsule consists of a single layer of cells (as in *Marchantia*, Fig. 44) or two to four layers and the structure of the capsule is never complex, such specialization as exists being directed to spore production and dispersal. In most liverworts, mixed with the spores are sterile elongated cells, with spirally thickened walls, which are called elaters. These, because of their hygroscopic properties, writhe about after dehiscence and aid spore dispersal.

We will see in the account of the moss *Funaria* that the capsule has a very complex structure (Fig. 52) but again this is chiefly related to spore production and dehiscence. The capsule of *Funaria* has functional stomata and well developed photosynthetic tissue. Liverwort capsules lack stomata but the statements so often made, that they lack photosynthetic tissues, is very far from the truth. For instance, the sporophyte of *Marchantia* is very strongly photosynthetic and has chloroplasts in the cells of the foot, of the capsule wall and in the elaters. The sporophyte of *Anthoceros* is also photosynthetic and has functional stomata.

Gametophyte

The bryophytes are distinguished from the pteridophytes and spermatophytes by the simplicity of their sporophytes and the permanent nutritional dependence of these on the gametophyte, and also by the fact that the dominant phase in the life cycle, the gametophyte, is simpler in organization than the dominant sporophyte of the pteridophytes and spermatophytes.

The gametophyte (Figs. 35, 46) is either a flattened lobed thallus or a leafy shoot which has rhizoids, which serve for anchorage and absorption, but has no true roots. A vascular system of the type seen in the sporophytes of the Pteridophyta and Spermatophyta is lacking.

FIG. 35. *Marchantia polymorpha.* Female gametophyte bearing two archegoniophores and, on the right, gemma cups (cupules), actual size.

Rhizoids

The rhizoids of the Hepaticae and Anthocerotae are unicellular and therefore resemble root hairs of other Archegoniatae rather than roots. In the mosses the rhizoids are multicellular with the cells arranged in single file, and here again they are not structurally comparable with true roots. In the moss genus *Andreaea* the rhizoids are cylindrical masses of flat cell plates.

Stem and Leaves

The stem in mosses usually shows differentiation into epidermis, cortex and central cylinder and in most mosses the leaves, the blade of which is usually one cell thick, have a midrib which has a central cylinder of specialized, thin-walled cells known as hydroids with or without thickened surrounding cells (Fig. 47B). In some mosses, e.g. *Polytrichum,* these "foliar bundles" are continuous with the hydroids of the central cylinder of the stem. It is incorrect to say that bryophytes are non-vascular, for it has been shown that these hydroids conduct water from the rhizoids into the stem and in some cases directly to the leaves. Nevertheless, in most mosses external conduction of water by capillarity on the surface of the plant and its absorption by thin-walled cells at the growing apex and at leaf bases is more important than internal conduction. The moss *Mnium* is interesting in being reliant chiefly on internal conduction. It is interesting that this genus has the leaves further apart, and less suitable for conduction by external capillarity, than in other mosses.

Some liverworts, known as leafy liverworts, have a definite stem but this shows little or no differentiation into different tissues. The central cells may be bigger or smaller than the cortical cells and usually have thinner walls but there is probably no specialized conducting tissue internally.

We will now consider two bryophytes, namely, the liverwort *Marchantia polymorpha* and the moss *Funaria hygrometrica*, both of which are cosmopolitan.

A LIVERWORT

Marchantia polymorpha

Distribution

Marchantia polymorpha occurs in many parts of the world, including both temperate and tropical regions. It grows in shady, moist places and it often reaches its best development on damp burnt soil, following forest fires or even local burning off. A form of *M. polymorpha* grows submerged in swampy meadows.

Gametophyte (thallus)

The thallus is flat, dichotomously branched, commonly 2–10 cm long, and possesses an indistinct central midrib. There are rhizoids and scales on the lower surface. It undergoes apical growth from a transverse row of initials. The upper epidermis shows hexagonal markings each hexagon corresponding to a small photosynthetic chamber below. In the centre of each hexagon is a small pore which opens into the chamber. The wall of the pore is not simple (Fig. 36); it consists of four vertical rows, each of four cells, arranged in the form of a barrel with its middle on the level of the epidermis so that half of the cells are above and half below the epidermis. The floor of each chamber bears numerous short, sometimes branched, filaments of cells (Fig. 36), which may touch the roof of the chamber. These filaments are very rich in chloroplasts and form the main photosynthetic tissue of the gametophyte. The remaining lower part of the thallus is several cells thick and the cells are parenchymatous and have numerous starch grains. Some of them, mucilage cells, secrete mucilage. The lower surface is covered with an epidermis composed of cells similar to those of the upper epidermis. These lower epidermal cells bear two types of outgrowths: scales (amphigastria) and rhizoids. The amphigastria are multicellular scales arranged in three or four rows on

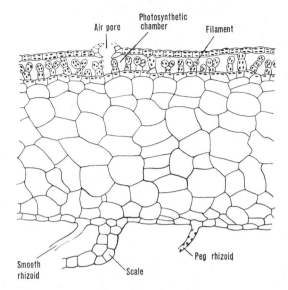

FIG. 36. *Marchantia polymorpha*. Vertical section through gametophyte.
Redrawn from Smith.

each side of the midrib. The scales of each row overlap and adjacent
rows also overlap. The scales protect the growing tip and also retain
water, by capillarity, which can be absorbed by the rhizoids. There are
two types of rhizoids (Fig. 36): smooth rhizoids and peg (tuberculate)
rhizoids. The smooth rhizoids emerge from behind the median scales
and penetrate the soil. The peg rhizoids arise behind the intermediate
scales or from the cells of the marginal scales. They lie parallel to the
underside of the thallus and form a system of conducting strands leading
forward to the growing point where water is readily absorbed.

Reproduction

Asexual reproduction is divisible into propagation by spores (p. 92),
and vegetative reproduction. Asexual reproduction accounts for more
propagation than does sexual reproduction. Vegetative reproduction occurs
by three chief means.

1. *Growth and death of parts of the thallus.* Cells of the thallus live
for only a month or two and therefore apical growth and branching,
followed by death of the cells of the posterior end as far as a dichotomy,
results in the production of two plants.

2. *Adventitious branches.* Adventitious branches sometimes develop from the ventral face of the thallus or even from such structures as the archegonia. These often become detached and give rise to new thalli.

3. *Gemmae.* Circular areas develop just behind the growing points (Fig. 35) and come to lie in depressions owing to upward growth of surrounding epidermal cells. The vessel thus formed is called a cupule (Figs. 35, 38, 39). Certain cells in its floor divide into a lower stalk cell and an upper primary cell. The primary cell divides horizontally and later vertically also to produce a biconvex multicellular body, a gemma (Fig. 37A) with a growing point in a small notch in the margin on each side.

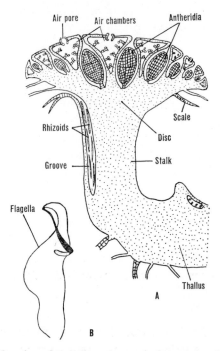

FIG. 37. *Marchantia polymorpha.* A, vertical section of an antheridiophore. B, antherozoid. From Parihar.

Specialized mucilage cells develop on the floor of the cupule and it is the swelling of the mucilage secreted by these when it imbibes water which breaks the gemmae from their stalks and forces them out of the cupule. If a gemma comes to rest on soil, rhizoids are put out from colourless cells in the epidermis and growth of the thallus proceeds from the two apices in the notches. Usually the central portion of the developing thallus dies so that each gemma produces two plants.

Sexual reproduction. In *Marchantia polymorpha* only one type of sex organ develops on a single gametophyte, i.e. the species is dioecious. The male organs (antheridia) are borne on an antheridiophore and the female organs (archegonia) on an archegoniophore (Figs. 35, 38). Both develop at the growing apex and form a direct continuation of the midrib. Their morphology closely resembles that of the vegetative thallus and they are undoubtedly modified apical branches.

Antheridiophore

In morphology the antheridiophore (Fig. 37) which is about 1–3 cm long, closely resembles a portion of the vegetative thallus which has turned upwards and grows vertically: ventilating pores and air chambers with photosynthetic filaments are present, as is the parenchyma and also lower epidermis and rhizoids. In transverse section (Fig. 40) the antheridiophore stalk looks like a narrow branch of the thallus, the margins of which have coiled downwards and inwards and have met below the midrib so as to create two vertical channels in which run the rhizoids. Antheridia develop on the upper surface of the antheridiophore which has the form of an eight-lobed disc. The antheridia are embedded in cavities sunk in the tissues between the air chambers. They develop in rows extending from the growing point of each lobe to the centre of the disc, the oldest being central. Each cavity contains a single large antheridium attached to a short basal stalk and has a tubular opening to the exterior. When the antheridium is mature, contact with water causes the apical jacket cells to break down and a mass of androcytes is extruded. These spread over the surface of the water and in a few minutes liberate the biflagellate antherozoids (male gametes, Fig. 37B) which swim by a serpentine movement of the flagella, one flagellum being directed anteriorly, the other posteriorly.

Archegoniophore

Like the antheridiophore this is thalloid (Fig. 43). Stages in its development are shown in Fig. 41A–D. By successive dichotomies it develops a terminal disc with eight lobes and, as in the antheridiophore, each lobe has its own apical growing point. Behind each growing point there develops a radial row of archegonia, the oldest archegonia being nearest

FIG. 38. *Marchantia polymorpha.* A, male gametophyte, seen from above, bearing two gemma cups on the left and two antheridiophores on the right, actual size. B, the same, seen from the side. C, disc of antheridiophore, viewed from above, showing rows of antheridia, × 4.

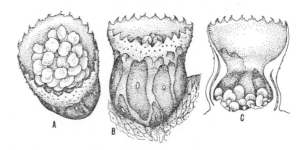

FIG. 39. *Marchantia polymorpha.* A, gemma cup containing gemmae, seen from above. B, same from the side. Note the diamond-shaped markings representing air chambers, each with a central pore on the thallus and, much larger, on the walls of the cupule. C, vertical section of gemma cup.

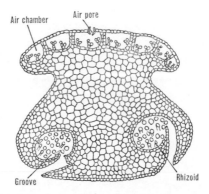

FIG. 40. *Marchantia polymorpha.* Transverse section of the stalk of an antheridiophore. From Parihar.

the centre. Before the disc of the archegoniophore is appreciably elevated above the thallus the first-formed archegonia are mature and fertilization has usually occurred. The antherozoids reach the archegonia by the agency of splashing or flooding rainwater and possibly by carriage on small invertebrates such as mites. After fertilization, and as the stalk elongates, a great expansion of the tissues comprising the centre of the

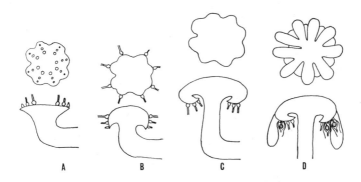

A   B   C   D

FIG. 41. *Marchantia polymorpha*. Diagrams of top views and vertical sections of stages in development of an archegoniophore. Slightly modified from Smith.

disc occurs and the margins of the disc are inverted by overgrowth so that the archegonia hang upside down and the oldest come to lie furthest away from the stalk (Fig. 41C). After this inversion a sheet of tissue grows out between each pair of lobes so that a curtain-like partition hangs down on each side of each row of archegonia. These outgrowths are known as involucres (*perichaetia*). Next a "ray" grows out, because of intercalary growth, between each pair of lobes. In *M. polymorpha* nine rays are produced (Figs. 41D, 42).

The neck of the archegonium (Fig. 43B) has a jacket of six vertical rows of cells. But the number of canal cells and the time at which the primary ventral cell divides to form the ventral canal cell and the oosphere are variable.

In some cases, e.g. some West African forms, the lobes of the antheridiophore disc are as long as, or longer than, the lobes of the archegoniophore, which lacks rays, and careful examination is necessary to distinguish between the male and female structures. The long lobes of the antheridiophores occasionally "take root" and develop as normal thalli.

D

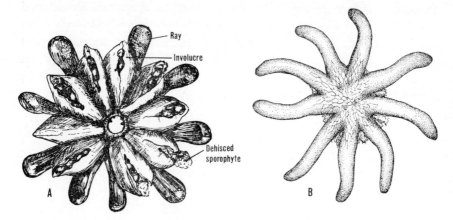

FIG. 42. *Marchantia polymorpha*. A, ventral view of a disc. The specimen is unusual in having nine instead of eight lobes to the disc. B, disc of archegoniophore, seen from above, showing the nine rays.

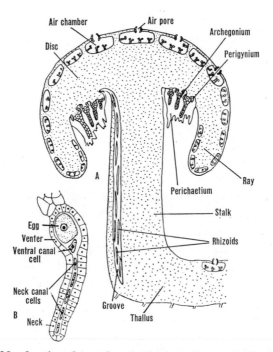

FIG. 43. *Marchantia polymorpha*. A diagram of a vertical section of an archegoniophore and a portion of the thallus. B, an archegonium. From Parihar.

Sporophyte

Division of the zygote produced by fertilization of the oosphere within the archegonium results in an embryo sporophyte. This differentiates into a foot, a seta or stalk and a capsule (Fig. 44). The lower portion of the foot is expanded and absorbs water and nutrients from the archegoniophore of the gametophyte. Meanwhile, fertilization induces certain changes in the archegonium and the surrounding tissues: the wall of the venter undergoes periclinal divisions (parallel to the outer surface) and the archegonium thus forms a thickened calyptra or cap over the embryo;

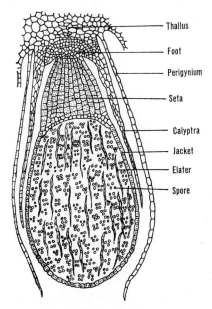

Thallus

Foot

Perigynium

Seta

Calyptra

Jacket

Elater

Spore

FIG. 44. *Marchantia polymorpha*. Vertical section through a mature sporophyte. Adapted from Parihar.

the cells below the base of the archegonium multiply to form a cylindrical sheath around the archegonium termed a pseudoperianth. The sporophyte thus has three concentric protective layers: an inner calyptra (jacket of archegonium), a middle pseudoperianth and an outer involucre.

The capsule of the sporophyte becomes differentiated into two layers: an outer amphithecium or jacket, one cell thick, and an inner mass of cells, the endothecium. The endothecial cells at the apex of the capsule may become sterile but the other cells elongate and about half of them undergo mitosis to form vertical files of four or five spore mother cells.

Each spore mother cell gives rise by meiosis to four haploid spores. The rest of the cells in the endothecium elongate greatly and develop spiral thickening of the walls. These are the elaters which function in dispersal of the spores. The walls of the jacket cells develop ring-like thickenings and dehiscence of the capsule then occurs (Fig. 45) but there are no definite lines of dehiscence.

FIG. 45. *Marchantia* sp. Dehisced sporophyte projecting from pseudo-perianth.

The spores are discharged by hygroscopic movements of the elaters. They germinate to give a filament of six to eight cells which may be two cells thick at the ends. A terminal cell then forms an apical initial and this cuts off cells so that the typical *Marchantia* thallus is formed. Spore dispersal does not occur until the seta has elongated greatly and the capsule has ruptured the calyptra and projects below the pseudoperianth and involucre.

Asexual production of numerous airborne cuticularized spores by the sporophyte lessens the dependence of *Marchantia* on sexual reproduction. The latter presents difficulties in those land plants which require external water for fertilization. Furthermore, the spores are an efficient means of dispersal. The occurrence of meiosis in the many spore mother cells instead of a single zygote greatly increases the probability of favourable genetical recombinations.

A MOSS
Funaria hygrometrica
Distribution

Funaria is a genus of mosses which occurs throughout the world. *Funaria hygrometrica* is cosmopolitan in temperate and warmer latitudes. Moss which forms a green carpet about an inch thick in shady places on walls, banks and level ground frequently belongs to this species. It is also a common colonizer of areas where other vegetation has recently been burnt off.

Gametophyte

The gametophyte has two successive forms: first a filamentous, alga-like, creeping protonema, which develops from a spore, and then a leafy upright gametophore (Fig. 46) which bears the sex organs. The gametophore is the typical "moss plant".

Protonema

A moss spore on germination gives rise to uniform filaments with numerous chloroplasts, and colourless cell walls of which the dividing walls are transverse, i.e. at right-angles to the axis of the filament. These chloronemal filaments ramify horizontally through or on the substratum. From them arises the fully developed protonema which is made up of (a) prostrate filaments with dark brown cell walls, *oblique* cross walls and few chloroplasts, which creep through or on the substratum and give rise at intervals to (b) thinner erect filaments with numerous chloroplasts, clear cell walls and transverse cross walls. The latter resemble the initial chloronemal filaments while the prostrate filaments resemble rhizoids of the later gametophore.

Later a bud arises as a lateral swelling from a cell of an erect filament, usually near its base, or, less commonly, from a brown prostrate filament. This bud cuts off one or two basal cells and then divides to form a tetrahedral apical cell with three cutting faces. This cuts off segments some of which give rise to leaves and others to rhizoids and hence a gametophore is formed. Several gametophores commonly arise as separate buds from a single protonema and on the death of the protonema, which soon occurs, become established as separate plants.

Gametophore

The gametophore (Fig. 46) consists of an upright monopodially branching stem, about 1–3 cm high, which bears ovate, pointed leaves which, at the apex, are arranged in three vertical rows corresponding to the three cutting-faces of the apical cell. Further down, the leaves become spirally arranged. Each branch arises below a leaf in contrast with the Spermatophyta. Basally the gametophore sends anchoring and absorptive rhizoids into the soil. Each rhizoid is a multicellular filament with the cells arranged in single file and separated by oblique cross walls. Where

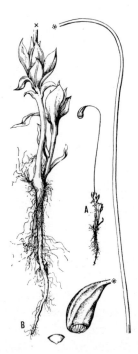

Fig. 46. *Funaria hygrometrica.* A, entire gametophore showing long female branch bearing a sporophyte and shorter male branch, actual size. B, the same, × 4, showing also the detached operculum to the left of the sporogonium.

the rhizoidal system is fully developed it can be seen that relatively stout brown rhizoids, each of which arises from a superficial basal cell of the gametophore, penetrate vertically for about two 2 cm into the substratum, and that each of these gives off colourless, finer, lateral branches which give rise in turn to even finer branches. There is thus a system analogous to the primary, secondary and tertiary branching of the roots of higher plants. There is, of course, no division into roots and root hairs. The whole of a branching rhizoid, arising from a superficial epidermal cell, is like a multicellular root hair and no vascular roots are present. Probably only the finer branches are concerned with absorption and the thicker basal regions serve solely for anchorage and conduction. Where rhizoids are exposed to light they develop chloroplasts and closely resemble protomenata.

The stem

The stem shows three clearly differentiated regions: the epidermis, cortex and central cylinder (Fig. 47A). The epidermis is usually one cell thick but is double layered in some places; it contains chloroplasts but

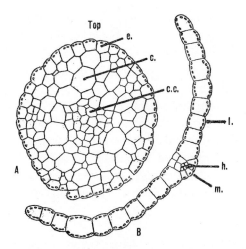

FIG. 47. *Funaria hygrometrica.* Transverse section of A, the stem and B, a leaf: c, cortex; c.c, central cylinder; e, epidermis; l, lamina; m, midrib; h, hydroids. Adapted from Smith.

has no stomata. Only in the younger parts of the stem does the cortex contain chloroplasts. Further from the growing point the outer cortical cells develop thickened reddish brown walls. The cells of the inner cortex remain thin-walled. Leaf traces, consisting of thin-walled elongated cells from the midribs of the leaves, end blindly in the cortex. The cells of the central cylinder are elongated and thin-walled and lack protoplasm.

At most they play only a minor role in conduction of water which occurs mainly by capillarity on the external surfaces of the plant (see, however, *Mnium*, p. 83).

The leaves

The leaves have a well defined midrib, which has a central cylinder of cells with slightly thickened walls (hydroids), and a fairly broad blade or lamina which consists of a single layer of cells (Fig. 47B). The cells of the lamina have numerous chloroplasts which can often be seen in the process of division. Again, there are no stomata, these being limited to the sporophyte generation. The gametophore has a remarkable ability to recover after severe drying if rewetted.

Reproduction

Vegetative reproduction. In mosses, as in liverworts, vegetative reproduction is of great importance, an importance perhaps related to difficulties of fertilization in terrestrial plants by free-swimming antherozoids. The following types of vegetative reproduction occur in *Funaria*.

1. *Gemmae.* During unfavourable conditions, including drying and injury, gemmae develop on the stem and leaves and also on the rhizoids where they are termed bulbils. These gemmae are capable of developing into leafy plants on return of favourable conditions and, as many may be produced on one gametophore, may result in considerable multiplication of the plant. Gemmae also develop by division of terminal cells of the protonemata.

2. *Primary protonemata.* We have already seen that a protonema developed from a spore (i.e. a primary protonema) usually gives rise to several gametophores which become separate plants on its death. Vegetative reproduction of the protonema by death of some of its cells and the development of the isolated parts as protonemata also occurs. In *Funaria* such division of the protonema is facilitated by development of special colourless separation cells.

3. *Secondary protonemata.* These are distinct from primary protonemata developed by splitting of the first-formed primary protonema. Secondary protonemata are developed (a) from rhizoids of the gameto-

phore which have become green owing to exposure to light; (b) as out-growths from detached or wounded aerial parts of the gametophore including stem, leaves, antheridium and archegonium; and (c) from parts of the sporophyte such as sterile cells of the capsule or of the seta.

4. *Apospory.* This term means production of a gametophyte from a sporophyte without the intermediary of spores. We have already considered an example of it in 3 (c) above. Secondary protonemata derived from sterile sporophyte tissue, and the gametophores they produce, differ from normal gametophytes in being diploid (like the sporophyte). They are, nevertheless, fertile. Union of gametes from the diploid gametophores gives viable sporophytes with four sets of chromosomes (i.e. tetraploids) or, where union is with normal gametes, triploid sporophytes. Apospory is not of common occurrence in *Funaria* under normal conditions.

Sexual reproduction. At first sight it appears that the male and female organs of *Funaria hygrometrica* are borne on separate plants but investigation of the development of a gametophore reveals that it is protandrous: at first the main shoot of the gametophore bears a group of antheridia at its apex; later a female branch develops as a lateral branch from the base of the male branch and attains a greater height than the male branch (Fig. 46A).

Antheridia

The male shoot is about 1 cm high. The leaves near its tip are crowded together and somewhat enlarged and form a rosette or perichaetium (Fig. 48A). At the convex expanded growing point numerous antheridia develop in no apparent order, so that all stages in development are present. The perichaetium with its antheridia is sometimes called the "moss flower" but, of course, has no homology with the true flower of an angiosperm. The flower-like appearance is enhanced by a reddish coloration of the central leaves of the perichaetium.

The mature antheridium has a stout multicellular stalk and a club-shaped body. The wall or jacket of the body of the antheridium is made up of a single layer of cells which, with the exception of one or two apical cells, which form a lid or operculum, contain chloroplasts. It surrounds a dense mass of androcytes.

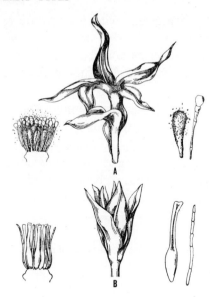

FIG. 48. *Funaria hygrometrica.* A, centre, tip of male shoot showing perichaetium, × 8; left, the same, with perichaetium removed to show antheridia and (longer) paraphyses; right, an antheridium and a paraphysis. B, centre, tip of female branch, × 8; left, same with leaves removed to show archegonia and paraphyses; right, an archegonium and a paraphysis.

Paraphyses

Intermingled with the antheridia are upright sterile hair-like structures termed paraphyses (Fig. 48A, 49) each of which is composed of a single row of four or five chloroplast-containing cells which distally are greatly enlarged. They probably function to retain water by capillarity, or perhaps to secrete water, for the developing antheridia. Paraphyses also occur on the female branches.

Dehiscence of the antheridium

If water collects in the cup formed by the perichaetium, ripe antheridia undergo dehiscence. Rupture of the opercular cells occurs and the androcytes are extruded as a sausage-shaped mass. The androcytes spread out over the surface of the trapped water. Each androcyte then undergoes metamorphosis into a biflagellate antherozoid.

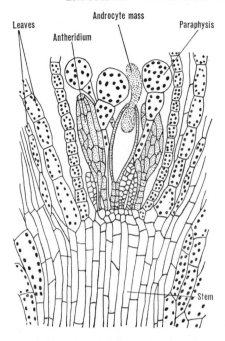

FIG. 49. *Funaria hygrometrica*. Vertical section of the tip of the male
branch. From Parihar after Sachs.

The archegonia

The archegonia (Fig. 50) develop on a special female branch, usually
at its tip. They are surrounded by leaves which differ little if at all in
appearance from those of a sterile branch. Intermingled with the archegonia are sterile paraphyses. The archegonium has a relatively long stalk,
a slightly bulbous basal portion or venter, and a long neck. The jacket
is two cells thick in the region of the venter but the neck is usually single-
layered, consisting of six vertical rows of cells. Inside the jacket there is
the usual axial column of cells: neck canal cells, of which there are six,
the ventral canal cell, and the egg. Of these, all but the egg disintegrate
by maturity to form a mucilaginous substance. The upper jacket cells of
the neck diverge to allow entry of the antherozoids.

Fertilization

The biflagellate male gametes (antherozoids) require external water
to reach the archegonia. Rainwater plays an important part in splashing
antherozoids from the perichaetial cup to the apices of the female branches

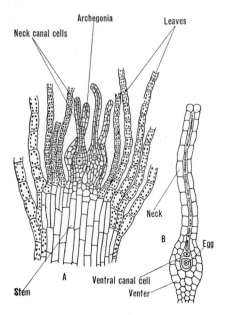

FIG. 50. *Funaria hygrometrica*. A, vertical section of the tip of the female branch. B, an archegonium. From Parihar after Sachs.

but it frequently must happen that the tips of the branches are totally immersed in water as is the case temporarily during heavy rain, so that the antherozoids can swim freely between the branch tips. It seems that the direction of swimming is random until the antherozoids are in the vicinity of an archegonium. After this they are attracted to the neck of the archegonium by chemical stimulation, i.e. chemotaxis occurs. Although several may penetrate the mucilage of the neck and reach the oosphere, only one enters the latter and effects fertilization. The nuclei have been observed to unite within 10 hr.

The sporophyte (sporogonium, Figs. 46, 51, 52)

The first division of the zygote within the archegonium marks the formation of the first rudiment of the sporophyte. Two apical cells, at opposite poles, are cut off as apical growing-cells, each with two cutting faces. The upper apical cell ultimately forms by its divisions the capsule and the major part of the seta or stalk of the sporophyte, the lower apical cell gives rise to the foot and the lower portion of the seta. The embryo

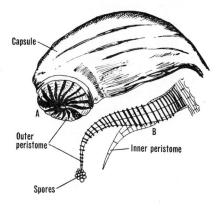

FIG. 51. *Funaria hygrometrica.* A, mature sporogonium showing intact peristome after fall of operculum. B, one outer and one inner tooth of the peristome. Redrawn from Parihar after Cavers.

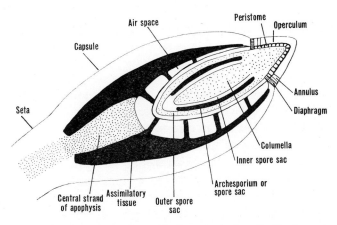

FIG. 52. *Funaria hygrometrica.* Diagrammatic longitudinal section of the sporogonium.

sporophyte is long, slender and upright. Its lower end burrows through the archegonium and into the apex of the female branch of the gameto-phore from which the foot absorbs nourishment. As the embryo increases in size, the archegonium around it enlarges but ultimately the archegonium ruptures at its base and the upper part is taken up with the sporophyte, as this is raised above the gametophore by gradual elongation of the seta.

This cap-like remnant of the archegonium is termed the calyptra. The seta has a well developed axial strand of cells which are believed to function in transporting nutrients from the gametophore to the capsule. The seta is wider within the base of the capsule where it forms an assimilatory zone termed the apophysis. This has an axial strand continuous with that of the seta. Surrounding its axial strand is a broad zone of chloroplast-containing cells which constitute a tissue very like the mesophyll of a leaf of a higher plant. Externally the epidermis in the region of the apophysis has stomata which also resemble those of higher plants.

The capsule (Fig. 52), is a complex structure with relatively little fertile tissue, the bulk being concerned with assimilation and dehiscence. The capsule may conveniently be divided into three regions; (1) the apophysis, the sterile assimilatory basal region; (2) the theca, a central fertile region; (3) the apparatus of dehiscence consisting of the operculum and peristome.

The apophysis

This has been discussed above.

The theca

The theca lies distal to the apophysis. Its axis is formed by a column of sterile, thin-walled parenchymatous cells, known as the columella. The upper end of the columella is convex and fits into the operculum; its lower narrow end connects with the apophysis by filamentous strands of photosynthetic cells. The columella runs up the centre of a barrel-shaped spore sac. Immediately internal to the sporogenous tissue is a layer of small cells (the outer layer of the columella) which forms the inner wall of the spore sac, usually called, misleadingly, the inner spore sac. The cells making up the outer walls of the spore sac are termed the outer spore sac, equally misleadingly. The sporogenous tissue within the spore sac consists of spore mother cells each of which divides by meiosis to give a tetrad of four haploid spores. Outside the outer wall of the spore sac is a wide cavity which is crossed by filaments of photosynthetic cells of which those connecting the columella with the apophysis are a part. Those connected to the spore sac run to the outer wall of the capsule. The capsule wall in this region consists of two to three layers overlain by the epidermis. The innermost layer is composed of loosely arranged cells containing chloroplasts; the outer two layers are a colourless parenchyma constituting a hypodermis. The photosynthetic layer widens below the fertile region and is continuous with the green tissue of the apophysis.

Operculum and peristome (Figs. 46B, 51)

The upper region of the capsule is specialized for dehiscence and spore dispersal. It is composed of two dome-shaped structures: a terminal operculum and an underlying peristome. These are marked off from the theca by a constriction. Below the constriction there is a transverse diaphragm composed of two or three layers of radially elongated cells. This diaphragm is interrupted centrally by the thin-walled cells of the columella. The diaphragm therefore forms a rim or ledge projecting inwards as far as the columella. The operculum consists of three layers of small, thin-walled cells bounded by the epidermis. It is, therefore, continuous with the outermost cells of the diaphragm. The peristome arises from the diaphragm just within the operculum. The basal, broadest part of the operculum, consists of two superimposed layers of swollen thin-walled epidermal cells. The two layers make up the annulus. The annulus functions in shedding the operculum. The peristome consists of an inner and an outer dome, each of which is composed of sixteen teeth, the tips of which meet at the apex. The two layers of teeth develop from a single dome-shaped layer of cells in the following way. The outer and inner (tangential) walls of the cell become thickened and cuticularized, whereas the radial walls remain unthickened. When the cells are mature the unaltered radial walls and the cell contents disappear, leaving an inner and outer cutinized dome each of which breaks in to as many teeth as there were cells around the circumference, i.e. sixteen.

Dehiscence of the capsule

When the capsule is mature it dries out and the cells of the annulus rupture so that the operculum is shed. The columella shrinks so that the spore sac comes into communication, through the rim of the diaphragm, with the cavity of the peristome. The peristomial teeth show hygroscopic movements. Each tooth is a two-ply structure, with an outer layer which shrinks when dry and lengthens when wet, while the inner layer is not affected by moisture changes. When the air is dry, the outer layer of the outer peristomial teeth shrinks and the teeth bend outwards. As a result, the spaces between the outer teeth widen. The inner peristomial teeth do not respond to moisture changes and act as a sieve which regulates the flow of spores outwards between the outer teeth. Shedding of spores is facilitated by hygroscopic twisting movements of the seta of the sporophyte. When the air is humid and spore-shedding undesirable, as the spore would tend to adhere in clumps and thus fail to disperse in the air, the outer peristomial teeth close owing to lengthening of the outer layer on absorption of moisture. The spores are thus prevented from leaving the capsule in conditions unfavourable for dispersal.

CHAPTER 5

Pteridophyta—Ferns and their Allies

FERNS and their relatives, psilophytes, club mosses, and horsetails, and some solely fossil forms which will not be discussed here, were until recently universally regarded as a single phylum, the Pteridophyta. In recent decades, however, a phylum Tracheophyta has been recognized which includes all vascular plants, from pteridophytes to the flowering plants. In 1956 one systematist, who has been widely followed, ceased to recognize the Tracheophyta as a valid grouping and instead made a separate "division" (i.e. phylum) of each of the pteridophyte groups mentioned in the first line of this paragraph. The latter worker also split the seed plants into several divisions (i.e. phyla) making the conifers a separate division from the flowering plants. The present authors consider that the group Tracheophyta is too broad and does not give sufficient emphasis to evolutionary innovations such as the reversal in the significance of the sporophyte relative to the gametophyte in seed plants as compared with pteridophytes. They also consider that the second, more recent, classification obscures, for instance, the fact that conifers and flowering plants have more in common than ferns and flowering plants.

The older classification, placing all pteridophytes in a single phylum, the Pteridophyta, and separating the seed plants as the phylum Spermatophyta, appears preferable to these systems. It is therefore retained here.

The Pteridophyta are divided into four classes, the Psilopsida, Lycopsida, Sphenopsida and Pteropsida. Each of these classes is represented by one living order. These orders are as follows.

1. Order Psilotales, e.g. *Psilotum*, psilotes.
2. Order Lycopodiales, e.g. *Selaginella*, club mosses.
3. Order Equisetales, e.g. *Equisetum*, horse-tails.
4. Order Filicales, e.g. *Dryopteris*, ferns.

FIG. 53. Examples of Pteridophyta. A, a psilote, *Psilotum triquetrum* (Psilotales), from Australia, × ½. B, sporangial triad, × 6. C, a club moss, *Selaginella trifurcata* (Lycopodiales), from Trinidad, habit from above, actual size. D, same from below. E, male strobilus bearing microsporangia, × 3. F, large leaf. G, small leaf, both × 6. H, a horse-tail, *Equisetum* sp. (Equisetales), from Madeira, × ⅛. I, whorl of leaves and J, strobilus with numerous sporophylls (sporangiophores), actual size. K, a single sporangiophore bearing several sac-like sporangia, × 4. L, a fern, *Squamosa hillebrandii* (Filicales), family Blechnaceae, × 1/24. M, part of one pinna, from below, × ½. N, midrib of one pinnule with elongated sorus on each side.

The ferns include the largest living Pteridophyta. Most ferns are herbaceous, but tree ferns, which are found in rain forest in many parts of the world, have been known to reach a height of 60 ft with a trunk 2 ft in diameter. These fern plants are an independent sporophyte generation and make a remarkable contrast with the minute "parasitic" sporophytes of the liverworts and mosses. The gametophyte is a minute, usually short-lived plant somewhat resembling a simple liverwort gametophyte. Some fossil representatives of the other orders were tree-like forms but the living representatives are all small plants.

Archegonium

The Pteridophyta indicate their relationships with the bryophytes and spermatophytes in having, as the female sex organ, a flask-like multicellular archegonium (Fig. 43).

Sporophyte

The sporophyte of all pteridophytes is, at maturity, independent of the gametophyte. The mature sporophyte has a vascular system with true xylem and phloem, and movements of water and dissolved mineral nutrients by capillarity on the external surfaces is unimportant. Usually the sporophyte is differentiated into stem, root and leaf but the most primitive members known, such as the Devonian fossil, *Rhynia*, had a dichotomously branching aerial body and a subterranean rhizome but no leaves or true roots.

The development of leaves relative to the stem varies in the Pteridophyta and it is possible to distinguish two groups: macrophyllous forms with a high development of leaves relative to the stem, the aerial parts of which may be inconspicuous, and microphyllous forms with relatively small or minute leaves, including the club mosses and horse-tails and also the Psilotales, containing *Psilotum*.

The spores are borne in bodies termed sporangia. The spores may be all alike, when the plant is said to be homosporous, or there may be many small microspores and fewer large megaspores, the heterosporous condition, as in *Selaginella*.

Vascular Tissue

There is great variability in the arrangement of xylem and phloem in the pteridophytes but histologically these tissues closely resemble those of seed plants. The protoxylem consists of annular and spirally thickened tracheids which, as in the seed plants, permit extension in the young growing plant while the metaxylem has tracheids with scalariform thickening and pitted walls, some groups even showing bordered pits like those of seed plants. The bracken fern, *Pteridium aquilinum*, which is found throughout the world, including tropical Africa, and the male fern, *Dryopteris filix-mas*, of Europe and Asia, including India, are unusual in the ferns, in having vessels, in the sense of vertical series of cells, arranged end to end with no cross walls. They differ from the vessels of the angiosperms in being of the same diameter as the tracheids. Pteridophyte xylem may also contain parenchyma.

The mature phloem consists of nucleated sieve cells without companion cells but with much phloem parenchyma. Secondary thickening is exceedingly rare in the present-day pteridophytes but was common in the tree-sized ancient Lycopodiales and Equisetales. The stele may be a protostele, comprising a solid core of vascular tissue, or a siphonostele with a central core of parenchyma. Within these two classes of stele there are numerous different arrangements of tissues. We will restrict our attention to a fundamental difference between the vascular anatomy of microphyllous and macrophyllous pteridophytes. In the microphyllous forms, e.g. *Selaginella*, where a vascular bundle runs out to a branch, there is, just above the point of departure, a gap in the vascular cylinder of the main stem, so that in transverse section above the point of branching, the ring of vascular tissue would be seen to be interrupted. In the region of departure of a leaf trace, i.e. a vascular bundle to a leaf, no gap occurs, however. In ferns, on the other hand, macrophyllous forms, gaps occur both at branches and at leaf bases. In this, they resemble gymnosperms and angiosperms, the spermatophytes.

Gametophyte

The gametophyte of the pteridophytes is usually a green, dorsiventrally differentiated thallus absorbing mineral solution by rhizoids but always lacking root and leaves. It is not unlike a simple liverwort gametophyte. There is a tendency in the ferns for it to become only one cell thick. In some species of *Lycopodium* and in *Psilotum* it is a colourless, subterranean, saprophytic organism requiring the presence of a mycorrhizal fungus (p. 20), for nourishment. There are no structures equivalent to the antheridiophores and archegoniophores which occur in some liverworts and the sex organs are normally borne on the ventral surface. Where heterospory is developed (in some ferns horse-tails and club mosses) the male gametophyte, developing from the microspore, is almost as reduced as that of the seed plants and the female gametophyte is nutritionally dependent on materials in the megaspore (Fig. 63). The significance of this reduction of the gametophyte stage is discussed on p. 122.

We will now deal in some detail with a polypodiaceous fern, *Dryopteris filix-mas*. The student should examine native ferns of the area in which he lives and compare them with the following description.

Further reference to the pteridophytes occurs on pp. 122–124.

THE MALE FERN
Dryopteris filix-mas
Distribution

The genus *Dryopteris* is cosmopolitan and *Dryopteris filix-mas* occurs in Europe and Asia, including India, where it grows in woodlands.

Sporophyte

The stem is rarely more than a foot long and is mostly subterranean lying obliquely to the soil surface (Fig. 54). Near the apex of the stem are several very large leaves (Fig. 55), often a yard long, known as fronds. Each has a strong tapering midrib consisting of a basal petiole and a more distal rachis. The rachis bears, on each side, a row of leaflets or pinnae, each with its own midrib, and the pinnae are further subdivided into pinnules, each of which has a relatively inconspicuous midrib and dichotomous vernation. Each frond develops from a single bud and constitutes a compound leaf. In bud, the axis of the frond (rachis and petiole) is coiled in one plane and each pinna is similarly coiled. Such folding of the young leaf is called circinnate vernation because of the similarity to a bishop's crozier (Latin *circinnus*). When young, the entire midrib is closed with small pointed delicate scales, termed ramenta. Characteristics of the ramenta are used in distinguishing between different species of ferns. The fronds do not uncoil until the year following their development. They then last only one season. They are replaced by new fronds developing at the apex in spiral succession. The old leaf bases remain and cause the stem to appear wider than it actually is. As new tissues are formed, as a result of activity of the growing point, the stem elongates, but it does not come to protrude appreciably further above the substratum. This is mainly because deposition of humus on the soil surface around the stem keeps pace with growth. The oldest basal parts of the stem die off and decay and thus the length of the stem, although it grows each

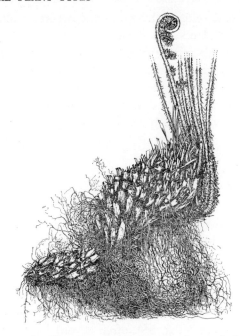

FIG. 54. *Dryopteris filix-mas.* Subterranean stem of the sporophyte showing old and current leaf bases, × $\frac{1}{8}$.

season, is limited. The very young sporophyte possesses a primary tap root but this is soon replaced by much branched adventitious roots, of which three usually grow at the base of each petiole.

Vascular tissue of the stem

In *Dryopteris*, the stele is broken up into a network of interconnecting bundles termed meristeles. Each meristele consists of a solid core of xylem, with protoxylem at its centre, which is surrounded by a cylinder of phloem and each has its own encircling endodermis with radial Casparian strips. The gaps in the network are leaf gaps, each lying above the point of departure of a leaf trace. Outside the meristele is a thick cortex which is bounded by the epidermis.

Vascular tissue of the root

In transverse section the root is very similar to a diarch angiosperm root (p. 151). The cortex consists of an endodermis, a thick-walled inner zone and a thin-walled outer zone.

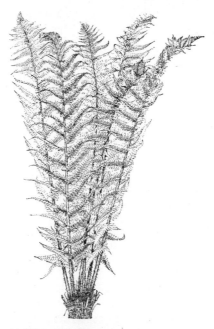

FIG. 55. *Dryopteris filix-mas.* Habit of the mature sporophyte above ground, $\times \frac{1}{12}$.

Sporangia

Dryopteris is homosporous. The sporangia are borne in clusters known as sori (Fig. 56) on the underside of mature leaves which may then be termed sporophylls. The sori are arranged in two rows, one along each side of the midrib of a pinnule. In some ferns the sporangia are naked but in *Dryopteris* the cushion-like swelling on which each sorus is borne gives rise also to a central stalk which bears a thin kidney-shaped membrane, the indusium (Fig. 57) which roofs over the sorus. Each sporangium arises from a single superficial cell of the placenta. By many divisions, each sporangium comes to consist of a small capsule with the shape of a biconvex lens, surrounding about 48 haploid spores produced by reduction division of spore mother cells. The capsule is borne on a slender stalk. The wall of the capsule is one cell thick and the constituent cells are flat and thin-walled except at the edge of the capsule where a row of cells with thickened inner and radial walls compose the annulus. The annulus is interrupted on one side by large thin-walled cells which comprise the stomium.

When dehiscense is about to occur, certain water glands on the stalk of the sporangium cease secretion of water, the indusium is shed, and the capsule begins to dry up. The thin outer walls of the annulus lose water rapidly and begin to contract, and adjacent thickened walls of the annulus cells are drawn together by cohesive force of the diminishing water of these cells. The result is that the stomium is torn open so that transverse

FIG. 56. *Dryopteris filix-mas.* Underside of a pinna composed of many fertile pinnules each of which has two rows of sori, × $\frac{2}{3}$.

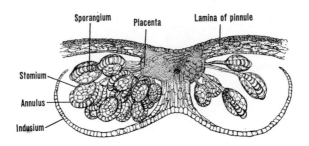

FIG. 57. *Dryopteris filix-mas.* Transverse section of a sorus, greatly enlarged.

dehiscence of the sporangium and shedding of the spores occurs. Periodically the "lid" of the sporangium snaps back into place, shedding adhering spores as it does so. This restitution of the lid is believed to be due to further drying out of the cells of the annulus so that the cohesive forces of the water disappear, air enters the cells and they resume their original size. It has been estimated that the output of spores from a mature plant is in the order of 500 million in a single season.

Gametophyte

After a period of dormancy a spore germinates, in favourable conditions, by bursting of its walls and emergence of a green cell. This gives rise to a branch which penetrates the soil as a rhizoid. The green cell divides to form a filament with a single apical cell, the transverse division of which extends the filament. After a time the apical cell also undergoes lateral divisions so that a rudiment of a thallus is formed. This develops into the mature green gametophyte or prothallus (Fig. 58). It is probably a secondary characteristic of fern prothalli that they are only one cell thick, with the exception of a cushion-like central region from which the rhizoids arise. The heart-shaped characteristic of a well formed prothallus is a result of the rapid enlargement of cells newly cut off from the apical cell which causes the apex to lie at the bottom of an indentation.

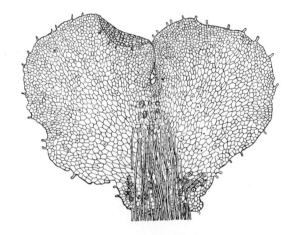

FIG. 58. Gametophyte of *Dryopteris*, highly magnified. Redrawn from Kny.

The prothallus is hermaphrodite but protandrous, the antheridia maturing before the archegonia. Both types of sex organ develop on the underside of the gametophyte though some antheridia occasionally develop dorsally. An antheridium has a jacket consisting of two superimposed ring-shaped cells, which surround the androcytes, which are produced by mitotic divisions of about 32 antherozoid mother cells, themselves the product of mitotic divisions of a single cell. The antheridium is closed by a cap cell. When the antheridium is mature, swelling of mucilage expels the androcytes, from each of which a flagellate antherozoid escapes into the surrounding water.

The form of the archegonia agrees with the generalized form described on p. 81. They differ from the archegonia of *Marchantia* but resemble those of some mosses, in having four instead of six vertical rows of jacket cells in the neck. Cross-fertilization between separate prothalli is the rule and is correlated with the protandry.

The embryo sporophyte develops by cleavage of the zygote. It derives nourishment from the gametophyte by means of a foot embedded in the venter of the archegonium. The young sporophyte (Fig. 59) puts out a small primary root and by the time the first leaf is large enough to supply the needs of the plant the gametophyte dies. The first five or so leaves produced by the sporophyte have a dichotomous lobing; subsequent leaves are pinnate. While the first leaves are developing, the primary root is replaced by adventitious roots.

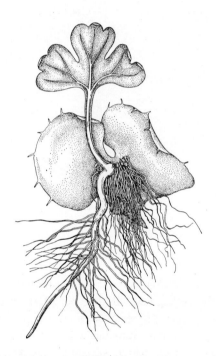

FIG. 59. Gametophyte of *Dryopteris* bearing young sporophyte, × approximately 15.

CHAPTER 6

Spermatophyta—Flowering Plants and their Allies

THE Spermatophyta, seed plants, have utilized a far wider range of terrestrial habitats than any other green plants and have established themselves as the dominant land flora. They have also successfully invaded fresh water. Their superiority over any other group of land plants in number of species is an expression of their unique adaptations to a terrestrial environment. They represent the culmination of several evolutionary trends which we have studied in the Thallophyta, Bryophyta and Pteridophyta.

Before dealing with the morphology of the Spermatophyta we will briefly review alternation of generations and the evolution and characteristics of terrestrial green plants.

ALTERNATION OF GENERATIONS AND THE EVOLUTION OF LAND PLANTS

The Ancestor of the Land Plants

The photosynthetic land plants belong to the Bryophyta, the Pteridophyta and the Spermatophyta. All resemble green algae in their photosynthetic pigments, and storage of starch. They resemble each other in possessing archegonia, although these may be greatly modified, and in having discoid chloroplasts. The gametophytes of some Bryophyta and the Pteridophyta show several points of similarity; and the Pteridophyta and Spermatophyta show many signs of relationship in the structure of the dominant phase, the sporophyte. It cannot be doubted that spermatophytes are advanced members of the pteridophyte stock. It seems likely that the bryophytes evolved from the same early archegoniate stock as the pteridophytes but the view that the two groups originated independently from green algae has some supporters.

One of the main difficulties in attempting to derive the archegoniate plants from green algae is to explain how multicellular, sterile-walled archegonia and antheridia could have evolved from the reproductive structures of the Chlorophyta. In the green algae, multicellular sex organs (gametangia) are rare. (They are, however, common in the brown algae.) In gametangia all the cells are fertile and become gametes. A purely speculative hypothesis has been put forward which derives archegonia and antheridia from the algal gametangium. According to this hypothesis, the gametangium developed an outer infertile jacket by sterilization of the outermost reproductive cells. This modification may have been selected because it reduced the danger of desiccation of gametes contained in the sex organs of an alga in a habitat which was prone to drying up. Such a modified gametangium would closely resemble an antheridium of a number of living archegoniate plants. Further sterilization of a female organ of this type, so that only a single gamete was produced, and the loss of motility of this gamete, i.e. the development of oogamy, would produce an archegonium. In support of the latter part of this hypothesis it may be noted that in the Archegoniatae, abnormal archegonia have been known in which many cells resembling developing antherozoids developed and that occasionally the ventral canal cell, as well as the oosphere, is fertilized and gives rise to an embryo.

The green filamentous form of the moss protonema and of the young gametophyte of some pteridophytes may be evidence of the descent of these groups from green algae. The algal ancestor is visualized, however, as having the form of a multicellular thallus or perhaps of a multicellular body with prostrate and erect branches. Where alternation of generations began is a matter of speculation.

Alternation of generations has been defined previously as the alternation of a haploid, gamete-producing plant, the gametophyte, and a diploid plant which produces spores by meiosis and is termed the sporophyte.

Alternation of Generations in Green Algae

In *Chlamydomonas* (p. 38) a unicellular haplophase which produces gametes alternates with a unicellular diplophase (the zygote) which produces zoospores (Fig. 60A). Because the zygote undergoes meiosis without the intervention of mitotic division and vegetative development, no alternation of generations can be said to occur in *Chlamydomonas*.

Three principal modifications of this type of life cycle occur in other green algae and involve interpolation of mitotic divisions in either the haplophase or the diplophase, or both, so that a multinucleate, and usually multicellular, plant is produced. In most green algae, e.g. *Oedogonium*, a multicellular haplophase alternates with a unicellular diplophase (zygote). This type of cycle is depicted in Fig. 60B; it does not constitute an alternation of generations. In some forms (Fig. 60C), e.g. *Codium*, vegetative (mitotic) division is interpolated between formation of the zygote and meiosis while the haplophase remains unicellular. As there are here vegetative haploid and diploid plants in the life cycle, alternation of generations is recognized. The third modification of the *Chlamydomonas* type of life cycle also involves alternation of generations; in it vegetative division occurs in both the haplophase and the diplophase (Fig. 60D). Into this category fall *Ulva*, the sea lettuce, and *Urospora*.

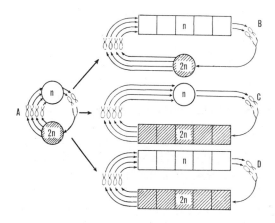

FIG. 60. Types of life cycles in the green algae (Chlorophyta).

In *Ulva* the two generations are identical multicellular flattened thalli which can only be distinguished at the time of reproduction. Every cell of the diploid plant retains the ability to divide meiotically and ultimately does so with the production of flagellated zoospores. In other green algae, e.g. *Cladophora*, meiosis is restricted to the tips of branches. Alternation of generations in which the two generations are identical is termed isomorphic alternation as opposed to heteromorphic alternation in which the two generations are structurally different, as in *Urospora*. In the latter a multicellular, filamentous haplophase alternates with a coenocytic diplophase.

Alternation of Generations in the First Archegoniate Plants

Having briefly surveyed alternation of generations in green algae, it will be clear that the possibility exists that the Archegoniatae inherited alternation of generations from their ancestral algae. The possibility must be borne in mind, nevertheless, that alternation developed independently in the Archegoniatae. Whatever the origin of this alternation, its advantages to early land plants are easily appreciated.

Advantages of Alternation of Generations in Land Plants

1. In a habitat subject to drying up, it is clear that reproduction by many cuticularized spores would greatly augment reproduction of the species by the less reliable means of sexual reproduction by motile gametes requiring external water in which to swim.
2. The possibility of a large number of genetic recombinations as a result of meiosis in many spore mother cells following a single union of gametes.
3. The airborne spores permitted wide dispersal of the species so that competition between individuals was minimized and more individuals survived.

Was the Sporophyte Primitively Dependent on the Gametophyte ?

Before the development of an archegonium the zygote would have germinated apart from the parent plant. With the advent of the archegonium, and the establishment of the first Archegoniatae, the zygote would have been retained in the parent body. If, as seems likely, there was alternation of generations, the embryo sporophyte developing within the archegonium would be in physical contact with the tissues of the gametophyte. The very development of archegonia and oogamy has been attributed above to the need for protection of the gametes against desiccation; and it would seem likely that initially the sporophyte, although green, would also be dependent on the gametophyte for some or even all of its inorganic nutrients. The *mature* sporophyte may have led a completely separate existence from the gametophyte, possibly on the death of the latter. In connection with this, it must be remembered that the diplophase in green algae is completely independent of the haplophase.

The First Archegoniate Plants—Summary

We can now summarize our deductions as to the nature of the first land plants.

1. They possessed a gametophyte which was a rootless, simple thallus or perhaps a branching filament more than one cell in diameter.

2. The gametophyte had a simple type of archegonium in which an immobile female gamete (oosphere) was fertilized by a free-swimming flagellated antherozoid.

3. The sporophyte developed from the zygote within the archegonium but, although as an embryo it was physically in contact with the gametophyte, it was probably green and only initially dependent for its nutrition on the gametophyte. It may well have become independent of the gametophyte following the death of the latter. Alternation may have been isomorphic.

We will now consider how the known archegoniate plants could have evolved from the hypothetical archegoniate ancestor.

Evolution of Liverworts, Mosses, Ferns and Seed Plants

In evolution from the ancestral archegoniate plant defined above there would be a possibility of emphasis on one generation relative to the other. Which was the dominant generation in the early descendants of the ancestral form can, perhaps, be deduced from an examination of the pteridophyte fossil *Rhynia* (order Psilophytales), its living relative *Psilotum* (Fig. 61) (order Psilotales) and the living liverwort-like bryophyte *Anthoceros* (Fig. 62). *Rhynia* had a dichotomously branching body consisting of a subterranean, creeping, rootless, rhizome and upright leafless, sporangium-bearing branches. Its gametophyte is unknown but that of *Psilotum*, which resembles *Rhynia* in many respects, is similar to the subterranean rhizome of the *Psilotum* sporophyte. The latter is nutritionally dependent on the gametophyte as an embryo but soon becomes free as was apparently the case in *Rhynia*. The sporophytes of both genera have true xylem and phloem and stomata with guard cells. The sporophyte of the bryophyte *Anthoceros* also has typical stomata but it is normally dependent throughout its life on the thalloid gametophyte. Where conditions for growth are very favourable, however, the green sporophyte may grow to three or four times its normal height, the sporogenous tissue at the base of the capsule may become sterile, and the weakly developed central core or columella may develop as a conspicuous conducting cylinder. Under these conditions the gametophyte may die and the sporophyte may persist, absorbing mineral salts in solution from the soil by means of the greatly enlarged foot and carrying out photosynthesis.

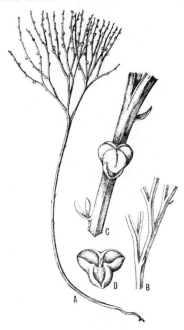

Fig. 61. *Psilotum*. A, habit of sporophyte, × ¼. B, portion of thallus showing dichotomous branching and minute leaves, actual size. C, portion showing triad of sporangia, × 3. D, dehisced sporangia.

It is commonly suggested that *Anthoceros* is a survivor of an ancestral stock of the pteridophytes which has failed to develop an independent sporophyte but it seems very likely that it is in fact derived from the pteridophytes by what could truly be termed degeneration. Just as the living club mosses, horse-tails and most ferns are dwarfs compared with the ancient pteridophytes with which they show relationship, so it seems possible that the sporophyte of *Anthoceros* has been greatly reduced. Its normal dependence on the gametophyte may be a result of this reduction.

Origin of Mosses and Liverworts

The mosses and liverworts, which have photosynthetic sporophytes (see p. 82), can be looked upon as descendants from the early isomorphically alternating stock. Permanent dependence of the sporophyte (as distinct from dependence only when young) on the gametophyte may have been secondarily acquired in the way we have discussed for *Anthoceros*. It would appear that liverworts, in which there are no stomata and

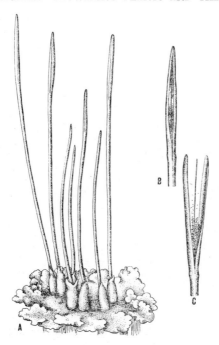

Fig. 62. *Anthoceros levis.* A, gametophyte bearing mature and immature sporophytes, × 2. B, tip of dehiscing sporophyte, × 4. In C the haploid spores are being released.

negligible vascularization, are descended from a more primitive form than are the mosses. Nevertheless, some workers regard elaters as modified spirally thickened elements of a now defunct vascular system, and therefore as an indication that the sporophyte was originally more complex. Certainly the bryophytes must be regarded as a side-line or blind alley in evolution because of the emphasis which they put on the gametophyte generation seen in the complex thallus of *Marchantia,* and the leafy shoots of the leafy liverworts and the mosses, and the rudimentary vascularization of the moss gametophyte. Such complexity as the sporophyte possesses is related chiefly to spore dispersal.

Whatever the evolutionary position of the bryophytes may be, they are well adapted to a terrestrial existence in the production of vast numbers of cuticularized, wind dispersed spores; the presence of stomata on the sporophyte; the possession by the gametophyte of absorptive and anchoring rhizoids; and the remarkable ability of the gametophyte in many to recover from desiccation. All bryophytes are under the disadvantage, so far as terrestrial existence is concerned, of having to rely on external water for fertilization by the free-swimming antherozoids. This perhaps adds to the advantages of vegetative propagation which is so common in the group.

Origin of Pteridophytes

In our discussion above the view has been expressed that certain fossil pteridophytes, the example taken being *Rhynia*, more closely resemble the primitive, ancestral Archegoniatae than do the bryophytes. This is supported by the great age of *Rhynia* fossils, which are Devonian, whereas the oldest bryophyte fossils are from later (Carboniferous) rocks. It is often said that the lack of bryophytes from the oldest strata is due to their softness and the consequent unlikeliness of their being preserved. But the conditions which permitted petrifaction of *Rhynia* so perfectly that histological detail is observable in prepared sections would presumably have preserved bryophytes had they been present. The possibility exists, nevertheless, that earlier bryophytes will yet be found.

The pteridophytes comprise a large and very successful group. They are often found in dry places, although many require humid conditions, and they are adapted to a wider range of terrestrial habitats than are the bryophytes. They exhibit all the adaptations to terrestrial existence which have been mentioned above for the bryophyte but the gametophyte easily suffers desiccation. The large, conspicuous sporophyte is truly vascular, possessing well developed xylem and phloem, and is divided into stem root and leaves. It becomes independent of the short-lived gametophyte early in ontogeny. The shortening of the gametophyte stage, with its susceptibility to desiccation and need for free water in fertilization, ensures sufficient exposure to moist conditions for development of the gametophyte even in regions of low rainfall. Furthermore, some gametophytes are able to omit the gametophyte stage completely by vegetative propogation of the sporophyte, and the need for external water in fertilization is eliminated in others by vegetative apogamy or by parthenogenetic apogamy. In apogamy the gametophyte gives rise to the sporophyte without fertilization: in vegetative apogamy, from vegetative cells of the gametophyte; in parthenogenetic apogamy, from an unfertilized egg cell. These modifications, which cut out fertilization, restrict the variability and adaptability of the species concerned, however, and, while they may ensure efficient reproduction in a limited range of habitats, they reduce the possibility of invading new habitats.

Certain of the Lycopodiales, e.g. *Selaginella* (Fig. 53C), have overcome the problem of desiccation of the gametophyte by the development of heterospory, i.e. many microspores and few megaspores are produced. Leaves bearing megasporangia are termed megasporophylls and those bearing microsporangia, microsporophylls. The large size of the megaspores enables storage of food, derived from the sporophyte, in the megaspore in sufficient quantities to sustain the female gametophyte which only partially emerges from the megaspore on germination (Fig. 63).

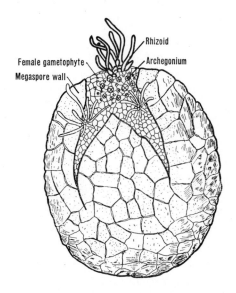

FIG. 63. Germinating megaspore of *Selaginella*. Redrawn from Cook and Mclean.

The microspores act virtually as antheridia and the male gametophyte is reduced to a single cell in the microspore. External water is still needed, however, for fertilization by the flagellated antherozoids. The advantages of such protection of the gametophytes from desiccation is partly offset by the reduction of the dispersive potentiality of the spores, the large megaspores being much less easily dispersed and fewer in number than the small spores of homosporous forms. In some species of *Selaginella*, the ova in the archegonia of the female gametophyte may be fertilized before the megaspore is shed from the strobilus.

The development of heterospory of a similar type in a few aquatic ferns appears to have a similar function (protection of the gametophyte from unfavourable conditions; but not in this case desiccation). The function of the retention of the female gametophyte within the megaspore in these aquatic forms is perhaps to shorten the gametophytic stage because of the poor conditions for photosynthesis which it experiences at the bottom of pools or amongst dense vegetation in contrast with the well illuminated site of the sporophyte.

Similar heterospory occurred in *Lepidodendron* of the Carboniferous, a relative of *Selaginella,* and in calamites, also from the Carboniferous, a relative of *Equisetum.* Both were tree-like forms which, unlike the ferns, were capable of secondary thickening. *Isoetes* (quillwort) is a small member of the Lycopodiales which may be a descendant of *Lepidodendron* and shows similar heterospory.

Those species of *Selaginella* in which the female gametophyte may be fertilized while still within the megasporangium on the sporophyte approach the seed plants in this condition.

Origin of Spermatophytes

Seed plants form a somewhat heterogeneous group (heterogeneous if certain fossil forms are included) with diverse morphological characteristics, the common feature of which is the possession of a seed. A seed is a ripened, fertilized ovule. An ovule may be defined in the broadest sense as a female gametophyte and its enclosing layers, namely the megaspore wall (embryo sac), the megasporangium (nucellus) and an integument, or two integuments, with an apical pore (the micropyle) see also, p. 217. Fertilization of the contained ovum before abscission converts the ovule into a seed.

It is sometimes difficult to decide whether the reproductive apparatus of a plant fulfils the above definition of a seed and therefore whether the plant can rightly be assigned to the Spermatophyta. For instance, *Lepidocarpon,* an extinct plant which flourished in the Carboniferous possessed an "integumented" ovule but the "integument" was derived from the sporophyll and therefore more nearly represented a carpel (p. 215) than a true integument. *Lepidocarpon* may therefore be looked upon as a blind alley in evolution which developed the carpel but failed to develop the true integument and it should be excluded from the Spermatophyta. Another Carboniferous plant, *Lyginopteris,* closely resembled ferns in general habit but the megasporangium was enclosed in two true integuments except at an apical pore, the micropyle, which probably held water. This ovule was probably fertilized by a motile antherozoid shortly before it detached from the sporophyte. *Lyginopteris* is placed in the order Cycadofilicales or Pteridospermae (seed ferns), an extinct group of the Spermatophyta. The seeds of the Cycadofilicales were naked, i.e. they were not enclosed by carpels, and the microspores alighted directly on the micropyle. Plants with naked seeds are grouped in the class Gymnospermae (literally "naked seeds") and we will now briefly discuss their present day representatives.

GYMNOSPERMAE

No embryos have been found in the fossils seeds of seed ferns and it seems likely, therefore, that the embryos did not develop in the seeds before they were shed. This is in marked contrast with the living orders of the Gymnospermae (the Cycadales, Ginkgoales, Coniferales, and Gnetales), in which the seed is embryonated before it is shed. All gymnosperms are characterized, however, by the nakedness of the seeds and in this are distinguished from the Angiospermae, the other class of the Spermatophyta, in which the seeds are completely enclosed and sealed in the megasporophyll (carpel).

Brief reference will now be made to three members of the Gymnospermae in order to complete the account of alternation of generations of which the present discussion is a part.

Cycas

The genus *Cycas*, which occurs in Africa, Australia and East Asia, is the most primitive of the order Cycadales. The general form of the plant (sporophyte) (Fig. 64) is similar to that of the tree fern and the leaves resemble those of ferns in that, when they are young, the pinnae and the main rachis are incurled (circinnate vernation). As in most gymnosperms, the microsporophylls and megasporophylls are borne in spirals in the form of cones (strobili; Fig. 65). All Cycadales are dioecious.

The microsporophylls are fleshy, wedge-shaped structures, becoming hard and woody when dried, which bear hundreds of microsporangia on their under-surfaces in an arrangement which resembles that of certain ferns. The megasporophylls (Figs. 65, 66) are borne on the main axis in series with the spirally arranged leaves and alternation of sporophylls and leaves occurs over the years. The megasporophylls are smaller than the leaves and lack chlorophyll but are otherwise very leaf-like. The integumented megasporangia or ovules, which are borne on the margins of the megasporophylls, are the largest in the Spermatophyta. The single integument of each seed is three-layered and the inner layer is stony. The micropylar canal is narrow and, at its base, the nucellus (megasporangium) develops a pit known as the pollen chamber. Four potential megaspores are produced in each ovule, but only one of these survives. By the time of pollination (see below) the contents of the

FIG. 64. *Cycas revoluta*. A native of China and Japan, showing habit of the sporophyte.

megaspore have divided to form a many celled gametophyte or prothallus and soon after pollination a number (usually three) of archegonia have developed. Each archegonium is exceedingly reduced, consisting merely of two neck cells and a large oosphere. The nucleus of the oosphere divides to form a ventral canal nucleus, which soon disappears, and an oosphere (female) nucleus.

A sticky fluid is exuded from the micropyle and in it are trapped wind-borne microspores. When this liquid dries the microspores are sucked down the micropylar canal and come to lie in the pollen chamber of the nucellus. Before it was shed from the microsporangium, each microspore divided to give a prothallus cell, an antheridial cell and a large tube cell which collectively constitute the male gametophyte. After pollination, the antheridial cell divides into a short stalk cell and a body cell which collectively make up the antheridium. The tube cell grows out through the wall of the microspore and penetrates the nucellus which it causes to break down in the region of the micropyle and from which it apparently absorbs nourishment. No further development then occurs until the archegonia are mature, a period of about 4 months. The body cell then divides to form two exceedingly large antherozoids, each of which develops a spiral band of cilia. The basal end of the microspore

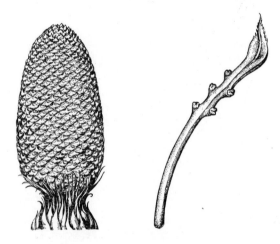

FIG. 65. Left, strobilus of male sporophyte of *Cycas celebica*, bearing many microsporophylls. Right, a single megasporophyll of *Cycas circinalis* bearing six ovules, × *ca.* ⅛. Both species are natives of Africa and India.

then enlarges to form an elongated sac, quite distinct from the rhizoidal structure hitherto mentioned, and this sac grows through the disintegrating nucellus and then ruptures to release the antherozoids freely into the cavity above the archegonia. The antherozoids then pass between the neck cells of the archegonia and one fuses with each oosphere. The cytoplasm and cilia are then cast off and the male nucleus penetrates the oosphere and fuses with the female nucleus. Unused male gametes disintegrate.

Although all the archegonia may be fertilized in this way, only one embryo reaches maturity. The fertilized ovule or seed consists, when mature, of the embryo, which is straight and has two cotyledons; the female gametophyte, which constitutes a nutritive tissue known as endosperm

FIG. 66. Female cone of *Encephalarctos* sp., a species in which the megasporophylls are not leaf-like, × *ca.* ⅛.

but not strictly homologous with the endosperm of angiosperms; and the integuments, of which only the outer fleshy and inner stony layers persist. Once shed, the seed germinates immediately. The absence of dormancy appears to be a primitive character.

Ginkgo

The order Ginkgoales is now represented by a single species *Ginkgo biloba*, which is believed to have existed from the Permian or even the Carboniferous period. It now occurs wild only in China. It is a dioecious tree with bilobed broad leaves (Fig. 67), the general habit of which resembles that of a conifer, but it is similar to *Cycas* in having flagellated antherozoids, an undoubtedly primitive character.

The only other order of the gymnosperms which we will consider in this brief account, the Coniferales, is by far the largest order of the class. Well known conifers are the pines (*Pinus* spp.), cedars (e.g. *Cedrus libani*, the Cedar of Lebanon), firs (*Abies* spp.), spruce firs (*Picea* spp.), Douglas

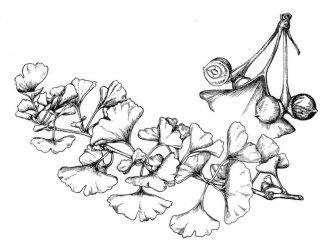

FIG. 67. *Ginkgo biloba.* Left, a branch bearing bilobed leaves, × ¼. Original. Right, ovules whole and in section. Redrawn from Kerner.

firs (*Pseudotsuga* spp.), junipers (*Juniperus* spp.), cypresses (e.g. *Cupressus* spp.), yews (*Taxus* spp.), redwoods (*Sequoia* spp.), larches (*Larix* spp.) and the Chile pine or monkey puzzle and Norfolk Island pine (*Araucaria* spp.). The Scots pine (*Pinus sylvestris*) will serve as an example.

Pinus

Pinus sylvestris is indigenous in Northern Europe. Like most conifers, and in contrast with the cycadales, the sporophyte is a tall tree. When young, the tree is conical in shape but as it ages the branches come to form an irregular crown on an often exceedingly tall trunk from which the lower branches are cast off. The main branches are of unlimited growth. They bear scale leaves and short spurs known as dwarf shoots each of which bears terminally a pair of needle-like green leaves in addition to scale leaves. The leaves are highly differentiated and like those of all conifers show xeromorphic characters (p. 318) such as thickening of the cuticle and sunken stomata. They are shed by abscission of the entire dwarf shoot; but the tree as a whole is evergreen.

The root system is initially a tap root but this soon is replaced by widely spreading, shallow lateral roots, the finer branches of which show mycorrhizal fungi in the cortex.

The stem and root anatomy is generally similar to that of a dicotyledonous angiosperm, though simpler. Both stem and root undergo normal secondary thickening. Notable differences from angiosperm vascular tissues are the absence of xylem vessels, the xylem consisting almost solely of tracheids with pits on the radial walls, and the absence from the phloem of companion cells though phloem parenchyma is present. The phloem sieve cells have sieve plates on their radial longitudinal walls and a few on their oblique transverse walls. This absence of phloem companion cells and xylem vessels is shared with the Cycadales but whereas the bulk of the stem in *Cycas* consists of a parenchymatous cortex and secondary thickening in the pericycle gives rise to alternating bands of phloem and xylem, in *Pinus* secondary thickening is initiated by cambium in the vascular bundles and a large part of the thickness of the stem is composed of tracheids which are responsible for most of the mechanical support. The anatomy of *Cycas* is thus nearer to the Pteridophyta and that of *Pinus* is similar to that of angiosperms.

The microspores, which are equivalent to the pollen grains of angiosperms, are borne on the underside of many microsporophylls. The microsporophylls are arranged spirally on a short axis which replaces a dwarf shoot and constitutes with it a male cone (Fig. 68). The term

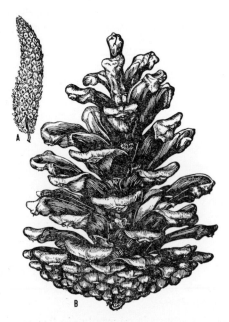

FIG. 68. *Pinus nigra.* A, male cone. B, female cone shedding seeds. Actual size.

"male" is here used in anticipation of the eventual production of male gametes by the prothalli developing from the microspores. The microspores are produced in tetrads by reduction division of their spore mother cells. They absorb nourishment from the walls of the sporangium which constitute a tapetum. Each microspore bears two conspicuous inflated air sacs which greatly facilitate wind dispersal (Fig. 69).

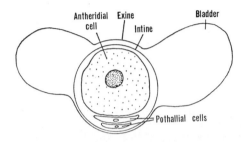

FIG. 69. *Pinus* sp. A microspore, greatly magnified.

The female cones (Fig. 70) are produced in clusters in place of shoots of unlimited growth. Each consists of a central axis with spirally arranged outgrowths. Each of these outgrowths consists of a lower bract scale and an upper large ovuliferous scale which bears a pair of ovules on its upper surface. It seems likely that each ovuliferous scale represents two leaves of a spur which became fused by their upper margins so that their ventral sporangia came to lie towards the main axis of the branch, i.e. on the upper surface of the ovuliferous scale. The bract scale is then to be regarded as a scale leaf in the axil of which the spur developed.

The ovule arises as a small protuberance on the upper surface of the ovuliferous scale which constitutes the sessile nucellus or megasporangium. An integument grows from the base of the nucellus and invests the latter except for a pore, the micropyle on the side towards the cone axis. Near the apex in the nucellus a single archesporial cell develops and this divides to form tapetal cells and a single megaspore mother cell. The megaspore mother cell divides meiotically to give four potential megaspores only one of which survives. No further development occurs until pollination.

When the megaspores are blown onto the female cone, the ovuliferous scales of which have temporarily moved apart, they are caught in a sticky secretion exuded from the nucellus and are drawn through the micropyle to the apex of the nucellus when the liquid dries, much as in *Cycas*.

The middle of the three walls of the microspore, the exo-intine, then breaks and the inner wall, the intine, grows through a permanent gap in the outer wall or exine, as a pollen tube. By this time the contents of the microspore have divided to give two prothallial cells of short duration, an antheridial cell, and a tube cell containing a "tube nucleus". The tube nucleus passes into the pollen tube which undergoes a very long period

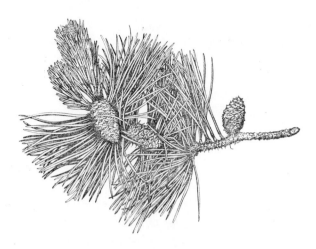

FIG. 70. *Pinus contorta.* Three young female cones after fertilization. Note numerous short shoots, each with two needle leaves, × ½.

of slow growth which is interrupted by winter. The antheridial cell later forms a body cell and a stalk cell. The body cell then divides into two male cells with large nuclei and very little cytoplasm.

Meanwhile, the contents of the megaspore in the ovule divide to form a many celled gametophyte or prothallus which derives nourishment from the inner wall of the nucellus. At the micropylar end of the ovule a number of archegonia (usually three) develops. The archegonia are very similar to those of Pteridophyta and differ mainly in the large venter and simple neck. An oosphere and ventral canal cell are present but there are no neck canal cells (Fig. 71).

The pollen tube later penetrates the neck of the archegonium and the stalk cell nucleus, tube nucleus and the two male cells enter the oosphere where all, except one male cell, disintegrate. The male and female nuclei then unite. Four embryos usually develop from the single fusion nucleus, a condition known as polyembryony. Each embryo typically has about ten cotyledons. The embryos derive nourishment from the inner layers of the prothallus and when the seeds are ready to be shed, in the cone's third year, only the outer layers of the prothallus persist as the endosperm which will be used in germination. The testa has by this time become stony. When the cone has again opened and the seeds are shed the testa takes with it a layer of the ovuliferous scale which forms a wing (Fig. 72). The latter aids in the dissemination of the seeds by wind.

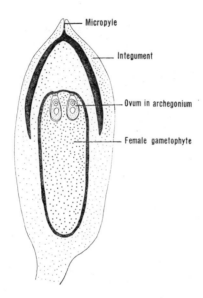

FIG. 71. *Pinus* sp. Diagrammatic longitudinal section of an ovule.

It will be seen from the above account that the conifers differ from their relatives, the Ginkgoales and Cycadales, and from all pteridophytes and bryophytes, in that the male gametes no longer bear cilia or flagella. Loss of motility is associated with the development of a pollen tube which delivers the male cells directly to the oosphere or female gamete. Reduction of the female gametophyte is extreme, though archegonia are still recognizable and are in fact somewhat better developed than those of *Cycas*. The integument of the seed bears structures which aid dispersal, and associated with this is the ability of the seed to remain dormant for short periods. The seeds of *Cycas* have no special means of dispersal and are incapable of dormancy.

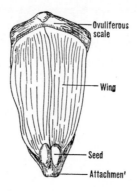

FIG. 72. *Pinus* sp. Adaxial view of a single ovuliferous scale bearing two winged seeds, from a second year female cone, × 1½.

We will now study the ultimate class of the Spermatophyta, and indeed of all plants, the Angiospermae, in which trends which we have dealt with above have reached their furthest development and in which two new structures, the ovary, formed by the megasporophylls (now known as carpels), which completely enclose the ovules, and the flower have developed (see p. 209).

ANGIOSPERMAE

Angiosperms are seed plants in which the ovules are completely enclosed in a chamber termed the ovary, the walls of which are formed from one or more megasporophylls or carpels. The class is further distinguished from the class Gymnospermae in that the microsporophylls (stamens) and the megasporophylls (carpels) are typically surrounded by modified leaves which constitute the perianth, and cause the whole reproductive axis to be termed a flower. The angiosperms are thus known as the flowering plants. The term flower is often used for any specialized reproductive axis and is even applied to the specialized leafy shoot bearing the reproductive organs in mosses. The name is, however, better restricted to the peculiar structure of angiosperms and is used only with this sense in the present work.

Before proceeding to a study of the flower we will briefly summarize the characteristics of living spermatophytes which taken as a whole, contribute notably to their success. A full understanding of this summary, will however, require a knowledge of the flower (p. 209).

SUCCESSFUL CHARACTERISTICS OF LIVING SPERMATOPHYTA

1. Reduction of the terrestrially vulnerable gametophyte, the female gametophyte being a minute body within the unopened megaspore; the male gametophyte a minute body retained within the microspore (pollen grain).

2. The retention of the megaspore within the megasporangium (nucellus) with consequent nourishment of the gametophyte by the sporophyte.

3. The enclosure of the megasporangium in one or more integuments which later constitute the protective and resistant seed coats.

4. The fertilization of the integumented megasporangium (ovule) before it is shed and partial nourishment of the resultant embryo sporophyte by the previous sporophyte (nutritive megasporangium wall or nucellus).

5. The independence of external water for fertilization which culminates in the delivery of the male nuclei directly to the female gametophyte by a pollen tube.

6. The onset of dormancy in the embryo prior to shedding of the fertilized ovule (seed) which facilitates dispersal and survival in unfavourable conditions.

7. The complete enclosure of the ovule (in the angiosperms) in the megasporophyll (carpel) and associated development of the flower, the significance of which will be discussed later.

8. The provision (in angiosperms) for nutrition of the embryo, of a special triploid tissue, the endosperm, produced by fusion of a male nucleus with two gametophytic nuclei. This has the added advantage that endospermic food reserves are laid by only if fertilization is successful.

CHAPTER 7

General Morphology of the Angiosperm. Plant Tissues

THE body of the sporophyte of an angiosperm is divisible into three parts: the root, stem and leaves (Fig. 73). The stem and leaves constitute the shoot.

The root is defined on p. 147. In what may be regarded as the basic type of root system there is an axial tap root which is positively geotropic, grows vertically downwards and is thicker than the other roots. This gives off smaller lateral roots which are clothed in root hairs and grow horizontally or diagonally downwards. These in turn may bear rootlets with no particular orientation. Other types of root systems are discussed on p. 147.

The stem is typically the aerial axis of the plant and bears leaves at regions, which are often swollen, termed nodes. Commonly the stem branches, the branches arising in the angle between leaf base and stem, i.e. in the leaf axil. Branches of the stem, even when greatly modified, are usually recognizable by their axillary position. Flowers, being compressed shoots, are typically borne in the axil of a leaf or of a reduced leaf termed a bract unless they are terminal on the stem.

Not the whole of the vertical axis of the plant is referable to as stem and root, however, as the region between the base of the seed leaves or cotyledon(s) and the radicle of the seedling constitutes the hypocotyl. If, in germination, the cotyledons are carried above the soil (epigeal germination), the hypocotyl is above ground; if the cotyledons do not emerge (hypogeal germination), the hypocotyl remains subterranean.

Primary growth of the plant occurs as a result of division of cells at the tips of the main axis and of branches of the root and shoot. Each group of cells is termed an apical meristem. Growth of the stem may be monopodial, in which the apical meristem of the main axis continues to

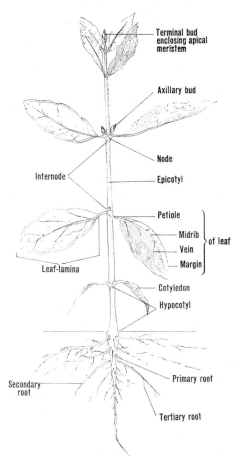

FIG. 73. The external morphology of an herbaceous dicotyledon
(germination epigeal).

produce new cells throughout the period of axial growth of the plant,
and the plant has a single main axis. Growth is sympodial where development of the apical meristem of the main axis ceases, often because of the
development of a terminal flower, and the main axis of growth is continued
in an axillary branch. If in a monopodially or sympodially growing
shoot system the main apical meristem is destroyed, as by desiccation
or pruning, a nearby axillary shoot takes over as the main axis of growth.
Often the growth of several axillary branches is accelerated in this way.
It is thus that a gardener produces bushy growth in a plant. It is now
known that the apparent co-ordination in development between the main

axis of growth and other branches is due to hormones, chemical substances which diffuse from cell to cell, which in plants are termed auxins. Auxins from young leaves are also known to be responsible for stimulating the growth of cambium and of roots so that an adequate supply of mineral salts in solution and of vascular tissue is ensured to cope with increased foliage.

Leaves are typically the main photosynthetic organs and accordingly each has a broad blade or lamina and a vascularized midrib from which branches or veins extend into the lamina. Usually the midrib continues basally as a bladeless stalk or petiole which attaches to the stem at the leaf base. Leaves which lack a petiole are said to be sessile. Leaves are further discussed on p. 188.

PLANT TISSUES

The plant typically develops from a unicellular zygote. This undergoes division to form the embryo and ultimately the mature plant. The embryo is a simple structure composed of few cells; these have undergone relatively little differentiation. It consists of an axis, bearing one or two cotyledons, and having a single apical meristem at each end. Subsequently, further growing tips with their own apical meristems develop and form the lateral roots and shoots of what is now the seedling. All growth by production of cells from apical meristems is termed primary growth and the plant body so produced the primary body. This development involves cell division and differentiation of cells to form tissues. Differentiation is the name given to the gradual specialization of cells from similar precursors which produces cells of different forms and functions.

Tissues

In its simplest form a tissue may be defined as a group of structurally similar cells, of similar origin, which perform the same function, e.g. parenchyma (storage and packing), collenchyma (mechanical), sclerenchyma (mechanical). Such a tissue is termed a simple tissue in contrast to tissues which are made up of more than one type of element (a term used for a constituent unit which may be a cell or may be derived from more than one cell). Such a heterogeneous tissue is termed a complex tissue and may be defined as a group of cells, of more than one type, which act together to perform the same function, e.g. xylem (conduction). The function of either type of tissue may itself be divisible into subsidiary functions; thus xylem vessels serve for longitudinal conduction of water and dissolved mineral salts while xylem ray parenchyma allows translocation to adjoining tissues. A tissue may also have additional, dissimilar functions, thus xylem fibres (and also vessels) give mechanical support. The numbers of types of tissues which are recognized is a somewhat arbitrary matter. In this account we will discuss only the chief types, four in number. These are: (1) a comparatively unspecialized ground tissue; (2) tissues whose main if not sole function is mechanical support; (3) tissues serving to prevent loss of water to the external environment and to reduce the entry of disease organisms, i.e. protective tissues; (4) vascular tissues, which include xylem for conducting water and mineral salts in solution; and phloem which has the function of conducting elaborated food materials.

Development and Differentiation

Before discussing these differentiated tissues, something must be said of the structure of the undifferentiated cell, which is the immediate product of the division of a meristematic cell, and the way in which it begins to differentiate.

When a meristematic cell divides the first "partition" between the two daughter nuclei is the cell plate which is believed to form from the fibres of the spindle. The cell plate grows centrifugally and when it reaches the cellulose of the original cell wall it splits into two layers between which pectin is laid down as the new middle lamella. A middle lamella is a non-cellulosic layer between the walls of adjacent cells and is composed of calcium and magnesium salts of pectic acid (collectively termed pectin); it may be regarded as a cement between the cells. If it is broken down the cells fall apart, a process which occurs naturally in over-ripe fruits. The new middle lamella comes into contact with the middle lamella of the old cell walls by dissolution of the intervening cellulose. The two layers of the cell plate are replaced by the bounding plasma membrane of the two daughter cells and the primary cell wall (composed of cellulose strands or microfibrils, hemicellulose and other polysaccharides, and pectin) is then laid down by each cell on its face of the middle lamella so that each new cell now has a complete cellulose cell wall. The undifferentiated cell has dense cytoplasm with a few, small sap-filled cavities or vacuoles. The sap in these vacuoles has a high osmotic pressure, chiefly owing to the presence of sugars. Osmotic uptake of water into the vacuoles from the cytoplasm and from neighbouring cells results in swelling of the vacuoles and an increase in the hydrostatic pressure or turgor pressure of the cell. Ultimately a single large vacuole forms and the cytoplasm becomes stretched as a thin layer, the peripheral cytoplasm, around it. The walls of the young cell are elastic and the increase in turgor pressure causes them to stretch so that the cell enlarges. The osmotic pressure of the cell remains fairly constant, despite the entry of water, because of a concomitant increase in dissolved solutes. In this way a fifteen-fold increase in size of the cell may occur.

In differentiation, the enlargement is made irreversible by addition of substances to the cell wall and plastic enlargement is said to have occurred, as opposed to elastic enlargement which is reversible. Although the cytoplasm surrounding the cell vacuole becomes greatly attenuated, its actual amount may increase four-fold. Some new cellulose microfibrils are deposited within the wall between pre-existing microfibrils, a process termed intussusception. Growth of the primary cell wall is, however, now believed from electron microscope studies to be mainly by the laying down of microfibrils on the inside of the wall, i.e. by apposition. Electron microscope studies show that the fibrils are first laid down transversely and somewhat diagonally as a network with the fibrils loosely held together where they cross. As the cell grows it elongates considerably and the predominantly transverse fibrils come to lie more and more longitudinally, slipping over each other where they cross. Since the fibres are chiefly laid down from the inside, by apposition, the oldest are external and the youngest internal and every orientation of fibrils is seen from almost transverse on the inside, to about 45° to the axis in the centre of the wall, and almost longitudinal in the outer region of the wall. Furthermore, the more peripheral the fibrils the larger become the spaces between them. Intussesception causes a certain amount of filling in of the interstices. Primary cell walls thus grow simultaneously in area and thickness. Most cells grow at more or less equal rates along their length, as has been shown by an even incorporation of radioactive carbon into their cellulose, but many grow most actively at or near the tip, as in the case of root hairs. The latter type of growth is fundamentally similar to the "multi-net" growth described above and differs almost solely in being localized.

The multi-net growth theory, though apparently a correct explanation of growth in most cases, does not satisfactorily explain growth of many root cells in which turgor pressure is too low to stretch the cell walls. Here growth is presumably due primarily to intussusception.

The secondary cell wall. In many cells a secondary cell wall is laid down by apposition on the inside of the primary wall when growth has ceased. The main constituent of the secondary wall is again cellulose but hemicellulose is much less important. The spaces between the molecules of which the fibrils are composed become filled with the woody substance lignin, pectic compounds and others. Deposition of the secondary wall usually coincides with lignification of the primary wall. The secondary wall may be very thick, as in sclerenchyma. Initially it is perforated by pores through which protoplasmic strands termed plasmodesmata interconnect the cells, but frequently communication with other cells is later cut off and the cell dies.

1. *Ground tissue*

Ground tissue is composed of cells known as parenchyma in which most of the metabolic activity of the plant occurs. These cells also have a supporting function, for the plant wilts if the water supply is insufficient to maintain their turgidity. A typical parenchyma cell, that is to say one in its least modified form, has a thin primary cell wall perforated by plasmodesmata in simple pits but no secondary wall. The cells are circular or approximately hexagonal in cross-section and are usually about two to several times longer than wide; they are in contact but intercellular air spaces which facilitate gaseous exchange are a conspicuous feature (Fig. 74).

The living contents or protoplast of the cell consist of cytoplasm in which is embedded the nucleus. Inside the nuclear membrane which bounds the latter is the nucleoplasm in which lie the chromosomes, bodies which bear the hereditary factors or genes. The cytoplasm is bounded externally by the cell membrane or plasmalemma which is about 75–100 Å thick, and internally, around the vacuole, by a slightly thicker membrane, the tonoplast. The vacuole of a parenchyma cell which is well supplied with water is typically large; it may be crossed by cytoplasmic strands and contains a watery vacuolar sap containing sugars, organic acids, proteins, including enzymes, and various inorganic ions. The cytoplasm contains, in addition to the nucleus, mitochondria and microsomes (the latter also termed ribosomes) which are minute bodies of great importance in metabolism, and also bodies termed plastids which, like mitochondria, are self-reproducing. Plastids may contain pigment (chromoplasts) or may be colourless (leucoplasts). The most intensively studied type of chromoplast is the chloroplast which is typically a biconvex proteinaceous disc containing chlorophyll. Parenchyma which contains chloroplasts is termed chlorenchyma and is commonly found near the periphery of herbaceous stems. Leucoplasts can often develop into chloroplasts if exposed to light but are normally associated with the storage of either lipoids (elaioplasts) or starch (amyloplasts). Also present in the cytoplasm are small vacuoles; food storage compounds, commonly oil, starch or protein; and various crystals, mostly regarded as excretory substances, including calcium oxalate. In addition, the cytoplasm is permeated by a complex system of intuckings of the cell membrane which constitute the endoplasmic reticulum. Further discussion of the ultramicroscopic structure of the cell is beyond the scope of this book.

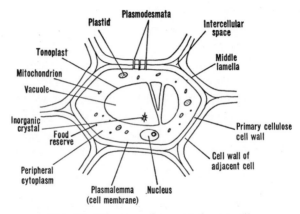

FIG. 74. Diagram of a parenchyma cell.

Physical evidence of the living state of the protoplast is given by cyclosis, streaming of the cytoplasm. If a few minutes are allowed to elapse between observations it can be seen that the nucleus moves with the cytoplasm.

Parenchyma cells frequently differ from the above description in having a secondary cell wall. In lignified parenchyma which may occur in various situations in the plant, including the pith, this may be fairly thick. Nevertheless, living, metabolically active contents persist in the mature cell.

2. *Supporting tissue*

(a) *Collenchyma cells.* Young, actively-growing plant structures are frequently supported by living cells whose walls have thick deposits of cellulose, especially at their corners. Such cells are called collenchyma

(Fig. 75C, D). Collenchyma cells are not confined to growing regions but are fairly characteristic of structures in which considerable strength has to be combined with elasticity. As cellulose is fairly elastic, collenchyma cells can be stretched quite a lot without being damaged.

(b) *Sclerenchyma fibres* (Fig. 75E, F). Fibres, which may be found in almost any part of a plant, are very elongated cells with tapering ends and thickened walls. During the development of a sclerenchyma fibre the thickened secondary cellulose wall becomes impregnated with fine longitudinal rods of silica, and lignin. Lignin is a material whose chemical nature has not been determined with certainty. It has a tensile strength which approaches that of steel. Mechanically it differs from steel in having greater elasticity and in breaking sooner after the limit of elasticity has been reached. After laying down the lignin the protoplasm of the fibre dies. The walls of fibres are often so thick that there is only a very small central lumen. Simple pits often occur.

3. *Protective tissue*

(a) *The epidermis.* The limiting layer of the stem and leaves is called the epidermis (Fig. 75D). Its cells are parenchymatous but are more tightly packed than in ground tissue. In terrestrial plants the epidermis secretes an outer, waterproof cuticle composed of cutin. Cutin is a complex waxy mixture of fatty acid derivatives.

(b) *Phellem or cork.* Under certain conditions of strain, a meristematic tissue called the cork cambium or phellogen arises under the epidermis and gives rise to cells whose protoplasts lay down suberin in their cell walls. Suberin is very similar to, if not identical with, cutin. Since suberin is impermeable to water the protoplasts die after they have surrounded themselves with it. These dead suberized cells make up the cork which forms the outer bark of old stems and roots (see also p. 174).

4. *Vascular tissues*

(a) *Water-conducting tissue.* The water-conducting tissue of plants is called the xylem or "wood". Xylem always contains a greater or lesser amount of parenchyma and wood fibres in addition to the lignified elements which carry water. Xylem has two main functions—water conduction and, secondary to this, mechanical support. Two distinct types of lignified elements occur in xylem.

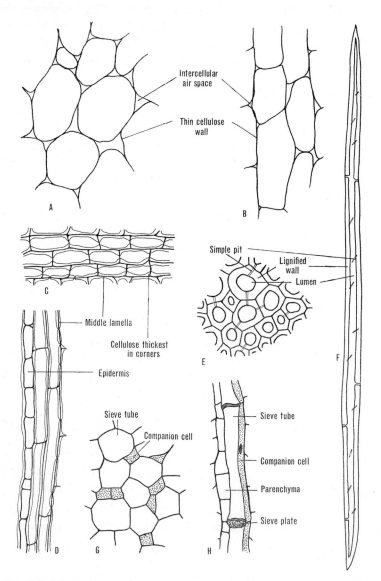

FIG. 75. Some tissue elements of the sunflower, *Helianthus annuus.*
Transverse and cylindrical sections respectively of (A and B) parenchyma,
(C and D) collenchyma and (E and F) sclerenchyma, with living contents
omitted in all cases. (G and H), transverse and longitudinal sections of
phloem including contents.

The tracheid, which is found in Pteridophyta and Spermatophyta, is the more primitive of the two elements. Tracheids show many similarities to sclerenchyma fibres, from which they can be distinguished by having chizel-shaped rather than tapering ends, and thinner walls which usually have bordered pits instead of simple pits. A bordered pit has a very thin, often perforated, pit membrane (composed of unthickened primary wall) roofed on either side by a dome of lignin with a central pore. Frequently the central portion of each pit membrane is thickened to form a torus. High pressure on one side of the pit pushes the torus against the far dome so that the pit becomes closed. Tracheids with very narrow transverse pits are called scalariform tracheids.

The second type of element, the vessel, is characteristic of the angiosperms. Vessels are, however, found in the xylem of certain species in the more primitive groups so it seems likely that this particular structure has been evolved independently in more than one group of terrestrial plants. Vessels, which are lignified tubes, are typically wider than tracheids. They are formed by the breakdown of the transverse walls of longitudinal rows of cells. Vessels range in length from a few centimetres to many metres. The vessels of tropical climbing plants are both very long and very wide. Protoxylem vessels have spiral or annular thickening of the walls while metaxylem vessels have reticulate or scalariform thickening or bordered pits (Fig. 76 and p. 145).

(b) *Food-conducting tissue.* The tissue which conveys elaborated food materials from one part of a plant to another is called the phloem or "bast" (Fig. 75G, H). The characteristic feature of phloem is that the cytoplasm of the conducting cells becomes continuous as a result of perforated regions, known as sieve plates, developing in their walls. In Pteridophyta and Gymnospermae the sieve plates occur on the longitudinal walls while in angiosperms they are found in the transverse walls. When fully formed, sieve tubes have no nuclei and their cytoplasm becomes coarse and permeable with no clear distinction between utricle and vacuole. Sieve tubes probably have a functional life of about one or at most two growing seasons. Secondary growth (see pp. 172–175) always results in the obliteration of old phloem and the formation of new. In angiosperms each row of sieve tubes is associated with a row of elongated, thin-walled, parenchymatous companion cells which are nucleated and have dense non-vacuolated cytoplasm. There are numerous simple pits in the walls between companion cells and sieve tubes. The functions of companion cells is not fully understood.

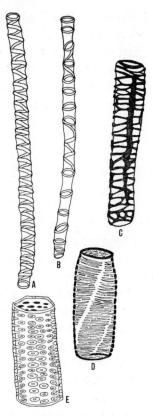

Fig. 76. Portions of various types of vessels of sunflower, *Helianthus annuus*. A, with spiral; B, with annular (and some spiral); C, with reticulate; D, with scalariform thickening. E, with bordered pits.

CHAPTER 8

Morphology of the Root

Definition

A root is typically a subterranean or aquatic multicellular axis or appendage of a plant the function of which is absorption of mineral salts in solution and anchorage of the plant; it differs from the shoot in having no chlorophyll and no nodes or lateral buds, in producing branches endogenously (p. 154), in having exarch protoxylem (p. 151) and in possessing a protective apical root cap.

There are exceptions to the points in the definition above, for instance some plants have aerial roots. These and other unusual types of root are dealt with on p. 155.

Types of Root Systems

Two major types of roots can be distinguished by their origin. These are "true roots" or primary roots, which are developed from the radicle of the seedling, and adventitious roots, which, although of normal structure, develop from the stem or leaves. The primary root branches to give secondary roots and these may give tertiary roots. The finest branches at any one time bear the root hairs. A primary root system is sometimes limited to a single large persistently growing tap root which is a direct downward prolongation of the radicle of the seedling, but frequently the branch roots which develop from the radicle soon equal or exceed the size of the radicle and branch repeatedly so that a fibrous root system results. Fibrous root systems are also typical of those plants, including most monocotyledons, in which adventitious roots replace the primary roots. Many forest trees and shrubs have tap roots, but the most familiar examples are probably those which are enlarged for storage of food materials and are eaten by man, such as carrots and turnips. Such tuberous tap roots resemble the tuberous adventitious roots of such plants as cassava but the latter should not be confused with tap roots.

DEVELOPMENT AND ANATOMY IN DICOTYLEDONS
Apical and Derived Meristems

At the apex of the root there is an apical meristem or promeristem (Fig. 77), a short region in which all the cells are capable of repeated division and are responsible for the initiation of the tissues of the mature root. In the root the apical meristem is protected, in its passage through the soil, by a hood-like root cap or calyptra. The outer layers of the parenchymatous cells which constitute the calyptra are continually

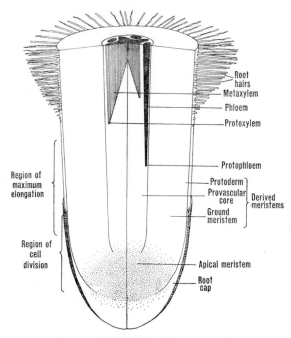

Root hairs
Metaxylem
Phloem
Protoxylem
Protophloem
Region of maximum elongation
Protoderm
Provascular core
Ground meristem
Derived meristems
Region of cell division
Apical meristem
Root cap

FIG. 77. Diagram of a root tip, from which a large wedge has been cut away, showing distribution of tissues. Adapted from University of Sydney Botany 1 Manual.

breaking down on contact with the soil particles and new cells are added internally by division of the cells of the apical meristem which lie nearest its tip. These cells are sometimes called the calyptrogen.

Immediately behind the apical meristem the young root axis is more or less clearly separated into three concentric layers the cells of which will give rise to the primary tissues of the mature root other than the calyptra. These three layers are the derived meristems and they occupy the region of elongation of the root. In this region the new cells become vacuolated, probably because of hydrolysis of starch and consequent osmotic uptake of water. Development of turgor pressure causes extension of the cells and additional cellulose is deposited on their walls. The three derived meristems are: (1) the procambium or provascular core which is central and gives rise further back to the vascular core (stele) of the root; (2) a ground meristem, outside this, which gives rise to the cortex; and (3) the protoderm or outer layer which is often not clearly separable from the ground meristem but is generally the precursor of the epidermis with its root hairs, i.e. the piliferous layer (Fig. 77).

The region in which the cells of the derived meristems become differentiated into the primary tissues of the root is termed the region of differentiation. The differentiation of the various tissues occurs at different rates and some cells alter over long periods. The term "region of differentiation" must therefore be regarded as a convenient label rather than a separate well-defined zone.

Differentiation of the Piliferous Layer

We have already discussed the formation of the root cap. In the region of differentiation, immediately behind the region of elongation, the cells of the protoderm develop very long tubular outgrowths, one per cell, which are the root hairs and give the tissue the name piliferous (hairy) layer. The root hairs form a bushy cone near the apex of the root with the shorter, younger hairs nearest the root tip. Each mature hair is several millimetres long and pushes its way between the soil particles to which it adheres closely by the mucilaginous outer coating of its wall. Absorption of water and mineral salts occurs mainly through the root hairs, which collectively constitute an enormous surface area. The root hairs anchor the root tip in the soil and therefore allow the elongation of the cells nearer the tip to force the calyptra further into the soil. It will be appreciated that the root hairs develop in a part of the root which is not actively elongating and they are not, therefore, rubbed off as they might be if they developed in the region of elongation. In some plants, e.g. the daisy, the root hairs have a long life and persist onto the older parts of the root, but in most they are short-lived and are found only near the root tip. In the latter case their death is associated with the development of the corky substance, suberin, in the outer layers of the root which consequently become impervious to water. It must be emphasized that each root hair is a prolongation of a single epidermal cell and that the vacuoles of root hair and epidermis are continuous.

Differentiation of the Cortex

The cells of the innermost layer of the ground meristem develop a band of thickening known as the casparian strip on their radial and transverse walls in most roots. The inner and outer (tangential) walls are unthickened. This cylinder of cells, forming the innermost layer of the cortex, is termed the endodermis. At a later stage the inner tangential walls, and often the outer walls also, of the cells of the endodermis become thickened except opposite protoxylem groups where passage cells (Fig. 78) maintain

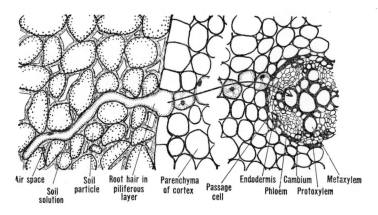

Air space / Soil / Root hair in / Parenchyma / Endodermis / Cambium / Metaxylem
Soil / particle / piliferous / of cortex / Passage / Phloem / Protoxylem
solution / layer / cell

FIG. 78. Transverse section of the root of *Ranunculus* showing the primary structure of a tetrarch dicotyledon root in which cambium is beginning to develop. The surrounding soil is indicated diagrammatically and an arrow indicates the path of water from the soil, via a root hair, to the xylem vessels.

communication between cortex and stele. The cells of the rest of the cortex, lying more peripherally, develop large vacuoles and their cytoplasm usually comes to contain numerous starch grains. They are rounded in cross-section, are several times longer than wide, have large intercellular spaces, and constitute a cortical parenchyma.

Differentiation of the Stele

The outermost layer of cells of the provascular core (procambium) remains parenchymatous, forming the pericycle. At a number of places around the periphery of the core, just within the pericycle, in the region of differentiation, a vertical series of cells becomes differentiated by deposition of annular or spiral bands of lignocellulose on the walls of each cell and breakdown of transverse dividing walls between the cells. These modified cells are the first-formed xylem or protoxylem vessels. The spiral and annular thickening allows for stretching of the vessels which occurs as a result of elongation of neighbouring differentiating cells.

On the same radius, and immediately internal to the protoxylem vessels, metaxylem vessels differentiate. These first appear further back from the tip than the protoxylem vessels; there they are less subject to stretching. They are therefore able to develop more rigid walls in which the ligno-cellulose covers a greater area of the walls, forming a ladder-like thickening (scalariform vessels) or leaving only small circular areas or pits unthickened (pitted vessels). The metaxylem vessels develop centripetally, with the oldest externally.

The xylem vessels are concerned with conducting mineral salts in solution, absorbed by the root hairs, to the rest of the plant.

By the time a root exceeds a few millimeters, the necessity arises for a special conducting tissue to bring organic nutrients to the root tissues, as diffusion of food materials from cell to cell is no longer sufficiently rapid or efficient to cope with the requirements of the dividing, elongating and differentiating cells. This conducting tissue which develops is the phloem or bast. It develops between the protoxylem groups and first appears at the same level as the protoxylem or behind it, or, sometimes, nearer the root tip. It consists of sieve tubes and their associated companion cells, and also of phloem parenchyma interspersed with these, and is often surrounded by phloem fibres which have thickened walls. It is not usually in contact with the xylem, on each side being separated from these by little-altered cells, the conjunctive parenchyma.

The phloem does not extend far towards the centre of the root but further back metaxylem continues to differentiate until the four (or more or less) bundles meet internally. Whether parenchyma is left centrally, as a pith, depends on the species. Where there are four points of protoxylem the xylem is said to be tetrarch (Fig. 78, 79A); where there are only two, diarch; and where there are more, polyarch (pentarch, etc.). The external location of protoxylem relative to metaxylem is the exarch condition.

ROOTS OF MONOCOTYLEDONS

A transverse section of the root of *Smilax* is shown in Fig. 80 and should be referred to while reading the following account.

The development of monocotyledonous roots closely resembles that of dicotyledonous roots but the following differences may be noted.

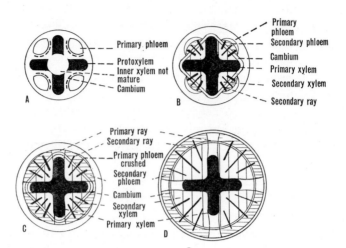

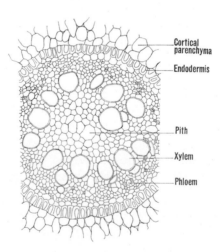

FIG. 79. Secondary thickening of a tetrarch root of a dicotyledon. A, primary structure. B–D, stages in secondary thickening.

FIG. 80. Transverse section of a root of a monocotyledon, *Smilax*, showing polyarch xylem and conspicuously thickened endodermis.

1. Monocotyledonous roots are usually polyarch, with sometimes as many as thirty xylem groups. Dicotyledonous roots usually vary between the diarch and pentarch conditions (two to five xylem groups).

2. They usually have a large central pith whereas in the dicotyledonous root the pith is usually small or the centre is occupied by xylem.

3. Secondary thickening of the root is rare in monocotyledons while it is normal in dicotyledons. In the rare cases where true secondary thickening occurs, as in the dragon tree, *Dracaena*, and in some members of the yam genus, *Dioscorea*, the cambium develops in the cortex, and never as in the dicotyledons between xylem and phloem. These genera also produce periderm (cork) from a phellogen (cork cambium) originating in the cortex just inside the piliferous layer. A similar development of cork occurs in the Liliaceae and Araceae.

4. The cells of the endodermis develop thickenings of suberin or of lignin on their radial and inner walls which is appropriately termed U-shaped thickening (Fig. 80), whereas in dicotyledons (Fig. 78) the thickening affects all sides of the cell.

5. It is characteristic of monocotyledons that the tap root usually dies off early in development and a fibrous root system made up of adventitious roots takes its place (Fig. 172), a situation which is much less common in dicotyledons. Furthermore, adventitious roots commonly develop from aerial nodes, e.g. prop roots of maize and *Pandanus* and aerial roots of orchids (see below); these are less common in dicotyledons.

Origin of Lateral Roots

Whereas rudiments of lateral appendages of the stem develop at the growing point and from the outer layers, i.e. are exogenous, lateral roots never arise near the root tip but arise behind the main region of differentiation and internally (endogenously) (Fig. 81). They arise opposite the protoxylem groups (Fig. 81B), when the number of rows they form equals the number of protoxylem groups, or between these groups and the phloem, when the number of rows developed is twice that of the protoxylem groups. Their development is endogenous, that is to say, they originate deep in the root. In the formation of a side root a small group of pericycle cells becomes meristematic (forming a secondary meristem) and develops the zonation of a root apex (Fig. 81B). Cell division continues and the young root penetrates the cortex, often pushing the endodermis, which secretes digestive enzymes, before it, until finally it ruptures all overlying tissues and projects from the parent root (Fig. 81C, D).

F

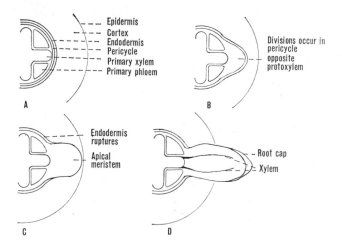

FIG. 81. A, tetrarch primary root of a dicotyledon before development of lateral root; B–D, stages in development of a lateral root. Diagrammatic. For explanation see text.

Secondary Thickening of the Root

Secondary thickening of the roots of monocotyledons is rare; it occurs by the development of a ring of secondary meristematic cells, i.e. a cambium, in the cortex.

Secondary thickening occurs in the roots of most dicotyledons (Fig. 79), the exceptions being among short-lived annuals and ephemerals and aquatic plants. The main effect is the addition of more xylem (secondary xylem) and more phloem (secondary phloem) by the activity of a cambium which develops in the conjunctive parenchyma between the phloem and the xylem and in the pericycle where this links adjacent arcs of conjunctive parenchyma (Fig. 79B). The cambium does not at first form a circle; it runs inward from the pericycle around the inside of each phloem group (Fig. 79B, C) and often has the appearance of a wavy ring. Secondary xylem is cut off on the inside and secondary phloem on the outside of the cambium. The actual cambium constitutes a single layer of cells. Each cell divides tangentially and either the inner or the outer daughter cell persists as a cambial cell until the next division. For any one cell, the alternation between cutting off a secondary tissue cell on the inside or the outside is irregular.

The wavy form of the cambium does not persist for long because more secondary xylem is at first cut off between the tips of the primary xylem than opposite the protoxylem groups and the cambium soon becomes a circular ring, as seen in a cross-section of the root (Fig. 79D).

Not all the secondary tissues cut off from the cambium are xylem and phloem, however; parenchyma cells are also formed and frequently in the same radius for many divisions so that "rays" of parenchyma are produced. The principal of these are the primary medullary rays, formed outside and radial to the protoxylem groups, owing to the fact that the cambium opposite these groups cuts off only parenchyma. Secondary rays develop where the cambium has been cutting off xylem and phloem and turns to producing parenchyma.

In most storage roots the secondary tissue is largely parenchymatous secondary xylem, but in the carrot it is a parenchymatous secondary phloem around a fairly woody core of secondary xylem.

SPECIALIZED ROOTS

The roots of some plants are specialized for functions which are not characteristic of roots. These functions include: photosynthesis, support of the shoot, aeration, reproduction, food storage and contraction.

Photosynthetic Roots

In some plants, in which the roots are habitually exposed to light, such as those of epiphytic plants and some vines, the roots contain chloroplasts. In the epiphytic orchid *Taeniophyllum*, of the Indo-Malayan region, the roots are the only photosynthetic organs and the shoots are leafless and bear only the flowers. In one tropical family, which includes the genus *Podostemon*, the members of which live only on rocks in rushing rivers, the root is thalloid, with the appearance of a liverwort gametophyte, or is filamentous, and is the only assimilating organ.

The adventitious climbing roots of *Philodendron* and even the prop roots of maize (Fig. 84) possess chlorophyll.

Support of the Shoot

1. *Prop roots*

There are two types of tree in the genus *Ficus* (the figs) which send down aerial adventitious roots from the branches. These roots grow into the soil, enlarge greatly and, besides absorbing water and mineral salts from the soil, act as supplementary trunks for support of the wide-spreading branches (Fig. 82). The first type of tree develops from a seedling in the soil and is exemplified by the famous banyan tree, common throughout

India, by other species of *Ficus*, of which fine examples are a tree at Akropong, Akwapim, Ghana, which is regarded as a fetish, and the tree outside Tabora, Tanganyika, near Livingstone's tembe, under which Stanley is said to have camped before finding Livingstone. The Moreton Bay fig of Australia is a further example. The second type develops from seeds dropped by birds on the branches of other trees, and strangles the tree by the great development of aerial roots and the shading of its leaves. The latter are known as "strangling figs".

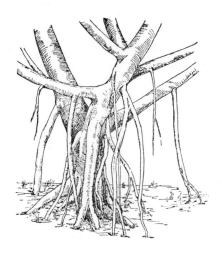

FIG. 82. Prop roots of a fig tree, *Ficus* sp. (above) and of the red mangrove, *Rhizophora racemosa* (below). Both specimens from West Africa. From Irvine.

A large number of other tropical plants produce prop roots. Examples are some species of mangrove, including several species of *Rhizophora* (Fig. 82); a number of species of screw pine, *Pandanus* spp. (Fig. 83), which occur throughout the tropics of the Old World; and maize (Fig. 84) and other grasses, including elephant grass and some bamboos, which send down prop roots from the lower nodes.

FIG. 83. Prop roots of screw pine, *Pandanus* sp.

FIG. 84. Prop roots of maize, *Zea mays*. These roots are also photosynthetic.

2. Buttress roots

In many species of trees of tropical rain forest throughout the world the roots arise from the trunk above soil level and radiate out from the trunk to form a conical, but much-divided, base resembling the buttressing used by Man to support buildings. Examples are *Terminalia arjuna* and the kapok tree, *Eriodendron anfractuosum* (Fig. 85). The trees are often very shallow-rooted, as sufficient moisture is obtainable near the soil surface, and the buttress roots have the effect of stabilizing the equilibrium of the trunk.

FIG. 85. Buttress roots of a kapok tree, *Eriodendron anfractuosum*.

3. Clasping (climbing) roots

Some climbing plants grip the stems of other plants, and other supports, by means of adventitious roots which develop at the widely spaced nodes. Examples are the West African black pepper, *Piper guineense*, *Culcasia* and *Philodendron*, climbing aeroids of tropical Africa and tropical America respectively; and the Indian plants *Vanilla* and *Piper betle* (Fig. 86).

Breathing Roots (Pneumatophores)

All roots respire, and most obtain oxygen directly from the external medium. In certain species of trees which form part of the mangrove vegetation of saline mud flats on all tropical shores, special negatively geotropic roots are developed which grow vertically, for a few inches to about a foot into the air and are the main site of oxygen intake for the root system. Below the mud, owing to decomposition of organic matter and poor aeration, the oxygen concentration is exceedingly low and without the special breathing roots, or pneumatophores, as they are called, the tree could not survive. Examples are the West African white mangrove, *Avicennia nitida,* and the Australian grey mangrove, *A. officinalis* (Fig. 87). Not all mangrove tree species have pneumatophores.

FIG. 86. Climbing roots of (above) *Vanilla* sp.; (below), *Piper betle.*

FIG. 87. Breathing roots (pneumatophores) radiating from a mangrove tree, *Avicennia officinalis.* Australia.

The pneumatophores are covered, even at the apex, by a corky layer well provided with lenticels, and within this is a very spongy cortex. Neither the pneumatophores, nor the horizontal subterranean roots which bear them, have root hairs but from the base of each pneumatophore short absorbing branch roots with root hairs are produced.

What can also be termed pneumatophores are produced by the aquatic plant *Jussieua repens*, the attractive, yellow buttercup-like flowers of which are familiar on ponds and dams in the tropics. Here the main roots send vertical buoyant roots towards the surface of the water, many actually emerging above the water. The cortex of these vertical roots has very large intercellular spaces and constitutes an aerenchyma through which air passes easily from the external medium. These roots serve also as "buoys" to keep the shoot at the surface. The main roots absorb mineral salts in solution from the water and from the mud at the bottom.

Reproductive Roots

The roots of many shrubs and trees form buds which in some cases are an important means of vegetative reproduction. Examples are the blackberry, *Rubus* and the guava, *Psidium guajava* (Fig. 88).

FIG. 88. Reproductive roots of guava, *Psidium guajava*.

Storage Roots

Storage of food materials, often as starch, in roots is not unusual but the roots of some plants are so enlarged that they deserve to be termed tuberous roots. The storage of food usually is related to overcoming annual unfavourable conditions such as winter or drought, i.e. perennation. These perennating roots are discussed on p. 303.

Contractile Roots

It will be clear that because a new corm or bulb develops above that of the previous season (Fig. 197), there will be a tendency for these organs to emerge above the soil surface. This is counteracted by the specialization of certain of the roots of the new corm or bulb as contractile roots which pull the developing organ down into the soil, so that those of successive years maintain approximately the same level in the soil. Examples of corms with contractile roots are *Crocus* and *Gladiolus*, and of bulbs, species of *Allium*. Rhizomes of some plants also have contractile roots, and the tap roots of *Taraxacum*, the dandelion, and other rosette-leaved plants contract sufficiently to maintain the new leaves at soil level. The seedlings of some orchids, e.g. the South American *Chloraea membranacea*, have contractile roots.

Contraction of the roots of corms and bulbs is due to collapse and shrinkage of cortical cells after depletion of their food reserves and may involve a 30 to 40 per cent shortening of the root.

Roots with a Velamen

Whereas many epiphytic plants, including the epiphytic aeroids, send aerial roots down to, and into, the soil, the epiphytic orchids have relatively short aerial roots which are specialized for absorbing rainwater and other water with which they come into contact, but do not reach the soil. The special absorptive roots possess an outer whitish, translucent layer often many cells thick, known as the velamen, which acts like a sponge. The cells of the velamen are dead, and empty, and their walls are supported by thickened ridges. The lumina of the cells are in communication with each other and the exterior by small holes in their walls. The spongy velamen readily absorbs and retains water. Root hairs are absent and probably could not survive the intermittent desiccation which they would encounter in this situation.

The velamen is probably equivalent to a multicellular epidermis. It is usually separated from the cortex by a thickened exodermis, which like the endodermis, has thin-walled passage cells. The cortex commonly contains chloroplasts. In *Taeniophyllum*, which was mentioned earlier, the velamen is confined to the underside of the root. Some soil-rooting orchids also have a velamen.

Water Roots

The roots of some aquatic plants do not reach the substrate and absorb mineral nutrients solely from the water. An example is the Nile lettuce, *Pistia stratiotes*, which is found throughout the tropics (Fig. 89). This plant has a floating rosette of leaves and sends a bunch of short roots into the water. These roots give off fine, short branches but no root hairs. *Pistia* reproduces vegetatively by stolons and is further interesting in showing "sleep movements", the rosette opening out in the day and closing up at night.

FIG. 89. Water roots of *Pistia stratiotes*, × ⅓.

CHAPTER 9

Morphology of the Stem

Definition

The stem of an angiosperm is typically an aerial axis which bears leaves at regions termed nodes and, axillary to the leaves, branches which may be vegetative or reproductive (flowers) or both. It differs from a typical root in these characters and also in possessing chloroplasts, in producing branches exogenously at the apex, in having endarch protoxylem, in usually having the phloem and xylem on the same radius and arranged in discrete peripheral bundles, and in lacking a protective apical cap.

Exceptions to most of these criteria occur but we need only note at this point a common departure which is apt to cause confusion of stems with roots by the uninitiated. Stems are not infrequently subterranean as is the case in rhizomes, stolons, corms and bulbs, but can then immediately be distinguished from roots by the presence of nodes bearing scale leaves and the development of buds in the axils of the latter.

DEVELOPMENT AND ANATOMY IN DICOTYLEDONS

Growth of the stem, as in the root, proceeds from an apical meristem but the meristem of the stem lacks a terminal calyptrogen as no protective cap covers the stem apex. The meristem (Fig. 90) is divisible into an outer tunica, the cells of which divide only at right-angles to the external surface, and a corpus, the cells of which divide in the plane parallel to the surface in addition.

The tunica is believed to be the source of leaves, and their axillary branches, which develop as minute rudiments exogenously immediately behind the apical meristem, unlike the branches of a root which develop endogenously and usually well behind the growing point. The young leaves enclose and protect the stem apex from desiccation, strong sunlight and other sources of damage. In the passage of the stem apex through

163

the soil at germination, it is protected by bending of the plumule or by a tough ensheathing coleoptile (p. 267).

The region of elongation is usually much longer than in the root and differentiation begins within it.

Formation of Procambium

In woody or not completely herbaceous plants, immediately below and continuous with the apical meristem there develops a meristematic ring which is bounded externally and internally by vacuolated cells of the cortex and pith, respectively. A number of types of development from this meristematic ring are possible. We will consider only the most common type, which occurs in most woody plants and also in many woody herbs including *Helianthus*. In these, at separate equally spaced points the meristematic ring forms procambium, i.e. a tissue which gives rise to the vascular elements and associated cells. Thus distinct longitudinal procambial strands, lying on a circle and connected by arcs of residual meristem, are formed. The residual meristem later acts as an interfascicular cambium which cuts off secondary xylem and secondary phloem so that these form continuous rings around the stem.

In extremely herbaceous plants, such as *Ranunculus*, the buttercup, there is never a continuous meristematic ring. Instead, from the first, there are separate procambial strands with non-meristematic tissues between them.

In all types of development where separate vascular bundles form, these bundles first differentiate at the bases of leaf rudiments so that the arrangement of bundles in a stem is from the first related to the arrangement of the leaves.

Development of Vascular Bundles in Extreme Herbs, e.g. Ranunculus

In *Ranunculus* procambial strands are the only remnants of meristematic tissue behind the apical meristem. Each procambial strand differentiates into a vascular bundle. The outermost cells relative to the stem centre become the first-formed phloem or protophloem and those nearest the centre of the stem differentiate as first-formed xylem elements or protoxylem. Next, the metaphloem develops internal to the protophloem and the metaxylem develops between the metaphloem and protoxylem. In woody herbs such as *Helianthus*, a narrow zone of undifferentiated meristematic tissue crossing the vascular bundles tangentially remains as the bundle cambium or fascicular cambium. In *Ranunculus*, in which no secondary thickening occurs, the whole of the procambium differentiates as vascular tissue and no cambium remains. Protophloem is distinguishable from metaphloem in lacking companion cells, and protoxylem from metaxylem by its ability to stretch; its elements accordingly have either spiral or annular thickening in contrast to the pitted scalariform and reticulate thickening of metaxylem elements.

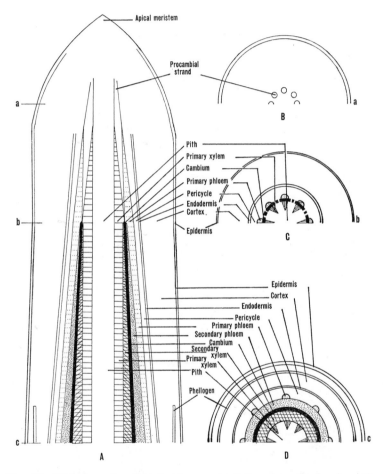

Fig. 90. Diagrams showing development of the stem (leaf primordia and nodes omitted). A, longitudinal section of tip of elongating and thickening stem. B, cross-section at level "a" through procambial strands. C, cross-section at level "b", showing primary structure but with interfascicular cambium developing. D, cross-section at level "c", showing secondary thickening.

It is commonly believed that the division of the vascular tissues into distinct bundles arranged in a circle near the periphery of the stem is the commonest arrangement in herbs and even in woody plants. However, it must be pointed out that the majority of herbs have a complete ring of procambium and, whether or not they later show secondary thickening, have a complete ring of primary xylem and primary phloem from the beginning.

Development of Vascular Bundles in Trees and Woody Herbs, e.g. Helianthus

Development of the vascular bundles from the procambium in *Helianthus* occurs as in *Ranunculus* but a tangential central band of fascicular cambium remains across each bundle. Furthermore a ring of procambium persists between the bundles and continuous with the fascicular cambium. This later gives rise to interfascicular cambium which is responsible for development of secondary tissues between the bundles.

The Primary Structure of a Dicotyledonous Stem (Figs. 90C, 91)

Particular reference will be made in the following account to the young stem of the sunflower.

As in the root, the stem is differentiated into a central cylinder containing the vascular tissue, and termed the stele, and an outer cortex.

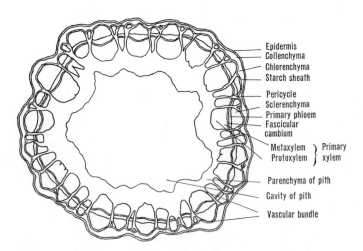

FIG. 91. *Helianthus annuus*. Plan of a transverse section of the stem showing primary structure.

Outside the cortex is a layer, one cell thick, the epidermis which corresponds to the piliferous layer of the root.

The epidermis is a single layer of closely fitting living cells which appear roughly rectangular in transverse section. The outer surface is covered by a thin, waxy cuticle which minimizes water loss. The only differentiations in sunflower are stomata with their bordering guard cells and simple hairs or trichomes. Chloroplasts are lacking.

The cortex

The cortex of the dicotyledon stem is always differentiated into parenchyma and an inner layer, one cell thick, the starch sheath or endodermis. Commonly also, as in *Helianthus*, a few layers of cells in the outer part of the cortex have very thick cellulose in the parts of the walls which originally bounded the intercellular spaces and these cells constitute a collenchyma. The collenchyma is a mechanical or skeletal tissue which is advantageously placed at the periphery of the stem to resist bending forces. It must not be forgotten, however, that it is a living tissue and that the cells contain chloroplasts and store starch. Collenchyma is absent from the root, which is subject mainly to longitudinal pulling and not to bending.

The cells of the cortical parenchyma have thin walls, large vacuoles and numerous chloroplasts and the intercellular spaces between them are large. They appear roughly circular in cross-section but are several times longer, as seen in longitudinal section, than broad, as is the case with the collenchyma. Amongst them, occasional schizogenous glands are visible, consisting of about four cells surrounding a cavity. These are present in many plants and secrete either "essential oils" or mucilage.

The innermost layer of the cortex is the starch sheath or endodermis, an undulating ring of cells arranged in single file with their radial walls in close contact. The endodermis curves outwards opposite each vascular bundle and centrewards between them. It is not as easily discerned as the endodermis of the root, as its walls are unthickened, but it can usually be detected by the great number and very small size of its starch grains. It possibly functions as a gravity receptor.

The stele

(a) *Pericycle.* Inside the endodermis is a layer, several cells wide, the pericycle. Where this is in contact with the outer limit of the vascular bundles, its cells have greatly thickened lignified walls, so that their cavities are almost occluded, and are elongated in the longitudinal axis.

When they mature their contents die. Their ends "dovetail" with those of neighbouring cells. These thickened cells are termed pericyclic fibres, and constitute a type of tissue which, wherever it occurs, is termed sclerenchyma. Sclerenchyma is another important mechanical or skeletal tissue.

(b) *Vascular bundles* (Figs. 92, 93). The vascular bundles are arranged in a circle near the periphery of the stele and are separated by regions of parenchyma known as the primary medullary rays. In cross-section each bundle is roughly egg-shaped in outline with the rounded end outwards.

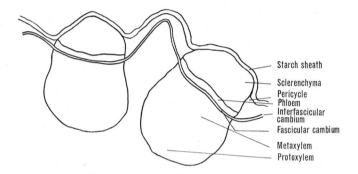

Starch sheath
Sclerenchyma
Pericycle
Phloem
Interfascicular cambium
Fascicular cambium
Metaxylem
Protoxylem

FIG. 92. *Helianthus annuus*. Plan of a transverse section through two vascular bundles. The interfascicular cambium has developed and secondary thickening is about to begin.

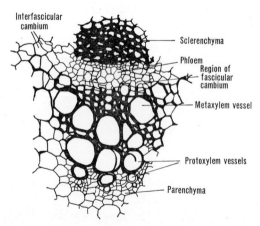

Interfascicular cambium

Sclerenchyma
Phloem
Region of fascicular cambium
Metaxylem vessel
Protoxylem vessels
Parenchyma

FIG. 93. *Helianthus annuus*. Transverse section of a vascular bundle.

Each is traversed by a tangential band, a few cells wide, made up of a single layer of cambium and the undifferentiated cells cut off by this. Outside the cambial zone lies the primary phloem consisting of outer protophloem and more central metaphloem. Inside the cambial zone lies the primary xylem, consisting of protoxylem nearest the centre of the stem and metaxylem next the cambium. A vascular bundle which has the xylem and phloem on the same radius with the xylem nearest the centre of the stem is said to be collateral. Much less commonly there is phloem external and internal to the xylem, when the bundle is said to be bicollateral. This is the case in *Cucurbita* (Figs. 94, 95), the cucumber, and in other Cucurbitaceae, including the pumpkin, melon and gourds. In some plants the phloem is surrounded on all sides by xylem, a condition which causes the bundles to be termed amphivasal (amphixylic or perixylic); the opposite condition where phloem surrounds the xylem is termed amphicribal (amphiphloic or periphloic). Where the bundle contains cambium, it is said to be open and where cambium is lacking, closed.

The primary xylem

The protoxylem consists of vessels with annular and spiral thickening, the annular being nearest the centre of the stem. It has already been mentioned that this type of thickening allows for the extension which occurs in the rapidly growing tissues of the young stem. The metaxylem is composed of vessels with scalariform thickening or pitted walls (p. 145). It also contains xylem parenchyma and some xylem fibres.

The primary phloem

The protophloem contains very narrow sieve tubes distributed among undifferentiated procambium cells. There are good reasons to regard the pericyclic fibres as part of the phloem. The metaphloem is a complex tissue with well developed sieve tubes, and also simple sieve cells (the later-formed elements being progressively wider); companion cells; parenchyma cells; and sclerenchyma in the form of fibres or sometimes sclereids. It closely resembles the later-formed secondary phloem. Where secondary phloem develops in large amounts, the primary phloem is in many plants crushed out of existence very early but in *Helianthus*, although there is considerable secondary phloem, the metaphloem continues to function almost throughout the life of the stem.

The fascicular cambium

The cambium of a bundle (fascicular cambium) consists of cells which are roughly rectangular in cross-section, with the length tangential. They usually appear to form a zone several cells wide radially, but only one cell in each radial tier is a true cambial cell; the others are the immediate undifferentiated products of division of a cambial cell and, if present, indicate that secondary thickening is commencing.

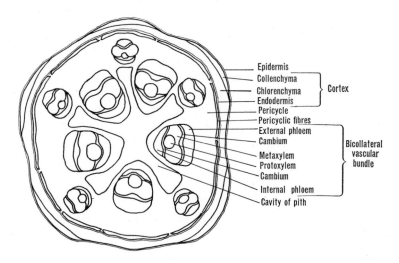

Fig. 94. *Cucurbita* sp. Plan of a transverse section of the stem showing primary structure including bicollateral vascular bundles.

The pith and medullary rays

It must be understood that the vascular bundles lie near the periphery of the stem and that the greater part of the stem, central to the bundles, consists of unthickened parenchyma with living contents, large vacuoles and abundant starch grains. This constitutes the pith. Similar tissue between the bundles, and continuous with the pith, constitutes the primary medullary rays. A line of undifferentiated procambial cells traverses each ray and connects with the fascicular cambium on each side. This interfascicular procambium is virtually indistinguishable from parenchyma and becomes noticeable only when its cells divide by tangential cross walls. This indicates that the interfascicular cambium which develops from the procambium is becoming active and that secondary thickening is beginning in the primary rays.

Secondary Thickening of the Stem (Fig. 90C, D)

The first sign that secondary thickening is occurring is the division of the fascicular cambium so that a radial tier of several cells is produced in place of the circle of cambial cells in single file. The mode of division is similar to that described for the root.

The cells cut off on the outside of the cambium differentiate as secondary phloem while those cut off on the inside become secondary xylem. These tissues closely resemble metaphloem and metaxylem.

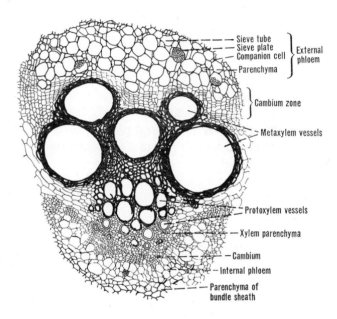

FIG. 95. *Cucurbita* sp. Transverse section of a vascular bundle.

When a small amount of secondary tissue has formed within the bundle, the interfascicular cambium becomes active. Its activity is first detectable by the appearance of tangential cross walls in the cells immediately adjacent to the fascicular cambium, which lie in the primary ray. The divisions progress from the neighbourhood of the bundles, across the ray, so that finally a complete arc of active interfascicular cambium joins the fascicular cambium on each side. The interfascicular cambium in many trees and woody herbs, such as *Helianthus*, cuts off secondary phloem to the outside and secondary xylem to the inside, so that a complete cylinder of these tissues is formed round the stem. In more herbaceous types, including *Vitis*, the grape vine, the interfascicular cambium cuts off parenchyma only, and therefore the secondary xylem and secondary phloem are restricted to the bundles between which persist the "primary rays" of parenchyma. Primary rays often persist in trees also. In *Helianthus*, when secondary xylem and secondary phloem are well developed it is difficult to determine the position of the original vascular bundles but these can be ascertained by looking for the sclerenchyma "cap" of each bundle.

Secondary rays, radial strips of parenchyma one to several cells in tangential width, and several cells deep, are cut off by the interfascicular and fascicular cambium at certain points in such a way that the secondary xylem and phloem are never far distant from parenchyma. The parenchyma is important for transference of organic food from phloem to xylem, for storage of food reserves, and for aeration of the stem via the large intercellular spaces. The cambium which gives rise to the secondary rays usually cuts off secondary xylem and phloem before it commences to produce parenchyma and for this reason a secondary ray rarely reaches from cortex to pith, although this is sometimes the case.

The arrangement of rays tangentially and vertically is such that every xylem element is, at some point along its length, in contact with the parenchyma of a ray.

Secondary thickening in the cortex of the stem and root

As a result of secondary thickening of the stele, the circumference of the stem and root is increased. In woody plants the increase in girth is very great and, as the epidermal and cortical cells have only a limited ability to stretch, the epidermis and cortex rupture and no longer effectively carry out their functions, which include protection, food storage and support. The mechanical support of any collenchyma is replaced by the additional, secondary wood and by phloem fibres. Protection of the internal tissues becomes the function of a new, secondary tissue, the cork or phellem. This is produced by the activity of a secondary meristem, the cork cambium or phellogen, which develops by transformation of cortical cells.

The phellogen cuts off cells both to the outside and to the inside. Those cut off to the outside have a tarry substance, suberin, deposited on their inner walls which is impermeable to water and to gases. Their contents soon die, therefore, and the cells come to form the tissue termed cork. The cells cut off to the inside of the phellogen are living parenchymatous cells and constitute a secondary cortex or phelloderm. Phellogen and the tissues it produces (phellem and phelloderm) are collectively termed periderm.

Successive layers of phellogen are usually produced—the first-formed layer is usually near, rarely in, the epidermis and when activity ceases, phellogen layers develop successively deeper into the cortex until even the pericycle of the stele may be involved. The cork cut off from each new phellogen causes the death of all tissues external to it because of its impermeability to outward passage of food materials. The dead tissues external to the most recently formed cork consitute what is popularly

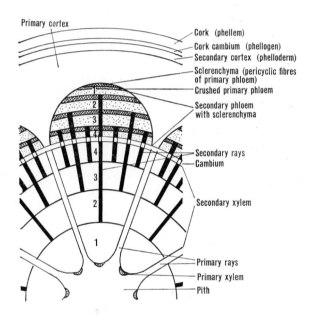

FIG. 96. Secondary thickening of the stem. Diagram of a portion of a transverse section through the stem of a woody perennial which is 4 years old and has persistent primary rays. In this specimen both the secondary phloem and the secondary xylem are laid down in annual rings. Each ring represents a season's growth. Successive xylem rings are discernible because of variations in the diameter of xylem vessels, and other features, during each season. Phloem rings are discernible because of a band of sclerenchyma produced each season. Annual rings are usually absent from plants which live in regions with little climatic variation but occur in plants living in those parts of the tropics which have pronounced wet and dry seasons and are characteristic of woody plants of the temperate zones. Periderm (phellem, phellogen and phelloderm) is also present.

termed bark. Where the original phellogen is deep-seated, successive phellogens usually form complete rings; where it is superficial they often form only arcs which are contiguous at their ends with pre-existing phellogen. The phellogen of roots almost always arises deep in the cortex.

The phellogen divides by radial walls as well as tangential walls and is therefore able to cope with increase in girth of the stem. When, however, it and associated tissues die owing to cork formation more centrally, increase in girth causes it to rupture producing the fissured appearance which is a frequent characteristic of bark.

If the cork were a complete barrier to the passage of gases, the stem and root would die. Breathing pores or lenticels are, however, developed (Fig. 97). The first lenticels usually arise beneath the stomata of the young

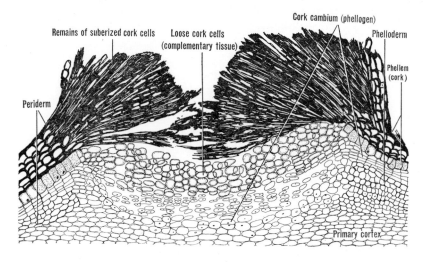

FIG. 97. Cross-section through a lenticel of *Sambucus*, elder.

stem. They are produced by the activity of a newly formed cambium which becomes continuous with the later formed phellogen. This cambium cuts off phelloderm to the inside and thin-walled unsuberized cells, which constitute the "complementary tissue" to the outside. The latter cells soon round off, often forming a powdery mass. Gases are able to diffuse in and out of the lenticel through the spaces between the cells of the complementary tissue and through the intercellular spaces of the phellogen and phelloderm.

New lenticels are formed each time a new phellogen is laid down.

Leaf fall involves processes closely related to cork formation. It is discussed on p. 194.

STEMS OF MONOCOTYLEDONS

The stems of monocotyledons differ fundamentally from those of dicotyledons in certain respects. The main points of difference are outlined below. In reading this account the cross-section of the stem of maize in Figs. 98, 99 should be consulted.

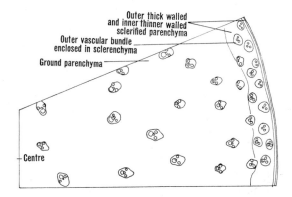

FIG. 98. Plan of a transverse section of a portion of the stem of maize, showing the distribution of vascular bundles.

1. Usually the vascular bundles are scattered and there is no differentiation of the stem into cortex and stele. In some stems, however, particularly stolons and rhizomes, there is an outer cortex which is bounded internally by a definite endodermis and inside this there is a central cylinder of ground tissue in which lie numerous vascular bundles. The latter are in some cases arranged in a ring.

2. The vascular bundles (Fig. 99) are closed, that is to say, they lack cambium and cannot undergo secondary growth. In rare instances there is feeble development of fascicular cambium, however.

3. Associated with the absence of cambium in the vascular bundles is the absence, usually, of secondary thickening. The relatively great thickness of the stems of most palms is due not to secondary thickening but to increase, as the plant ages, in the width of the apical meristem, and increase in cell size, though some of them do have a form of secondary thickening. In no case where there is significant secondary thickening does the cambium develop in the bundles, however. In the dragon tree,

Dracaena, and in *Yucca*, also, secondary thickening occurs. In young *Dracaena* stems the closed bundles are scattered throughout the width of the stem. A cambium later develops a short distance below the epidermis. This cuts off a small amount of parenchyma to the outside and, on the inside, produces secondary vascular bundles separated by parenchyma, which may or may not be lignified. The new bundles consist of a little phloem surrounded by xylem tracheids. Periderm is also produced by a peripheral phellogen, as in some other monocotyledons.

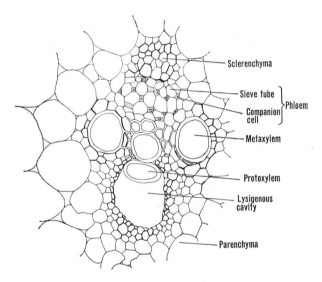

FIG. 99. Transverse section of a vascular bundle in the stem of maize. Note the absence of fascicular cambium, as is characteristic of mono-cotyledons.

The structure of a vascular bundle of maize is seen in transverse section in Fig. 99. Each bundle is "capped" externally, or is surrounded by sclerenchyma. Just within its outer margin is an area of phloem with very clearly distinguishable, large, pale sieve tubes and smaller, dark, companion cells with dense contents. Internal to the phloem are two large, circular, pitted metaxylem vessels between which are tracheids of much smaller diameter. The protoxylem consists of one or more annular vessels situated in the median plane of the bundle and, internal to these, a few spirally thickened vessels some of which have usually broken down to leave a cavity, the lysigenous cavity.

Types of Branching of the Shoot (Fig. 100)

The simplest type of branching occurs by division of the apical meristem into two so that the axis of a shoot (or root) forks. Such branching is described as dichotomous. The two branches of the dichotomy are not necessarily equal in size and growth potential. Dichotomous branching is exceedingly rare in the shoots of seed plants and is not common in their roots but is frequent in pteridophytes (e.g. *Selaginella*), bryophytes

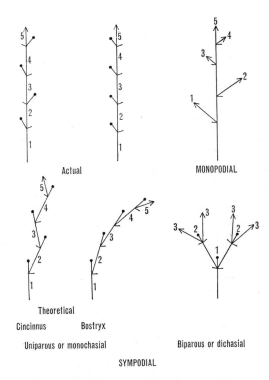

FIG. 100. Types of branching of the shoot. An arrow indicates that growth is proceeding; a black disc that growth has ceased. The numbers indicate the sequence of development.

(e.g. *Marchantia*) and algae (e.g. *Fucus*). The only angiosperms which show true dichotomous branching are the two palms *Hyphaene thebaica* and *Chamaedorea martiana*.

The normal type of branching in spermatophytes is lateral and, in shoots, axillary. In axillary branching each branch arises in the axil (p. 136) of a leaf. Where the same apical meristem maintains the power of division and the lateral branches are all physiologically subordinate to the terminal bud, growth and branching are said to be monopodial or racemose. Where the apical meristem normally ceases to be active (often because it forms a flower, as in *Jacaranda* or *Tecoma*) one or more axillary shoots continue growth of the shoot. This type of growth and branching is said to be sympodial or cymose. Even in a monopodially growing shoot system, if the main apical meristem is destroyed, as by desiccation or pruning, a nearby axillary shoot takes over as the main axis of growth (see also p. 137).

Where branching is racemose, each node may bear a single branch, a pair of branches or a whorl, according as there is one leaf or are two or more leaves at the node. Even where there is a single leaf at a node, there may be several axillary buds. Where branching is cymose and the leaves alternate, growth of the shoot is typically continued by only a single axillary shoot and the branching is said to be uniparous or monochasial. Where the leaves are opposite (i.e. paired), both axillary buds may develop as shoots on cessation of growth of the terminal bud. Such double branching is said to be biparous or dichasial. If the terminal bud shrivels away, the shoot appears to have forked and the dichasium is sometimes termed a false dichotomy. Sometimes multiparous branching occurs in which more than two branches develop at each node.

In uniparous cymes, successive daughter axes produced on cessation of activity of the preceding growing points may be developed alternately on opposite sides, when the shoot is termed a cincinnus, or on the same side, when it is termed a bostryx (Fig. 100). Theoretically a cincinnus should have the form of a zigzag and a bostryx that of a spiral, but in fact each successive new growing shoot, although axillary, pushes the preceding apex to one side and comes to lie in line with the main axis. The shoot as a whole then superficially resembles a monopodial shoot. A uniparous cyme can always be distinguished from a monopodium by the fact that its leaves lie on the opposite side to the apparent branches, while in a monopodium the branches lie between the axis and the leaf.

Branching of Inflorescences (Figs. 101, 102)

An inflorescence is a shoot which bears a number of flowers and typically has the leaves reduced to bracts. The stalk or pedicel of each flower lies in the axil of a bract and commonly bears minute bracts termed bracteoles. Bracts and bracteoles are usually absent in the Cruciferae. As a flower is a compressed shoot and an inflorescence bears a minimum of two flowers, all inflorescences are branched. Their branching may be racemose (monopodial) or cymose (sympodial) or, commonly, the main axis (peduncle) develops in a racemose manner and side-branches are produced which bear flowers in a cymose arrangement. Racemose inflorescences differ from cymes in the order of opening, and of ages, of the flowers; in racemose inflorescences the flowers open from below upwards, the youngest being nearest the apex, whereas in cymose inflorescences opening is in the reverse order and the youngest are borne below the oldest. Where inflorescences have become flat-topped (see below) the sequence of opening is towards the centre where racemose, and away from the centre where cymose.

Racemose inflorescences (Fig. 101)

There are several types of racemose inflorescence of which the chief are:

1. The raceme. Here the flowers are stalked (pedicellate) and the peduncle is elongated so that the pedicels of individual flowers are at some distance from each other. The raceme may be simple, e.g. *Crotalaria*, or compound, where it is a raceme of racemes known as a panicle, e.g. many grasses, including *Avena* and *Festuca*.

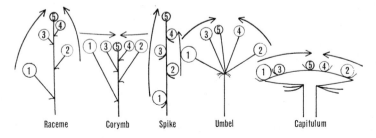

Raceme   Corymb   Spike   Umbel   Capitulum

FIG. 101. Types of racemose inflorescences. The numbers indicate the sequence of opening of flowers.

2. The corymb. This is a simple raceme in which the pedicels of the lower, older, flowers have elongated so that all the flowers lie approximately on the same level, e.g. many Cruciferae, including candytuft, *Iberis*.

3. The spike. A simple raceme with sessile flowers, e.g. *Piper*, *Plantago*.

4. The umbel. A simple raceme in which the internodes are so reduced that the individual pedicels all appear to spring from the top of the peduncle. The bracts are borne in a whorl, at the base of the pedicels,

which is termed an involucre. The umbel is characteristic of the Umbelliferae, in which the inflorescence is commonly an umbel of umbels (compound umbel).

5. The capitulum is a simple raceme in which the internodes are again
greatly reduced and the flowers (florets) are crowded together on the
expanded and flattened or dome-shaped end of the peduncle which is
termed the disc. It is typical of the Compositae and is discussed on p. 280.

Cymose inflorescences (*Fig.* 102)

The main feature of cymose inflorescences is cessation of growth of the
main axis by production of a flower prior to the development of axillary
lateral branches which continue the growth of the inflorescence. They
are divisible into uniparous and biparous cymes.

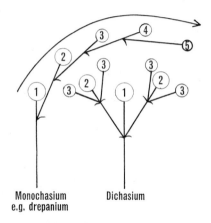

Monochasium   Dichasium
e.g. drepanium

FIG. 102. Types of cymose inflorescences. The numbers indicate the
sequence of opening of flowers.

1. The uniparous cyme or monochasium. This occurs in plants with
alternate bracts. Only one flower is produced at each node. There are
four types of monochasium.

(a) The drepanium has each successive flower developed on the same
side of the main axis and in the same plane, e.g. *Juncus*.

(b) The bostryx, or screw, has each successive flower developed on
the same side but at right-angles, e.g. *Hypericum*.

(c) The rhipidium has the flowers alternating in the same plane, e.g.
Iris.

(d) The Cincinnus bears alternate flowers which are mutually at right-angles, e.g. *Tradescantia*.

2. The biparous cyme or dichasium. Here the bracts are opposite (paired) and a flower develops in the axil of each bract. The stalk of each flower in turn gives rise to a pair of axillary flowers. They are common in the Caryophyllaceae and Gentianaceae. Often in the Caryophyllaceae one of the branches at each node is weakly developed or may be supressed so that a cincinnus results.

SPECIALIZED STEMS

The primary functions of the stem are supporting the leaves in a situation satisfactory for photosynthesis and acting as a pathway for translocation of water and mineral salts to the leaves and the growing points and of organic food materials from the site of their elaboration in the leaves to all other parts of the plant. Stems are frequently modified for other functions, however. These include: photosynthesis, protection, support of the shoot by special modifications, reproduction, storage and water absorption.

Photosynthetic Stems

The stems of herbs and of young woody plants usually have chloroplasts in the cortex which augment photosynthesis by the leaves. In some plants, photosynthesis is carried on mainly or wholly by the stem which shows more or less structural modification for this function. A stem which carries out most of the photosynthesis of a plant is termed a cladode or phylloclade.

In the Old World genus *Asparagus* (Fig. 103), of which *A. officinalis* yields young shoots which are regarded as a delicacy in many parts of the world, and which includes the wild asparagus fern of tropical regions, the leaves are reduced to minute scales in the axils of which are borne what appear to be short green rod-like leaves. These "leaves" are, as their axillary situation reveals, modified stems functioning as leaves and are therefore cladodes. There is evidence that in *Asparagus* the cladode is equivalent not to a vegetative internode but to a sterilized flower stalk, hence their arrangement like the flowers in two axillary cymes. The subgenus *Myrsiphyllum* of *Asparagus* is particularly interesting in having cladodes which have the form of leaves, the true leaves being reduced, again, to minute scales.

Cladodes also occur in *Casuarina*, the she-oak or whistling pine (an angiosperm, despite the latter name) which is native to the Australian region but is cultivated throughout the world as a windbreak and timber tree. In *Casuarina*, the scale-like leaves are arranged in a whorl around the photosynthetic stem at each node so that the shoot has a remarkable resemblance to that of a horse-tail fern. Cladodes also occur in *Muehlenbeckia platyclados*, a native of Australia (Fig. 104).

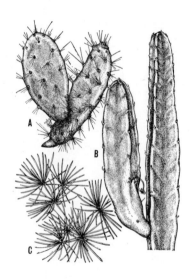

FIG. 103. Cladodes. A, *Opuntia robusta*, a cactus. B, *Stapelia grandiflora*, an African succulent. C, *Asparagus zuluensis*, an African species. All × ½.

The true cacti which are, with the exception of the African *Rhipsalis*, restricted as natives to the New World offer fine and varied examples. Perhaps the prickly pear, *Opuntia* spp. (Fig. 103), which has been introduced, often to become a pest, into many parts of the world is the most familiar example of a cactus. Here the stem forms a flattened oval green pad and the branches are similar. The nodes are represented by small round cushions termed areoles which bear innumerable minute spines termed glochids which easily enter the skin if the cladode is handled. Many species bear long sharp spines on the areoles in addition. In those species which lack obvious spines very small finger-like green leaves are borne in place of the spines and suggest that the two organs are homologous.

In tropical and South Africa, certain members of the Asclepiadaceae, e.g. *Stapelia* (Fig. 103) and *Edithcolea*, and members of the Euphorbiaceae, have cladodes as their only photosynthetic organs. These plants, like the cacti, are usually found in arid regions and resemble the latter in storing water in the cladodes, but differ from cacti in containing a white latex and, in euphorbias, in having paired spines, developed from stipules. Another example is the anchor plant, *Colletia paradoxica* (Rhamnaceae), (Fig. 105) which is cultivated in many parts of the world as a thorn hedge or as an ornamental plant. Here the branches of the cladode form triangular thorns in the axils of tiny leaves which soon fall.

FIG. 104. Cladodes of *Muehlenbeckia platyclados*, × ½.

Protection

Browsing of herbivorous animals on the foliage of plants has favoured the development of protective spines or thorns in many species. These may develop from almost any part of the plant (see specialized leaves, Chapter 10) and commonly arise by modification of branches of the stem. An example has already been seen in *Colletia* (Fig. 105). Familiar examples are the spine of lime trees and other *Citrus* spp. (Fig. 106A) which are borne in the axils of some of the foliage leaves. Further examples are *Haematoxylon*, the tropical American leguminous tree from the heart wood of which the dye haematoxylin is obtained; Old World shrubs of the genus *Carissa* (Fig. 106B); and the climber *Bougainvillaea* (Fig. 106C) in which their main function is for climbing.

Specializations of the Stem for Support

Some plants are described as climbers because the stem lacks the ability on its own to support the shoot system, and the plant climbs on an external support. Climbers have been divided into twiners, those climbing by tendrils or by sensitive hooks, root climbers and scramblers, names which indicate the means of attachment to the support. With the obvious exception of root climbers, all of these classes contain plants in which the climbing organ is a modified stem.

FIG. 105. Cladode of *Colletia paradoxica*, anchor plant, × ½.

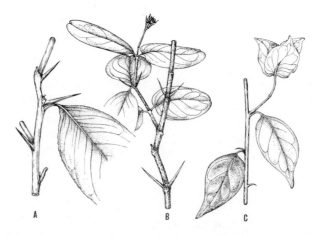

A   B   C

FIG. 106. Spines of A, *Citrus* sp.; B, *Carissa carandas* and C, *Bougain-villaea*, representing modified axillary branches.

Twiners

Twiners are plants which climb by coiling round the support, a pheno-menon known as circum-nutation. They may have additional means of attachment such as adventitious roots or prickles.

Examples of annual twiners are morning glory, *Ipomoea purpurea*, and many beans including the runner bean, *Phaseolus multiflorus*. Examples of perennial climbers are Dutchman's pipe, *Aristolochia elegans* (Fig. 146), the sweet potato, *Ipomoea batatas*, and species of yams, *Dioscorea* spp. All these plants coil anti-clockwise (viewed from above) with the exception of *Dioscorea dumetorum*, which coils clockwise and differs from other yams in having compound leaves with three leaflets.

Plants climbing by tendrils or by sensitive hooks

Tendrils. Some plants climb by means of whip-like processes termed tendrils which are sensitive to touch and respond by coiling round sup-ports if they are in contact with these for a sufficiently long period. They are developed from stems or from leaves (including stipules). Leaf tendrils are discussed on pp. 201 to 203. Some stem tendrils are illustrated in Fig. 107.

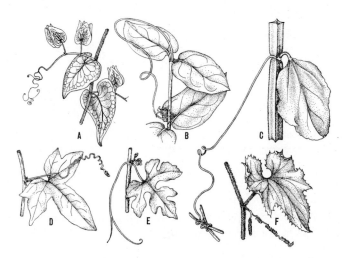

Fig. 107. Stem tendrils of A, coral creeper, *Antigonon leptopus*; B, *Landolphia* sp.; C, *Cissus quadrangularis*; D, the passion flower, *Passiflora foetida*; E, the vine, *Vitis candicans*; F, the bottle gourd, *Lagenaria alassenica*

G

Stem (i.e. inflorescence) tendrils occur in the tropical American coral creeper, *Antigonon leptopus* (Polygonaceae) (Fig. 107A), which is cultivated throughout the tropics; *Landolphia* spp. (Fig. 107B) of Africa, which include the beautiful East African white-flowered *L. florida*, and climb by tendril-like axiliary hooks (species of *Landolphia* yield a type of rubber); *Cissus quadrangularis* (Fig. 107C), a succulent climber of arid regions; the passion flower, *Passiflora* (Fig. 107D), an American climber grown all over the world for its fruit; the vine, *Vitis* (Vitaceae) (Fig. 107E), and the bottle gourd *Lagenaria* (Fig. 107F) and other Cucurbitaceae. The nature of the tendrils in the latter family is in doubt; in *Vitis* they are probably the ends of shoots in a sympodially growing plant.

Sensitive hooks. Some plants develop axilary hooks which are sensitive and curve around supports and become woody, e.g. *Hugonia mystax* and *Artabotrys* spp. (Fig. 108). Examples also occur in the tropical genus

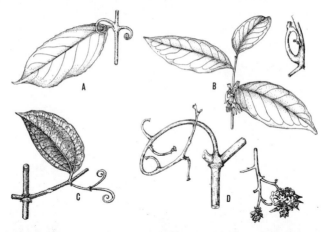

FIG. 108. Axillary hooks of A, *Hugonia planchonii*; B, *Artabotrys nitidus*; C, *Strychnos* sp.; D (left) *Landolphia oweniensis*, (right) *Landolphia klamei*.

Strychnos, including *S. nuxvomica* of India from which strychnine is obtained; and in *Landolphia* spp. The distinction between tendrils and sensitive hooks is not always clear-cut.

Root climbers

Examples of plants which climb by means of their roots are given in Chapter 8.

Scramblers

Scramblers are plants which climb by leaning on external supports, usually other plants, but do not coil around them in any way. They often maintain a purchase on the support by means of thorns or of spines which may be curved to form a hook which is not, however, sensitive in that it does not respond to contact by coiling.

Examples are the rose, *Rosa*, which has epidermal hooked thorns; *Bougainvillaea spectabilis*, which has hooked thorns which represent modified branches (Fig. 106C), although this is not always apparent as the thorns often emerge from the stem some distance above their origin in an axil. These thorns also protect the plant.

Reproduction

Many plants reproduce vegetatively by means of modified stems including rhizomes, stolons, bulbs, corms and tubers. These are discussed under perennation in Chapter 15.

Storage

The stems (cladodes) of cacti and euphorbias store water, and food is often stored in subterranean stems (rhizomes, corms and tubers) which are discussed in Chapter 15.

Absorption

The stems of many water plants are not cuticularized and are able to absorb water and mineral salts.

The haustoria or suckers of mistletoes, *Loranthus* spp., which are parasitic on trees and shrubs throughout the world, are exogenous in origin and lack root caps and are perhaps to be regarded as absorptive stems.

CHAPTER 10

Morphology of the Leaf

A LEAF is typically the main photosynthetic organ of a plant; accordingly it has a broad flattened blade or lamina and is supplied with mineral salts in solution, via xylem elements, and supplies elaborated organic food to the rest of the plant via phloem elements, the xylem and phloem forming veins throughout the lamina; the veins may communicate with the vascular tissue of the stem through a bladeless stalk or petiole or, lacking this, may be sessile on the stem. However modified, a leaf may be recognized by the presence in the axil, between the leaf base and stem, of an axillary bud. This bud may be in an exceedingly rudimentary state but its presence can often be demonstrated by cutting off the apical meristem of the shoot. This stimulates development of axiliary branches.

DEVELOPMENT

We need consider development of the leaf only very briefly. The leaf is initiated by periclinal divisions (parallel to the surface) of the apical meristem below the extreme tip of the stem. Also the surface layer or layers undergo anticlinal divisions (at right-angles to the surface) and a minute bulge, the leaf buttress, is thus formed. At first this grows laterally and the extent to which it encircles the stem is related to the degree of sheathing of the stem by the leaf. This is usually very extensive in monocotyledons. Outward growth of this primordium then occurs in two ways: first repeated divisions occur at one point which constitutes the apex of the developing leaf. Often it is possible to distinguish two initials, namely, an apical cell and a subapical cell. The apical initial divides anticlinally (transversely) and causes increase in length of the leaf primordium; the subapical initial divides anticlinally and periclinally and increases the length and thickness of the primordium. Secondary growth proceeds by anticlinal and periclinal divisions of the derivatives of the initials which themselves soon cease to divide. This second type of growth is termed intercalary growth and accounts for all the later growth and development of the leaf, which may continue for more than one season. The development of the characteristic flattened form of the leaf, that is, the development of the lamina, is dependent on the activity of two longitudinal bands of meristem, which become active during the early stages of development of the primordium, and of their derivatives; these result in increase in width and depth of the lamina. Once the characteristic number of layers of cells has developed in the thickness of the leaf, the derivatives of the marginal meristems divide, so that extension in area but not in thickness occurs. Both periclinal and anticlinal divisions continue at the marginal meristems until growth of the leaf ceases. The particular shape of a leaf is due to differences in rate and type of growth in different parts of the leaf.

ANATOMY (FIG. 109)

Like the root and stem, the leaf consists of a dermal system which is here the epidermis; ground tissue and the vascular system. The epidermis is usually persistent as there is usually no secondary growth of differentiated regions of the leaf. Nevertheless, secondary growth sometimes occurs in the petiole and the main veins and bud scales develop some periderm.

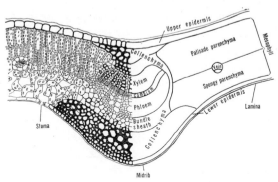

FIG. 109. Transverse section of a dorsiventral leaf of an angiosperm.

Epidermis

The epidermis of the leaf consists of closely packed cells, frequently with wavy outlines as seen in surface view. The outer walls are usually thicker than the inner and are impregnated with a fatty substance, cutin, and are overlain by a layer of cutin which constitutes the cuticle. This cutinization and cuticularization is characteristic of all aerial parts of the plant. Cutin is impermeable to water and gases and is most developed in plants of arid regions (xerophytes), as compared with those of plants of fairly moist regions (mesophytes). In addition to cuticle, leaves are sometimes covered with a waxy layer or "bloom".

The epidermal cells have living contents and contain plastids which usually store starch. Chloroplasts are almost always absent from epidermal cells with the exception of the guard cells of the stomata which normally are green. In some leaves the epidermis is more than one cell thick owing to periclinal division. Such a multiple epidermis occurs in the leaves of the India rubber tree, *Ficus elastica*. The same appearance is sometimes produced where one or more colourless subepidermal layers develop from the ground tissue and a multiple epidermis can only be distinguished from this formation by studies of development.

Stomata

Stomata are strictly speaking minute intercellular pores traversing the epidermis, but the term stoma is often extended to include the pore and the two cells which always flank it, the guard cells. Stomata are usually very much more common on the leaves than on the stem and are absent from typical roots. In mesophytic plants the stomata occur chiefly if not wholly on the under-surface of the leaf.

In dicotyledons the guard cells are sausage-shaped in surface view. The cells adjacent to the guard cells may be normal epidermal cells, when the stoma is said to be anomocytic (Fig. 110), or may be modified as subsidiary cells. Three types of arrangement of subsidiary cells relative to the guard cells exist: the guard cells may be surrounded by three subsidiary cells of which one is much smaller than the other two, the anisocytic arrangement; or by two subsidiary cells paralleling the guard cells, the paracytic arrangement; or by two subsidiary cells set transversely to the guard cells, the diacytic arrangement. These arrangements have been found to be of taxonomic value at the generic and higher levels. Guard cells of grasses and other monocotyledons have bulbous ends (Fig. 111).

The guard cells may be on the same level as the rest of the epidermis but in hydrophytes they are frequently borne on prominences, and in xerophytes they are usually at the bottoms of pits—situations which are clearly correlated with the amount of available water and the control of transpiration. It has been shown experimentally that a plant which typically has sunken stomata can be induced to develop raised stomata if grown in a humid atmosphere.

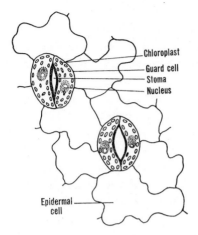

FIG. 110. Anomocytic stomata of sunflower, *Helianthus annus*, in surface view, greatly enlarged.

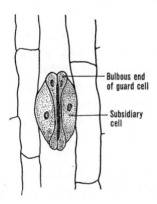

FIG. 111. Stoma of a grass in surface view, greatly enlarged.

The two guard cells of a stoma are formed by the longitudinal division of a single mother cell. The pore develops by dissolution of intercellular material. They are covered with cuticle on the outer surface and on those bounding the pore and the chamber into which the pore opens, i.e. on all free surfaces. When the guard cells are turgid, they separate and the pore opens; when they lose water and become flaccid they move together and the pore closes.

Mesophyll

The ground tissue of a leaf is divisible into mesophyll and vascular tissue. The characteristics of the mesophyll are those which suit it to its function as the main photosynthetic tissue of the plant. Its cells have abundant chloroplasts, large vacuoles, thin walls permitting rapid diffusion of gases and water, and very large intercellular spaces which communicate directly or indirectly with the external air. In the leaves of mesophytes the mesophyll is usually differentiated into one or more upper layers of cells which are elongated in the direction at right-angles to the upper surface and constitute the palisade parenchyma and a lower zone of irregularly shaped cells, several cells in height but not distinctly layered, which is termed the spongy parenchyma.

Cells of the spongy parenchyma are usually in contact with each other only at the tips of branch-like extensions of the cells. The spongy parenchyma consequently has the form of a three-dimensional network enclosing large intercellular spaces. The intercellular spaces between palisade cells are narrower but the palisade parenchyma has a larger internal free surface than has the spongy parenchyma.

The typical mesophytic leaf with palisade parenchyma above (adaxial) and spongy parenchyma below (abaxial) is called a dorsiventral leaf. Shade leaves of mesophytic plants with typically dorsiventral leaves often have a palisade parenchyma at both surfaces of the leaf with the spongy parenchyma between them and, somewhat surprisingly, the same is often true of the ordinary leaves of xerophytic plants. A leaf with palisade cells at both surfaces is called an isobilateral or isolateral leaf.

Vascular System

The vascular bundles supplying the lamina of a leaf are visible as "veins" in surface view. One to many leaf trace bundles run from the stem throughout the length of the petiole to the leaf base or directly to the latter if the leaf is sessile. The course of the bundles thereafter is variable. In dicotyledons the pattern of veins (venation) is usually net-like or reticulate. In reticulate venation there may be a single, median, main vein which is visible externally as a thickening of the leaf, the midrib, or there may be several main veins, also usually raised as ribs. From these main veins diverge branch veins and these again branch, and the branches meet, so that a network of veins is visible dividing the mesophyll into very many small regions sometimes termed areoles. There may or may not be minute veins ending blindly in the areoles.

In monocotyledons, reticulate venation is not infrequent but the vast majority show parallel venation in which large main veins are not developed (although a midrib may be present) and there are many relatively small veins running approximately parallel to each other in a longitudinal direction or more transversely. Parallel venation resembles reticulate venation in that there are cross connections between the veins. These connections may be almost straight transverse striations or may form a network as complex as that seen in reticulate-veined leaves.

The arrangement of xylem and phloem in the petiole and in the veins of a leaf is easily understood if reference is made to the origin of the vascular system of the leaf from that of the stem. The simplest case we can take is that in which the xylem and phloem completely encircle the stem so as to form continuous cylinders. Here a gap in the vascular cylinder occurs just above the point of departure of a bundle to the leaf. The gap is termed a leaf gap and the bundle to the leaf a leaf trace. The leaf trace has the appearance of a portion of the vascular cylinder which has been deflected outwards, leaving a corresponding gap in the cylinder. As the xylem of stem cylinder is internal to the phloem, it will be understandable that the xylem of the leaf trace running in the petiole will be dorsal (adaxial) relative to the phloem. The situation is more complex in plants where the vascular cylinder is divided, as in extreme herbs and vines, but orientation of xylem relative to phloem is the same.

This orientation of xylem to phloem persists throughout the veins of the leaf but in the smallest, microscopic, veins, the phloem usually peters out and the vein ends as a single xylem tracheid. Only very exceptionally (cf. hydathodes) are xylem elements, however small the vein, exposed to the intercellular spaces. The smaller veins are surrounded by a single layer of cells which make up the bundle sheath. These cells usually contain chloroplasts. The larger bundles are surrounded by several layers of cells which usually contain few or no chloroplasts and some of these cells are often thickened with cellulose at the corners to form collenchyma. The large amount of ground tissue in the midrib (if this is differentiated) and the larger veins, accounts for their prominence as ribs; the collenchyma adds greatly to their efficacy as a supporting skeleton for the leaf.

Cambium is commonly absent from the vascular bundles of the leaf but is not infrequently present in those of the petiole where secondary thickening then occurs.

Abscission of the Leaf—Leaf Fall (Fig. 112)

The periodic shedding of leaves by trees and shrubs is a familiar phenomenon. In the tropics it often occurs at the beginning of the dry season, while in temperate and colder latitudes it occurs as winter approaches. In both cases the ensuing season brings conditions which are unfavourable for growth. Evergreen trees which retain their leaves throughout the year exist in both regions and, indeed, make up the majority of tropical trees. These are adapted in various ways to meet the adverse conditions of the unfavourable season, the most notable adaptation being a xerophytic leaf. The evergreen trees differ from the deciduous trees, i.e. those which become bare in the adverse season, by shedding their leaves, and replacing them with new leaves, constantly so that the tree is never bare of foliage.

Leaves are not broken off haphazardly by external forces but are shed as a result of modifications of the leaf base which may occur many months before shedding. Although abscission literally means the cutting away or shedding of the leaf we must therefore consider these modifications under this heading.

The narrow zone at the base of the leaf where separation of the leaf from the plant always occurs is known as the abscission zone and it is often externally visible even in the young leaf. It may appear as a groove or a differently coloured band around the base of the petiole. Within this band, from the start, the mechanical tissue is reduced, collenchyma and sclerenchyma are at a minimum, and even the vascular bundles may be reduced in diameter.

Within the abscission zone, days or weeks before abscission, a separation layer develops. It is the breakdown of the cells, or at least their middle lamellae, in this layer which causes abscission of the leaf. Dissolution of the cells seems to be under the control of auxins and when it occurs is so complete, including even the parenchyma of the vascular bundles, that only the vascular elements attach the leaf to the plant. These are finally broken by external factors, usually wind, and the leaf falls.

Usually, before abscission occurs, a protective layer is formed below the separation layer. The protective layer hinders entry of disease organisms into the leaf scar and in cold climates minimizes frost damage. The layer is commonly formed by deposition of suberin and/or wound gum in cells beneath the separation layer or even in the cells of the separation layer, and the scar is thereby rendered impermeable to gases, water and many organisms. The vascular elements are usually sealed by tyloses, precipitates of insoluble and impermeable materials. The development of the protective layer is not usually the cause of death of the leaf, the abscission being under the control of auxins as noted above.

After abscission, often in the following year, the protective layer may be augmented by the development of a periderm across the scar, continuous with the periderm of the stem.

The process of abscission has many variants and the above account must be regarded as a generalized account only.

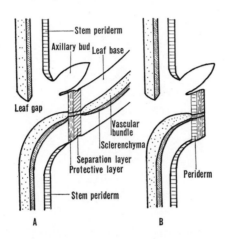

FIG. 112. Abscission of a leaf. A, before leaf fall. B, after leaf fall.

Leaves of Monocotyledons

The leaves of monocotyledons are usually distinguished from those of dicotyledons by the following features.

1. They have parallel veins (Fig. 113) whereas the leaves of dicotyledons are "net-veined" (reticulate venation). There are many exceptions to this difference, however. The dicotyledonous genus *Plantago* has parallel venation and the monocotyledons *Paris* and some Araceae have reticulate venation.

2. Monocotyledonous leaves are rarely lobed or compound. Where they are compound, as in palms, the mode of development is quite different from that of dicotyledonous compound leaves, a single leaf rudiment becoming divided up by death of some of its cells. Monocotyledonous leaves are usually parallel-sided and this, with their parallel venation, has led to the view that they are not true leaves but are phyllodes, i.e. photosynthetic petioles in the absence of a leaf blade.

3. They have indefinite intercalary basal growth; such growth is due to the presence of a persistent meristem at the base of the leaf. In dicotyledonous leaves growth does not occur after expansion of the young leaf is completed.

FIG. 113. Leaves of a monocotyledon, the banana, seen from above. As is usual in the monocotyledons the veins are parallel, in this species running transversely from a well developed midrib. Note the leaf mosaic, an arrangement of the leaves so that there is very little overlap and therefore good exposure to light.

4. Monocotyledons usually have sheathing leaf bases; that is to say, the base of the leaf wholly or partly encircles the stem and usually ensheathes the stem for one or more internodes. In dicotyledons the attachment of the leaf to the stem is localized and sheathing of the stem is rare. An extreme development of sheathing leaf bases in a monocotyledon is seen in the banana, *Musa*, in which the "trunk" is made up entirely of concentric sheathing leaf bases, the true stem being restricted to a wide, short cone at the base of the plant. Only when flowering occurs does the stem become more extensive, the inflorescence growing up through the middle of the leaf bases. In its relative the traveller's tree, *Ravanela madagascariensis*, on the other hand, there is a woody stem, although this is hidden by sheathing leaf bases.

5. The leaves of monocotyledons rarely, perhaps never, show a true opposite arrangement; they normally alternate or are scattered. In dicotyledons opposite leaves are common and probably predominate.

VARIATION IN LEAF FORM
Simple and Compound Leaves

The leaves of most plants have a single lamina arising from the petiole or directly from the stem. These are termed simple leaves. The shape of the lamina is usually constant for a species, although, in many, "juvenile leaves" of the young plant differ markedly from the leaves of the older plant. A great variety of form occurs between different species. This variation can be classified into variation of outline (shape); of the apex; of the base; and of the margin of the lamina. Within each of these classes there are relatively few different forms. These forms are named and illustrated in Fig. 114.

A compound leaf is a leaf the lamina of which is composed of two or more discrete parts termed leaflets which arise separately from the petiole or from an extension of the petiole termed the rachis. The following criteria distinguish a compound leaf from a branch which bears leaves.

	Compound leaf	*Branch*
1.	Has an axillary bud in the axil of its main stalk	Has no axillary bud
2.	The leaflets have no axillary buds	Leaves have axillary buds
3.	Has no terminal bud	Has a terminal bud

The separate leaflets of a compound leaf develop as separate rudiments in the primordium of the leaf and development of a compound leaf does not proceed by division of an already formed simple leaf, even in bud. The only exception seems to be in some palms where the compound leaf does arise from a simple leaf by death of cells and subsequent division of the lamina.

Forms of compound leaves are named and illustrated in Figs. 114, 115.

Stipules

The leaves of many species of angiosperms have leaf-like outgrowths at the base of the petiole, and often adherent to the petiole, termed stipules. The morphological origin of these is obscure. Their function is frequently to protect the leaf rudiments, in which case they often fall shortly after the leaf unfolds. In some plants they are more or less important photosynthetic organs. In *Smilax* (Fig. 120) the leaf base tendrils are possibly stipules and in some plants (p. 200) the stipules form spines.

Some other plants with stipules are: *Hibiscus*; *Cassia*; *Ficus*; *Morus* (mulberry); *Pisum*; *Rosa*; *Musanga* (West African corkwood or umbrella tree), and *Pellargonium* (the garden geranium).

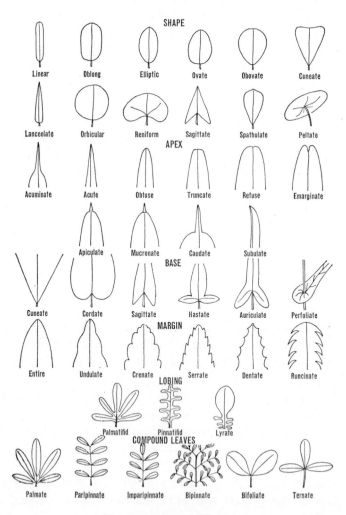

FIG. 114. Forms of leaves.

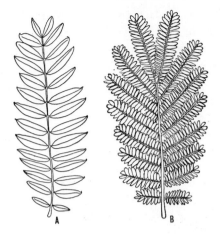

Fig. 115. A, pinnate compound leaf of *Cassia spectabilis*. B, bipinnate compound leaf of *Jacaranda*. Both are paripinnate.

Specialized Leaves

Leaves may be specialized for protection, support of the shoot, attraction of pollinators, reproduction, storage, water absorption, and catching and digesting animals (carnivorous leaves).

Protective leaves

Leaves normally protect the growing point of the shoot. They also may be specially modified to protect developing buds. These protective bud scales often show little similarity to the foliage leaves of the young shoot which they protect but cases where gradations exist between the two organs indicate that bud scales are merely specialized foliage leaves which have become thickened, often by the formation of periderm, and suberized.

Spines and thorns commonly arise by modification of leaves. The least extreme modifications are the development of prickles on the margins of the leaf as in the case of the circum-tropical yellow-flowered weed, the Mexican prickly poppy, *Argemone mexicana*, and the development of a spiny apex to the leaf as in the sisal, *Agave sisalana*, and other agaves. Another simple modification is the development of epidermal thorns on the rachis of the compound pinnate leaf of the rose, but these thorns are to be regarded as modifications of the epidermis rather than of the leaf, as they occur on the stem also.

The most extreme modification occurs in the cacti, e.g. *Opuntia*, the prickly pear, where the spines are believed to represent leaves and protect the cladodes from browsers. In many xerophytes the leaves are needle-like, but this is probably in many cases, an adaptation of leaf form which minimized desiccation rather than protection against browsing.

Stipules are modified as spines in some *Acacia* spp., in *Euphorbia* (Fig. 116) and in *Capparis* (Fig. 117) and in *Acanthus* spp., (Fig. 116D). *Acanthus ilicifolius* forms part of the mangrove flora and, in addition to stipular spines, has prickly leaves.

Spines give only limited protection from herbivores, as many of the latter are adapted to eating spiny plants.

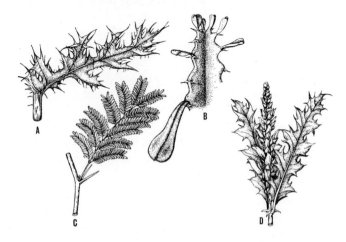

Fig. 116. Protective leaves. A, leaf of the Mexican prickly poppy, *Argemone mexicana*, showing marginal prickles. B, cladode of *Euphorbia* sp. showing small leaves, which are shed early, and paired stipular spines. C, *Acacia farnesiana*, bipinnate compound leaf with paired stipular spines. D, *Acanthus* sp., prickly leaves and stipular spines.

Fig. 117. *Capparis zeylanica.* Stipular spines.

Sensitive leaves

The leaves of *Mimosa pudica* and some other plants are sensitive to touch and respond to it by folding up (Fig. 118). This has a protective function, as it makes the leaves less attractive to Herbivores. These movements in *Mimosa* are due to the activity of organs called pulvini at the base of each leaflet of the compound pinnate leaf. Pulvini also account for "sleep movements" of leaves and for folding of some leaves in strong sunlight. In the former case their function is perhaps to reduce heat loss, and in the latter to prevent overheating and excessive transpiration.

Fig. 118. Leaf of the sensitive plant, *Mimosa pudica*, before (above) and after (below) being touched.

Supporting leaves

In many plants one of the main functions of the stem, raising the leaves into a suitable situation for photosynthesis, is performed by the leaves.

Grasping leaves. Leaves or parts of leaves may be modified for grasping and thus raising the shoot into an advantageous position. In such cases the stem is usually weak. The commonest types of grasping organs developed from leaves are leaf tendrils and hooks. Sometimes intermediates occur between the two. In the beautiful *Gloriosa* lilies (Fig. 119) of tropical Africa and Asia, the tips of the leaves coil round other plants and raise the shoot, often many feet. In the garden pea, *Pisum sativum*, the apical pinnae of the compound, pinnate leaf lack blades and are

FIG. 119. *Gloriosa simplex*, showing tendrillar leaf tips, × ½.

developed as tendrils (Fig. 120B); and in *Tropaeolum* (garden nasturtium) and *Clematis* the petioles coil round other objects (Fig. 120C, D). In *Smilax* (Fig. 120A), two tendrils arise from the base of the leaf and are usually regarded as stipular tendrils. As stipules are rare in the monocotyledons, however, it is possible that these tendrils are special outgrowths of the leaf. In *Bignonia unguis-cati*, a cultivated climber with large yellow flowers, like those of *Tecoma* and *Jacaranda* of the same family (Bignoniaceae), the compound leaves have two leaflets and a terminal group of three grapnel-like hooks (Fig. 121) which grip the support on which the plant is climbing and, if this is slender, become tendrillar. Many other members of the genus have leaf tendrils. In the rose, epidermal thorns form hooks on the leaf rachis.

Supporting leaf bases. In the banana, *Musa*, and other members of the Musaceae, the stem is very short but the leaves have sheathing bases which are arranged concentrically so as to form a "trunk" from the top of which radiate the leaf laminae. The inflorescence stalk grows up through the centre of the leaf bases.

In grasses, there is a soft intercalary growth zone above each node and the sheathing leaf base surrounding this has an important supporting function. In many other monocotyledons, the sheathing leaf bases participate in support of the stem. In the water hyacinth, *Eichornia crassipes*, the petioles are swollen "buoys" which support the plant in the water (Fig. 122).

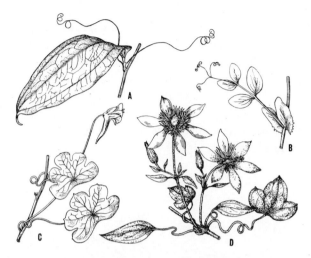

Fig. 120. Leaf and stipular tendrils. A, *Smilax* sp., stipular (?) tendrils.
B, garden pea, *Pisum sativum*, tendrils developed from terminal leaflets.
C, *Tropaeolum tuberosum*, a relative of the garden nasturtium, petiolar
tendrils. D, *Clematis triloba*, petiolar tendrils.

Fig. 121. Flowering shoot of *Bignonia unguis-cati*, showing leaf hooks,
× ¼.

Attractive leaves

Perianth members are not the only leaf-like organs which may be adapted to attracting insects or other pollinators. In some plants the perianth is inconspicuous and leaves, or modified leaves termed bracts, act as the attractive organs. Examples are *Euphorbia pulcherrima*, commonly known as poinsettia, which has brilliant red leaves around the inconspicuous flowers; and *Bougainvillaea spectabilis* (Fig. 123A), the brightly coloured "flowers" of which are groups of three coloured bracts; from the midrib of each bract arises a single, small, tubular, cream-coloured true flower. An attractive, flower-like structure which is not part of the perianth is termed a pseudanthium.

FIG. 122. Water hyacinth, *Eichornia crassipes*, showing buoyant, swollen petioles which keep the plant afloat, × ¼.

Reproduction

The leaves of some plants are organs of vegetative reproduction. The leaves of *Bryophyllum* have several notches in their margins from which small plants develop when the leaves fall to the ground (Fig. 206). In *Kalanchoe*, groups of small plants develop at the tips of the tubular, stem-like leaves (Fig. 205); the young plants usually develop fine aerial roots before they are detached (abscised) and fall to the ground. Leaves of some *Begonia* spp. readily root if detached from the plant.

Storage leaves

Water storage. Many plants of arid regions store water in tissues specialized for this function. Such plants are commonly termed succulents (Fig. 116B). In many of these the storage organs are the leaves. Thus in the *Aloe* and *Mesembryanthemum* (Fig. 124) of Africa and the *Agave* spp. (including sisal) of America, the leaves contain special chlorophyll-free parenchymatous cells with thin walls and very large vacuoles which are filled with a watery or mucilaginous sap which is rapidly added to in the brief periods of rain.

In the mainly epiphytic family Bromeliaceae (which include the pineapple) of tropical America and the West Indies, many species have the leaves grooved above and arranged to form a sort of funnel which collects water. The water is absorbed by special hairs at the base of the leaves and is stored in the leaves in a "water tissue". Many other plants collect water at the leaf bases, e.g. banana and the canna lily; in these it probably helps to prevent desiccation of the developing inflorescence.

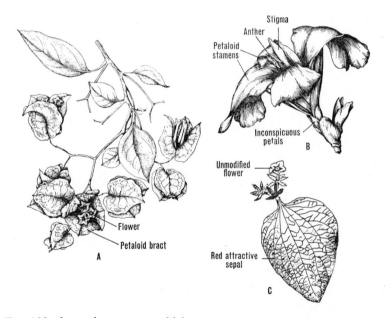

FIG. 123. Attractive organs which are not part of the corolla. A, *Bougainvillaea* (from S. America), brightly coloured, attractive bracts and relatively inconspicuous white flowers. B, *Canna indica* (cosmopolitan in the tropics), brightly coloured, attractive petaloid stamens most of which are sterile. C, *Mussaenda erythrophylla* (from tropical and S. Africa), one sepal of some flowers greatly enlarged, bright red and resembling a foliage leaf in form.

Food storage. The most striking example of storage of food reserves in leaves is afforded by bulbs. These are condensed subterranean shoots, the leaves of which are swollen by food reserves. They are discussed under perennation in Chapter 15.

Water absorption

We have already seen that many members of the pine-apple family have water-absorbing hairs on the leaves. Some plants which live in places where dew and mists are the only sources of water for most of the year have similar hairs. The leaves of aquatic plants can usually absorb water directly from the external medium.

FIG. 124. Succulent leaves of *Carpobrotus* (= *Mesembryanthemum*) sp., from Australia, × ½.

Carnivorous leaves

A large number of species of tropical plants are able to catch and digest insects by means of specialized leaves. They include the sundew, *Drosera*; the aquatic bladderwort, *Utricularia*; and the pitcher plant, *Nepenthes* (Fig. 125).

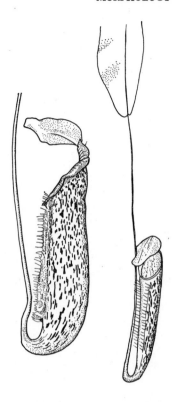

FIG. 125. Pitchers of *Nepenthes* sp. On the right it can be seen that the pitcher is a modification of the end of a leaf. Left, × ⅓. Right, × ⅙.

The leaves of *Drosera* bear many tentacles traversed by vascular bundles and ending in swollen heads which secrete a sticky substance which traps small insects. Having caught an insect they secrete proteases and absorb the amino acids produced. The tentacles are sensitive to touch and to nitrogenous compounds and respond by bending over to participate in the digestion of the trapped insect.

Phyllodes

A phyllode is a flattened, leaf-like petiole. Phyllodes are developed in many species of *Acacia* where they replace the leaf blades as photosynthetic organs (Fig. 126). The leaves are fully developed only in the young plant.

FIG. 126. Phyllodes of *Acacia* sp., actual size. In the young plant bipinnate leaves, phyllodes and intermediates between these coexist.

CHAPTER 11

Morphology of the Flower

THE flower is a shoot of limited growth, with much-shortened internodes, which bears typically four types of organs. These, from the apex downwards, are the carpels (collectively the gynaecium), the stamens (collectively the androecium), the petals (collectively the corolla) and the sepals (collectively the calyx). A study of the vascular anatomy of these organs suggests that they are ultimately homologous with leaves. The carpels are apparently megasporophylls and the stamens microsporophylls (see p. 125). The petals appear to be sterilized microsporophylls (and it is a fact that increase in numbers of petals in cultivated flowers is associated with decrease in the number of stamens) while the sepals appear to be morphologically bracts. A bract is a small leaf with relatively undeveloped lamina in the axil of which a flower or inflorescence branch arises.

Those parts of the flower which are concerned directly with reproduction, the carpels and stamens, are termed the essential floral organs while the perianth members, the petals and sepals, which play an indirect part in reproduction, are termed the inessential or accessory floral organs.

The stalk of an individual flower is a pedicel and the stalk of an inflorescence, i.e. an axis with more than one flower, is a peduncle. Each pedicel normally arises in the axil of a bract which may be indistinguishable from a normal leaf of the species or may be much-reduced or absent. Minute bracts, known as bracteoles, may occur on the pedicel. The bracteoles may be closely adpressed around the flower as an involucre, the upper bracteoles of which may be indistinguishable from the sepals.

The position of the bract is used to orientate its axillary flower in descriptions. The side of the flower towards the bract is said to be anterior or ventral and the side towards the main axis is said to be posterior or dorsal. The antero-posterior plane coincides with the plane of symmetry in zygomorphic flowers (see below). When the members of each set of floral organs (e.g. the petals) are uniformly developed and all the parts are arranged around a common centre a flower is said to be regular or actinomorphic, e.g. *Ranunculus* (Ranunculaceae). Where the members of a set are not uniformly developed or are arranged so as to create a bilateral symmetry the flower is irregular or zygomorphic, e.g. *Tecoma stans* (Fig. 186) (Bignoniaceae), *Crotalaria* (Leguminosae). Some flowers have no plane of perfect symmetry, e.g. *Cassia spectabilis* (Leguminosae) in which a petal on one side only is greatly enlarged.

A spiral arrangement of leaves (spiral phyllotaxy) is the commonest type in vegetative shoots but spiral arrangement of floral organs is found only in a few families, notably the Magnoliaceae, e.g. *Liriodendron tulipifera*, the tulip tree; Ranunculaceae, e.g. *Ranunculus* (Fig. 174); and Nymphaceae, e.g. *Nymphaea*, the water lily. These families show many primitive features which, with the widespread occurrence of a spiral leaf arrangement in vegetative shoots, suggest that a spiral arrangement of floral parts is primitive. In many flowers the members of a given set of floral organs come off the flower axis at the same level and constitute a whorl. There may be more than one whorl in a set. Flowers with all parts in whorls are said to be cyclic. Other flowers show an intermediate condition in which some sets are arranged in whorls and others spirally. They are said to be spiro-cyclic.

In spiral flowers the parts are usually large in number and are not united. A calyx with free sepals is said to be polysepalous; a corolla with free petals polypetalous; an androecium with free stamens polysteminous; and a gynaecium with free carpels apocarpous. In cyclic or spiro-cyclic flowers the members of a whorl are frequently united. Such union of the members of a single whorl is called cohesion. Union of members of different sets, e.g. stamens with petals, is called adhesion.

Cohesion of sepals, i.e. synsepaly, renders the calyx synsepalous or gamosepalous and is sporadic even in a single genus. Cohesion of petals, i.e. sympetaly, renders the corolla sympetalous or gamopetalous and characterizes whole families, e.g. the Bignoniaceae (p. 284). Cohesion of stamens, i.e. synstemony, is relatively rare but is characteristic of some Leguminosae, in which the filaments of the stamens are fused, e.g. *Crotalaria* (Fig. 127), and all Compositae, in which the anthers alone are fused, e.g. *Zinnia*, *Helianthus* (Fig. 183) and *Cosmos*. Cohesion of carpels, i.e. syncarpy, is exceedingly common and is further discussed below.

Adhesion of the calyx to the corolla and of the androecium to the gynaecium are uncommon. Intimate union of the androecium and the gynaecium, to give a gynostemium, does, however, occur in some plants, e.g. *Aristolochia* (Fig. 128), in Orchidaceae and in *Passiflora* (Fig. 134). Adhesion of stamens to the corolla is common. Stamens borne on the corolla are said to be epipetalous. Because consecutive floral whorls normally alternate, the stamens in a whorl adjacent to petals alternate with the petals and are therefore antesepalous. As the position of each stamen therefore corresponds to the gap between two petals it is understandable that epipetalous stamens are usually found only where the petals are coherent, i.e. the corolla is sympetalous, as in *Tecoma stans* (Fig. 186).

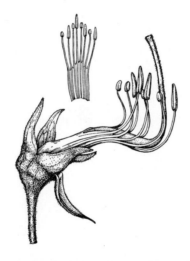

FIG. 127. *Crotalaria capensis*. Below, flower with petals removed to show fused filaments of the stamens, × 2. Above, united stamens removed.

Where epipetalous stamens are opposite the petals, i.e. antepetalous, as in the genus *Primula*, it is because an outer whorl of antesepalous stamens has been lost. The degree of adhesion varies; it may involve only part or the whole of the filament.

In most flowers the floral axis or receptacle is either conical or convex and the carpels therefore occupy the highest position in the flower. The flower is then said to be hypogynous because the other floral organs lie below the gynaecium, and the gynaecium is said to be superior, e.g. *Ranunculus* (Fig. 174A), *Tecoma*, *Crotalaria*, and *Hibiscus* (Fig. 129D, E). In some flowers, however, the receptacle is flattened and expanded in such a way that the carpels lie on the same level as the other floral organs. Such a flower is said to be perigynous. In extreme perigyny the receptacle may have the form of a flask enclosing the carpels but remaining open apically, e.g. the rose (Fig. 129B). In this extreme perigyny the carpels, although still considered to be superior, do in fact lie below the bases of the other floral organs. Were the rim of the receptacle to unite over the carpels and the walls of the flask-shaped depression in the receptacle to unite with the carpels, an inferior ovary and an epigynous flower would result. It must not be thought, however, that all cases of epigyny originated in this way. Examples of epigynous flowers are *Aristolochia* (Fig. 128) and *Cucurbita* (Fig. 129C).

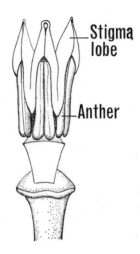

FIG. 128. *Aristolochia elegans*. Androecium and gynaecium fused to form a gynostemium, × 3.

It will now be convenient to discuss four devices which the student must learn to use which facilitate the description of flowers. They are the floral diagram, the floral formula, the half flower and the longitudinal section.

Floral Diagram

A floral diagram (Figs. 175, 181) is a diagrammatic plan of a flower with the parts represented in the same transverse plane. The anterior, ventral, part of the flower is always below in the diagram. The perianth members are represented by crescents, sepals and petals if differentiated, being distinguished by some slight differentiation of the crescents; stamens are represented by points or by outlines of the transverse sections of the anthers; the gynaecium is shown as it appears in cross-section. Bracts and bracteoles and the main axis are also represented. The relative sizes of the members of a whorl can be indicated and peculiar structures such as spurs are diagrammatically represented. Cohesion in a whorl is indicated by linking brackets and adhesion of adjacent whorls by straight lines joining the parts concerned. Where epipetalous stamens are present the position of their anthers and any grouping of the latter can be shown; otherwise the anthers are shown where the filaments arise. Sometimes the positions of parts believed to have been lost in the evolution of a group are indicated by crosses.

FIG. 129. Hypogynous, perigynous and epigynous flowers. A, *Ranunculus*, hypogynous with an apocarpous gynaecium, × 1. B, *Rosa*, perigynous with an apocarpous gynaecium, above, × ½, below, × 1½. C, *Cucurbita*, cucumber, epigynous with a syncarpous ovary, × ½. D and E, *Hibiscus*, hypogynous with a syncarpous ovary; D, × ½; E, × 1½.

Floral Formulae

Basically a floral formula consists of four symbols: K for the calyx; C for the corolla; A for the androecium; and G for the gynaecium; the symbols being arranged in that order. Where the perianth is not differentiated into sepals and petals, the letter P replaces K and C. After each symbol is placed a number which represents the number of parts, e.g. K5. Cohesion of parts is indicated by a bracket around the number of coherent parts, any separate members being separated by a + sign, e.g. A(9) + 1. Also, where more than one whorl occurs in a set a + sign separates the members in each whorl, e.g. C3 + 3. Adhesion is indicated by joining with a horizontal bracket the symbols of the parts joined, e.g. $\overparen{C(5)+A(5)}$. The top of the receptacle is indicated by a horizontal line which is therefore placed below the number of carpels in the gynaecium if the latter is superior, e.g. G(5̲), but above the number if the gynaecium is inferior, i.e. G(5̄). When the number of parts in a set is large or indefinite, the number is indicated by an infinity sign, e.g. A ∞. The sign ⊕ before the formula indicates that the flower is actinomorphic and ·|· or ↑ shows that it is zygomorphic. It is not necessary to indicate separately whether the plant is hermaphrodite or unisexual. As an example of a floral formula we may take that of *Tecoma stans* which is: ↑ K(5) $\overparen{C(5)\ A5}$ G(2̲).

Half Flowers

The half flower is an accurate representation of a complete half of the flower as it appears when the flower is longitudinally bisected and viewed in the antero-posterior, median plane. It is only slightly, if at all, diagrammatic.

Longitudinal Sections

A longitudinal section shows only the cut surfaces resulting from bisecting a flower in the antero-posterior plane. Only surfaces in this plane are shown. If a half flower is depicted a longitudinal section is unnecessary.

We will now discuss the morphology of the gynaecium and of the ovule.

The Gynaecium

For the purpose of description of the structure of the various types of ovaries it is convenient and customary to look upon the angiosperm carpel as a leaf-like organ. The validity of considering it to be such is discussed briefly on p. 217.

If there is more than one carpel and each carpel is free from the others, as in *Ranunculus* and *Rosa* (Figs. 129A, B; 130A–C), a gynaecium is said to be apocarpous. Each carpel then constitutes a separate ovary with its own stigma (receptive surface for pollen). An individual ovary of an apocarpous gynaecium or of a gynaecium consisting of a single carpel has the appearance of a megasporophyll bearing ovules on its margins which has folded along its midrib so that the margins have come together and coalesced in such a way that the ovules are enclosed. The same is true of a gynaecium consisting of a single carpel, as in pea (Fig. 130D–F).

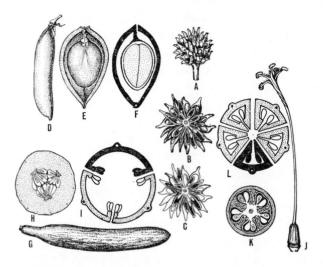

FIG. 130. Whole and sectioned fruits demonstrating the main types of ovaries. A–C, *Ranunculus*, buttercup, apocarpous gynaecium. D–F, *Pisum*, garden pea, monocarpellary superior ovary with marginal placentation. G–I, *Cucurbita*, cucumber, inferior, tricarpellary ovary with parietal placentation. J–L, *Hibiscus*, pentalocular superior ovary with axile placentation. Each fruit is shown whole, in cross-section, and in diagrammatic cross-section with one carpel distinguished in black or (*Ranunculus*) cross-hatched.

On one side of the ovary a longitudinal ridge is often visible; this is known as the dorsal suture and is believed to be the midrib of the folded mega-sporophyll. A corresponding longitudinal line on the other side is believed to be its united margins which internally form the placenta on which are borne the ovules. The stigma is considered to be the apex of the sporophyll which may or may not be elongated to form a stalk or style. The dorsal suture has the appearance in some cases of a well developed "midrib" from which arise conspicuous lateral veins, as in *Aconitum* (Ranunculaceae).

While it is commonly accepted that the individual ovary of an apocarpous gynaecium is homologous with a leafy megasporophyll, there is much controversy as to the true nature of syncarpous ovaries (i.e. ovaries made up of fused carpels), but it will be convenient at the present stage of the discussion to continue to accept the carpel as a leaf-like structure.

When two or more carpels are united to form a syncarpous ovary two alternative structures commonly occur. Constituent carpels may be united to each other by their margins so that only a single cavity exists in the ovary and the ovules borne on the margins of the carpels lie on the periphery of the cavity (Fig. 130G–I). Such an ovary is described in terms of the number of carpels and is said to be bi-, tri-, quadri- or multicarpellary according as the number of carpels is two, three, four or more (specific prefixes for numbers greater than four may be used if desired). Placentation of the ovules is said to be parietal and the number of placentas is taken to indicate the number of carpels involved. A familiar example of a pentacarpellary ovary with parietal placentation is that of *Carica papaya*, the pawpaw.

Alternatively, the margins of all the carpels may be united so as to form a common central column in the ovary from which radiate to the periphery septa formed by the "laminae" or "blades" of the carpels (Fig. 130J–L). In this case the ovary has as many loculi as carpels. Such an ovary is described in terms of the number of loculi and not in terms of the number of carpels. It may be bi-, tri-, quadri- or multilocular (and again the specific prefixes for numbers greater than four may be used if desired). Examples are the pentalocular ovary of *Hibiscus* (Fig. 130J–L) and the hexalocular ovary of *Aristolochia* (Fig. 146).

Not all ovaries fall into these two categories, however. In some ovaries no septa occur but there is, nevertheless, a central column projecting from the base of the ovary and bearing the ovules. The placentation in this case is said to be free central. At least in some cases, e.g. the family Caryophyllaceae, it appears that this type of ovary is derived from a septate ovary with axile placentation by loss of the septa. Similar to free central placentation is basal placentation in which the ovules arise from the base of a unilocular ovary.

In the genus *Nymphaea*, the water lilies (Nymphaceae), the ovules are not limited to the margins of the carpels of the syncarpous ovary but are borne all over the inside of the ovary. Such placentation is said to be superficial. Superficial placentation also occurs in the flowering rush *Butomus*.

A particularly bizarre ovary occurs in the pomegranate, *Punica granatum*. In *Punica* there are two whorls of carpels which, by intercalary growth, come to lie one on top of the other; the lower, originally inner, whorl, of three carpels has axile placentation while the upper whorl of five carpels has parietal placentation.

Some ovaries have false septa. These may be derived from intrusive placentas, where placentation is parietal, or may be distinct structures. A false septum occurs in *Cheiranthus*, the wall flower and other Cruciferae

(Fig. 145), and in *Tecoma stans*, and several occur in *Papaver*, the poppy. It must be understood that the view that the individual ovary of an apocarpous gynaecium arose by folding and marginal fusion of an open megasporophyll and that syncarpous ovaries arose in the ways described above is hypothetical, and that these stages are not followed in the development of mature carpels from their rudiments. There is thus no direct evidence that the angiosperm carpel is derived from a leafy megasporophyll. The form of the individual carpel in apocarpous gynaecia makes it difficult to doubt this origin, however. Furthermore, most carpels resemble leaves in containing chlorophyll, in bearing stomata, and in their venation, and they sometimes have palisade tissue and hairs and glands similar to those of foliage leaves. The close resemblance of the megasporophylls of *Cycas* in the related gymnosperms and of the seed ferns to foliage leaves has already been mentioned.

There is some doubt, however, as to whether the megasporophyll is descended from the foliage leaf or has derived with it from a common ancestral structure which may have been a flattened branch.

Whatever the origin of the megasporophyll may be, it seems reasonable to accept that the angiosperm carpel as seen in the apocarpous gynaecium is derived from a leafy megasporophyll by folding in the manner outlined above. The conventional view of the constitution of the syncarpous ovary must be retained because of its nomenclatorial value but its validity is uncertain. As examples of alternative views we may briefly note that Saunders considers the "trilocular" ovary to consist not of three carpels but of three central solid carpels and three peripheral sterile valve carpels and the "bicarpellary" ovary with false septum of the Cruciferae, e.g. wall flower, to consist of two median fertile solid carpels forming the false septum and two lateral sterile "valve carpels". The monocarpellary ovary of the Papilonaceae, e.g. *Pisum* (Fig. 130D–F) and *Crotalaria*, which is usually regarded as a remarkably perfect example of a folded megasporophyll, is considered by Saunders to contain a third type of carpel the pseudo-valve carpel which is not homologous with the individual carpel of an apocarpous gynaecium.

The Ovule

The ovule is the body which, on fertilization of its contained female gamete, becomes the seed. It consists (Fig. 131) of an embryo sac containing the female gamete or oosphere, fertilization of which produces the zygote and hence the embryo; a surrounding multicellular layer, the

H

nucellus; and one or two integuments which invest this except for an apical pore, the micropyle. The ovule is borne on that part of a carpel known as the placenta, either directly or on a stalk called the funicle.

The nucellus arises as a small protuberance on the surface of the pacenta, normally by division of a subepidermal cell or cells. Subsequent growth results in the formation of a stalk, the funicle. A subepidermal cell at the apex of the nucellus differentiates as the archesporial cell. This usually divides to form a primary parietal cell, which becomes incorporated in

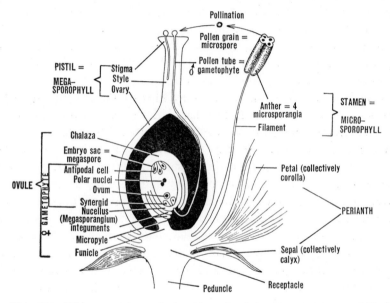

FIG. 131. Diagrammatic vertical section of a flower showing the essential organs.

the nucellus, and a primary sporogenous cell. The latter then becomes transformed into the megaspore mother cell or divides and one of its products undergoes the transformation. The megaspore mother cell typically divides to form a row of four cells of which only the one nearest the chalaza, as the basal, funicular end of the nucellus is termed, develops as an embryo sac. As soon as the archesporium develops, the integuments commence development from the base of the nucellus.

The nature of the ovule is disputable but it is generally considered that the embryo sac is a megaspore and that division of its single nucleus produces a reduced female gametophyte and that the nucellus is the megasporangium. The nature of the integuments is extremely uncertain but it seems likely that the two are not homologous with one another. The nature of the embryo sac will be discussed later.

Variation in the structure of the ovules is considerable. The presence of two integuments (the bitegminate condition) is apparently primitive and reduction to one integument (the unitegminate condition) is very common and characterizes most of the advanced families. In some families integuments are lacking. Reduction of the nucellus also occurs. Great variation in the origin and composition of the embryo sac exists but typically it is the single persistent member of the tetrad formed by reduction division of the spore mother cell and the single nucleus of this megaspore gives rise to eight nuclei. Three of these nuclei come to lie at the micropylar end and three at the chalazal end of the embryo sac, while two migrate to the middle of the embryo sac (Fig. 131). The three micropylar nuclei constitute the egg apparatus; each nucleus appropriates cytoplasm and two of them secrete cellulose cell walls and become synergidae ("help cells") while the other constitutes the female nucleus or oosphere, the wall of which contains cellulose only in places and is elsewhere a free plasma membrane. The three nuclei at the chalazal end usually become cells, with cellulose walls, and are known as the antipodal cells, or antipodal nuclei if naked. The two nuclei which migrate from the poles to the centre of the embryo sac are termed the polar nuclei and lie free in the scanty cytoplasm of the embryo sac. They usually unite before fertilization of the oosphere. When the pollen tube releases its two male nuclei into the embryo sac, one of the male nuclei unites with the two polar nuclei, or the product of their fusion, to give the primary endosperm nucleus, which later divides to form the cellular tissue known as endosperm. The latter nourishes the embryo. It is used up by the cotyledon(s) before the seed is shed in the case of non-endospermic seeds, but in endospermic seeds persists for some time after this.

Several interpretations of the embryo sac have been suggested but the most convincing hypothesis is that attributable mainly to Porsch (1907). Its main points are as follows.

The embryo sac is a germinated megaspore, the contents of which are a greatly-reduced female gametophyte or prothallus. The vegetative parts of this prothallus have completely disappeared but two archegonia are still represented in a much-reduced form. The egg apparatus represents one of these archegonia and the antipodal cells represent the other. Each polar nucleus represents a liberated ventral canal cell of an archegonium.

Support for this hypothesis is supplied by some species, e.g. *Ulmus americana*, in which the antipodal cells act as an egg apparatus and the micropylar cells act as antipodal cells, suggesting that the two groups are equivalent; by the parasite *Balanophora indica*, in which the embryo sac is U-shaped, so that the antipodal cells and egg apparatus are near together, and in which either group may be fertilized; and the lily, *Crinum*, which is said to have a functional egg apparatus at each end of the embryo sac, a condition which occurs anomalously in some gymnosperms.

We have seen that the polar nuclei unite with one of the male nuclei, and in support of the view that the polar nuclei are ventral canal cells the evidence of some gymnosperms in which the ventral canal cells are fertilized may be cited. In some gymnosperm genera, probably after such fertilization, the ventral canal cell gives rise to a small mass of tissue which is perhaps homologous with endosperm.

The posture of ovules relative to the placenta is variable. Orthotropous ovules are straight, with the micropyle at the furthest point from the placenta. Anatropous ovules have the funicle lengthened and the ovule turned on itself so that the micropyle faces the placenta. In hemitropous ovules the long axis of the ovule is parallel to the placenta and the funicle is attached to its middle. Campylotropous ovules resemble the last, but in addition the body of the ovule is bent so that the micropyle faces the placenta. Amphitropous ovules appear anatropous but the micropyle faces the placenta because the body of the ovule is bent into a U-shape. In circinotropous ovules the funicle is very long and encircles the ovule.

The Androecium

Brief reference was made to the androecium on p. 209. We will now discuss it in more detail.

The stamen is typically differentiated into a fertile microspore-producing head, the anther, and a sterile stalk, the filament (Fig. 132).

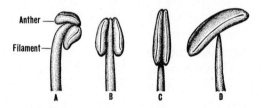

Anther

Filament

A   B   C   D

Fig. 132. Types of stamens. A, apicifixed. B, adnate (dorsifixed). C, innate (basifixed); D, versatile.

In some primitive families, however, the differentiation is incomplete. Where there is a distinct anther this possesses a distinct central column of tissue which is known as the connective and which attaches to the filament. The anther is typically bilobed, there being a lobe on each side of the connective. Each lobe contains two pollen sacs or microsporangia (Fig. 133). At maturity the anther is bilocular in transverse section owing to confluence of the two pollen sacs of each lobe.

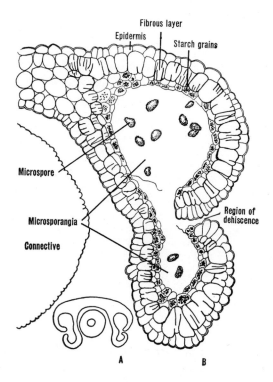

FIG. 133. Transverse sections of the anther of *Lilium*. A, plan. B, half of the anther, greatly magnified.

The anther is said to be basifixed or innate if its connective is a direct continuation of the filament (Fig. 132C), e.g. *Datura*, *Ranunculus* and *Cassia*; dorsifixed or adnate if the filament runs along and is fused with its back (Fig. 132B), e.g. *Nicotiana*, tobacco; apicifixed if the filament attaches to the upper end of the connective (Fig. 132A), e.g. *Tecoma* and *Lamium*, dead-nettle; and versatile if the filament is attached to a single point on the connective so that a hinge or articulation is formed (Fig. 132D), e.g. *Gloriosa*, gloriosa lily, and *Passiflora*, passion flower (Fig. 134), and the grasses, e.g. *Triticum*, wheat.

Cohesion of anthers is the syngenesious condition. It occurs throughout the Compositae (p. 283), and in some Solanaceae. It is less widespread than cohesion of filaments, the adelphous condition. In the monadelphous condition which is seen in the Malvaceae, e.ĝ. *Hibiscus* (Fig. 129D), and certain Papilionaceae, e.g. *Crotalaria* (Fig. 127), the stamens are united by their filaments into a single group, whereas in the diadelphous condition two groups of stamens are created by the union, as in *Arachis hypogaea*, the groundnut, and *Pisum sativum*, the garden pea (Fig. 180), both of the Papilionaceae. Several groups of stamens are thus formed in the Annonaceae, e.g. *Annona muricata*, the soursop; this is the polyadelphous condition.

FIG. 134. *Passiflora* sp., Passion flower, in which the stamens have versatile anthers and are united with a superior ovary to give a gynostemium.

Adhesion of stamens to an undifferentiated perianth is called epiphylly; to the petals, epipetaly; and to the sepals (a rare condition) episepaly. Epipetaly has been discussed on p. 211. The degree of adhesion varies; it may involve only part or the whole of a stamen. Adhesion of the stamens to the gynaecium (e.g. to form a gynostemium as in *Aristolochia*) was mentioned on p. 210 (Fig. 128). It is rarer in the case of superior ovaries than inferior ovaries but is seen in *Passiflora* (Fig. 134).

The presence in a single flower of more than one type of functional stamen is known as heterostemony. A simple example is seen in the Bignoniaceae, e.g. *Tecoma stans* (Fig. 186), and in the Labiatae and Scrophulariaceae in all of which there are two long and two short stamens, the didynamous condition. In the Cruciferae, e.g. wall flower, four are long and two are short, the tetradynamous condition. Heterostemony is particularly well developed in *Cassia* (Fig. 178) and in *Commelina* (Commelinaceae), species of which are common blue-flowered weeds, which has three posterior stamens with enlarged yellow connectives which are attractive to insects.

Staminodes

Stamens which have lost their function of producing pollen are known as staminodes. They may be greatly reduced structures as in the case of the single dorsal staminode of *Tecoma stans* (Fig. 186), which is occasionally absent, and the four staminodes of *Mangifera indica*, the mango. Less commonly, they may be conspicuous owing to their fulfilling another function as in *Canna indica*, the canna lily (Fig. 123B), and *Mesembryanthemum*, in which they are expanded and coloured (petaloid) and perform the function normally assigned to petals, which are inconspicuous in *Canna* and absent from *Mesembryanthemum*.

Reduction in the number of stamens is a common feature of angiosperm evolution and is generally associated with increased efficiency of modes of pollination, but splitting of stamen rudiments, i.e. chorosis, does occur though it is rare. True branching of stamens is also uncommon. It is well shown in *Ricinus communis*, the castor oil plant.

Development of the stamen

Early in its development the stamen rudiment becomes four-lobed in outline. Each lobe represents a microsporangium. Some of the sub-epidermal cells enlarge and develop denser contents and an archesporium is thus formed. This typically consists of a row of cells running vertically through the length of the lobe. Each of these cells undergoes a division tangentially to the surface of the sporangium. The outer cells thus formed, the primary parietal cells, give rise by tangential and radial divisions to two or more concentric layers of cells which lie under the epidermis and constitute the endothecium of the anther walls. The inner cells, the primary sporogenous cells, produced in the division of the archesporial initials, divide in such a way that a solid mass of archesporial tissue is formed. Radial divisions of the cells in the wall of the anther are sufficiently rapid to separate the archesporium from the anther wall so that four pollen sacs become recognizable. The archesporial cells later round off as pollen mother cells, each of which by two divisions which involve meiosis gives rise to a tetrad of haploid microspores.

The radial walls of the cells of the subepidermal layer become thickened by lignin laid down in a network and this layer constitutes the middle layer or fibrous layer which, on dehiscence of the anther, serves by its hygroscopic action to aid in release of the pollen. There may be more than one middle layer but the inner layer of cells in the endothecium always becomes the tapetum, the function of which is to nourish the developing microspores. Unlike the middle layer, which is generally interrupted at the connective, the tapetum is continuous around the archesporium, deriving both from the sporangial wall and from the connective. Its cells become plasmodial and show cytoplasmic streaming, and put out pseudopodia which envelop the pollen mother cells which they nourish. Layers of the anther wall additional to the middle layer and tapetum are crushed.

Dehiscence

Prior to dehiscence the two pollen sacs of each lobe usually become confluent. Dehiscence normally occurs only along a stomium which consists of a row of small cells in the furrow between the two pollen sacs. Dehiscence is thus usually by longitudinal rupture, as in *Ranunculus* and *Tecoma*, although it is not infrequently by formation of an apical pore, e.g. *Cassia*, or pores, e.g. *Solanum* spp., and in some flowers it occurs by transverse, e.g. *Hibiscus*, or even U-shaped splitting. Stamens which shed their pollen outwards, e.g. those of *Ranunculus*, are said to be extrorse. Most flowers, however, shed their pollen inwards, towards the gynaecium, and their stamens are said to be introrse.

CHAPTER 12

Pollination and Fertilization

POLLINATION

The term pollination is applied to the transference of microspores, collectively known as pollen, to the stigma of a flower. Self-pollination is the transference of pollen from the anthers to the stigma of the same flower and is sometimes called autogamy, but the latter term is more correctly restricted to self-*fertilization*. Cross-pollination is the transference to the stigma of a flower of pollen from another flower of the same species on the same or a separate plant. Cross-pollination is sometimes called allogamy but again the term should strictly be confined to cross-*fertilization*. Allogamy is divisible into geitonogamy, where fertilization is between two flowers on the same plant, and xenogamy, where separate plants are involved.

Pollination is brought about by three main agents: wind, animals and water, the types being called respectively anemophily, zoophily and hydrophily. Gravity and direct contact of anthers and stigma are, however, very important in many species.

Entomophily

Wind-pollination was undoubtedly the common method of pollination in the first angiosperms, and the development of the attractive perianth, of nectar-secreting glands, of scent and of rough, sticky pollen, which are characteristic of so many angiosperms, appears to have been stimulated by the abundance of insects in the Tertiary period. The insects initially visited flowers to obtain pollen, a rich protein source, as a food, or to eat the floral organs, or to suck up liquid secretions which may have been exuded by, or were contained within, the flower. Although these early flowers were wind-pollinated, it seems likely that casual pollination by visiting insects would have been sufficiently effective to prove advantageous to the plant and that selection occurred for those characteristics

which attracted insects, viz. sterilization and expansion (and often coloration) of the stamens to form readily visible structures, the petals, and the
development of glands for exuding sugary secretions, the nectaries. As
a conspicuous perianth would generally be attractive to insects only over
short distances, those flowers which could be detected from afar by distinctive odours would possess an advantage, and selection for scent
would have occurred so that glands which secrete diamines, trimethyl-
amine, aromatic alcohols, and aliphatic acids and alcohols and other
volatile substances were developed.

Evolution of angiosperms has gone hand in hand with that of insects
and many remarkable examples of mutual dependence have resulted.
Thus some flowers have become so specialized for entomophily that only
a single species of insect can bring about pollination, and the insect in
turn has become largely dependent for its food supply on a few species
of flowers and in some cases on a single species.

The butterflies and moths (Lepidoptera), the bees and wasps (Hymenoptera) and the hoverflies (Diptera) all have the mouth parts specialized
for sucking nectar and, in the case of bees, for kneading pollen. This
specialization and other aspects of insect evolution have been associated
with the specialization of flowers since the Tertiary for entomophily,
including the progressive concealment of nectar. Various biological
groups of flowers may be recognized with reference to the extent of their
modification for insect pollination. Two main divisions of flowers are
recognized: those visited for pollen and those visited for nectar. The
divisions overlap, however, as some flowers produce both nectar and
pollen in sufficient quantities to be exploited.

Pollen flowers

Pollen flowers produce excess pollen as an attractant for insects, especially bees, and usually lack nectar. Examples are found in the genus
Cassia where special stamens produce pollen which is collected by bees and
does not effect pollination. Zygomorphy in *Cassia* is related to the functional distinction between the two different types of stamens (see p. 275).

Nectar flowers

Nectar flowers secrete nectar as the chief attractant for insects. The
nectar may be freely exposed, as in the Umbelliferae and some *Euphorbias*,
and therefore available to short-tongued insects, e.g. dipterous flies,
small Hymenoptera such as ichneumons, and beetles, or partly concealed

by scales, as in *Ranunculus*, or by hairs or a short perianth tube. In the later type the nectar can be reached only by insects with tongues longer than about 3 mm, so that many Diptera and Coleoptera are excluded. Zygomorphy is not usually developed in the above types. Other flowers have the nectar completely concealed, e.g. *Ricinus*, *Thevetia* and *Tecoma*, so that it is available only to insects with tongues longer than about 6 mm. Concealment is usually by lengthening of the corolla tube. Zygomorphy, sometimes with the development of a nectar-secreting spur, is common. Zygomorphy often produces a floral mechanism which can be exploited by only a limited group of species, as in the Leguminosae, or by a single species, as in the case of *Aconitum* (Ranunculaceae), which depends exclusively on a single species of humble bee. Many are exclusively bee-pollinated, and in some the corolla tube or nectar spur is so long (nearly 1 ft in the Madagascar orchid, *Angraecum sesquipedale*) that only Lepidoptera can exploit them. Many moth flowers are night-opening and night-scented and whitish or pale in colour, e.g. *Nicotiana* and *Cereus*.

Some flowers are visited by flies not for pollen or nectar but because they have a carrion-like smell. Examples are *Stapelia*, some species of which closely resemble dead animals in appearance, *Aristolochia* (Fig. 135), and some Araceae. Many fly-pollinated flowers have purple, brown and yellow mottling of the perianth. Some of these nauseous flowers do not provide food for the visiting flies and rely on the reproductive instinct of the flies for visitation.

Before leaving the subject of entomophily an example of obligate interdependence of a flower and a single species of insect may be mentioned. The *Yucca* (Liliaceae) and the moth *Pronuba yuccasella* have established a symbiotic relationship. *Yucca* is pollinated by the moth which collects pollen from one flower, lays its eggs within the ovary of another flower of the same species which it penetrates with the ovipositor, and then cross-pollinates the flower by placing the pollen on its stigma. The caterpillars feed on the developing seeds but leave sufficient for propagation of the plant.

Entomophily in *Ranunculus*, *Tecoma*, *Thevetia* and *Pisum* will be dealt with under these genera in Chapter 14.

Ornithophily

Entomophily, although the most important is not the only form of zoophily. Some flowers are pollinated by birds and are said to be ornitho-philous. Examples are *Strelitzia reginae*, an African relative of the banana

(Musaceae), which is pollinated by a species of sun bird (Nectarinidae), for which it is highly specialized, and some species of *Bignonia* (Bignoniceae) which are pollinated by humming birds.

Malacophily

Some flowers, e.g. *Aspidistra lurida, Chrysanthemum leucanthemum,* and some Araceae are pollinated by snails and slugs. Pollination by molluscs is termed malacophily. That any flowers are exclusively malacophilous is doubtful.

Chiropterophily

Pollination by bats, i.e. chiropterophily, has been observed in *Bauhinia megalandra* (a tropical American member of the Caesalpiniaceae), in *Parkia clappertoniana* (a West African tree of the family Mimosaceae), and in the baobab *Adansonia.*

Hydrophily

Pollination by the agency of water is termed hydrophily. Angiosperms have secondarily invaded the water and most have retained wind or insect pollination and raise their flowers above the water. Hydrophily is uncommon and perhaps its rarity is due to the damaging effect which water normally has on pollen, the possibility of premature germination of the pollen, and, above all, the efficacy of the other modes of pollination.

Anemophily

Anemophily, wind pollination, was undoubtedly the normal method of pollination in primitive angiosperms but in many existing species in which it occurs it is secondary.

Wind-pollinated flowers normally lack devices which are attractive to insects: the perianth, nectaries and scent. The sexes are often separate and the male flowers are usually far more abundant than the female flowers, thus allowing for vast wastage of microspores. The stigmas are usually feathery and the stamens pendulous, frequently with versatile anthers. Dispersal of pollen is often further aided by a pendant habit of the male inflorescences, e.g. catkins, and the pollen grains are usually very light and smooth-walled. Mechanisms commonly exist to prevent dispersal of pollen when clumped together by moisture. Sometimes the flowers are immobile but the stamens shed pollen explosively.

Some flowers which are normally insect-pollinated are wind pollinated if entomophily fails. In *Cyclamen* the flowers are adapted for insect pollination, but if this fails the microspores lose their stickiness and become powdery, thus adapting to wind dispersal.

Pollination in *Zea mays*, is dealt with under that species in Chapter 14.

Advantages of Cross-pollination

It will be clear that only rarely do two plants produced from separate seeds have the same genetic constitution. Fertilization resulting from cross-pollination between two separate individuals (xenogamy) will therefore result in more new combinations of genes than is possible by autogamy and, where the two individuals possess different alleles at the same gene loci, characters may appear in the progeny which could not have occurred if self-pollination had been effected. Experiments have shown that, particularly after some generations of self-pollination, the result of xenogamy is often an increase in the vigour of the progeny as compared with the parents. This phenomenon is known as heterosis or hybrid vigour. Self-pollination is likely to result in homozygosity for any deleterious genes which may have originated by mutation. It is not surprising therefore that mechanisms have evolved which favour allogamy by reducing the possibility of autogamy. It must be remembered, however, that we must distinguish allogamy between flowers on the same plant (geitonogamy), which has no genetic advantages over autogamy, from xenogamy.

Mechanisms Favouring Cross-pollination

The following mechanisms reduce the possibility of, or prevent, self-pollination and thereby favour cross-pollination.

1. *Dichogamy*

If the androecium and gynaecium are not mature at the same time, self-pollination is impossible and if pollination occurs it must be cross-pollination. This phenomenon of temporal separation of maturation is termed dichogamy. Dichogamy is divisible into protandry, in which the stamens mature before the gynaecium becomes receptive, and protogyny, in which the gynaecium matures first. Protandry is very common and is the commonest method of preventing or allaying self-pollination, whereas protogyny is relatively rare. Some tropical families which show protandry are the Compositae, Lobeliaceae, Malvaceae, and Bignoniaceae, e.g. *Tecoma stans* (Fig. 186). Protogyny is met with in *Aristolochia elegans* (Figs. 135, 136).

Where the dichogamy is complete, and all the flowers on the plant simultaneously reach the same stage of maturity, cross-pollination within the same plant (geitonogamy) is impossible and only xenogamy can occur.

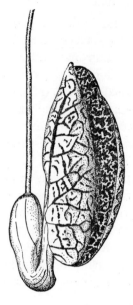

FIG. 135. *Aristolochia elegans.* A flower with brown and cream markings of the perianth which, with its odour, are attractive to flies, × ½.

If protogyny is imperfect and the stigma is still receptive when the first stamens of the same flower commence to shed their pollen, autogamy is possible and may be resorted to if allogamy has failed. In imperfect protandry, when anthers are still shedding pollen after the stigma has become receptive, self-pollination is very likely, though if the growth rate of own pollen is slower than that of pollen from other flowers, allogamy can still occur.

2. Dioecism

When each individual of a species produces flowers of one sex only, the species is said to be dioecious. Dioecism is perhaps an extreme case of dichogamy in which the function of either the gynaecium or the androecium is completely suppressed. It will be clear that dioecism completely prevents autogamy and geitonogamy and that only xenogamy is possible. A familiar dioecious plant is *Carica papaya*, the pawpaw (Fig. 189), in which pollination is brought about by night-flying moths.

3. Heterostyly

Heterostyly was first described by Charles Darwin in the genus *Primula*. In most species of this genus two types of flower exist, both of which are hermaphrodite (Fig. 137). A single plant bears only one type and there are no intermediates. In one type, the pin-eyed type, the style is long so that the stigma occupies the mouth of the gamopetalous corolla, and the five epipetalous stamens are borne well down inside the corolla tube. In the other type, the thrum-eyed type, the style is short so that the stigma is situated low down in the corolla tube on the same level as the stamens of the pin-eyed type, and the stamens occupy the mouth of the corolla tube, thereby occupying the position of the stigma in the pin-eyed type. It

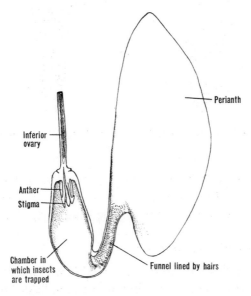

Fig. 136. *Aristolochia elegans.* Half flower, × ¾. The gynaecium matures first and is pollinated by insects, bearing pollen from another flower, which enter the perianth funnel. They cannot escape until the hairs lining the funnel wither by which time the stamens have shed their pollen. This pollen may be conveyed by the escaping insects to other *Aristolochia* flowers.

will be clear that the amount of pollen collected on the sides of an insect visiting one type of flower will merely be augmented if another flower of the same type is visited, but that if the insect visits a flower of the other type, the pollen will be transferred to the stigma and that xenogamy will occur. Additional mechanisms help to prevent self-pollination, thus the pollen grains of the short-styled flowers are spherical and are larger than the pollen grains of the long-styled flowers, which are oblong, and the stigma of one type of flower is adapted to receive pollen from the other type and is less suitable for its own pollen. The stigmas of the long-styled flowers are rougher and have larger papillae, whereas those of the short-styled flowers have smoother stigmas. There is also a physiological mechanism which tends to prevent autogamy: self-pollination is found to be much less effective in producing seed than is cross-pollination.

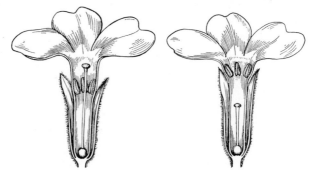

Fig. 137. Half flowers of (left) a pin-eyed and (right) a thrum-eyed primrose.

Heterostyly is remarkably widespread and has been shown to occur in seventeen families. In *Primula*, where two types of flowers exist, it is called dimorphic heterostyly. Trimorphic heterostyly also exists.

4. *Self-sterility and incompatibility*

Failure of self-pollination to produce seed is widespread and is known as self-sterility. It has been found in most cases to be due to failure of the microspores to germinate or of the pollen tubes to grow normally. The inhibition of normal development has been attributed to differences in osmotic pressure between microspores and stigma, but it seems likely that inhibition is an immunological response similar to those which occur in transplants of animal tissues.

As flowers of different plants may be fairly similar genetically (and therefore immunologically), it is not surprising that self-sterility may extend to whole populations or races. Thus cultivated members of the Rosaceae, e.g. the apple, show complete or partial sterility within a single strain and it is necessary to plant together two or more strains to produce fruiting. The phenomenon of self-sterility within whole populations is called incompatibility.

An extreme case of self-sterility occurs in members of the Orchidaceae, where, if self-pollination occurs, the microspores are rapidly killed. Sterility is not usually so extreme, however, and in some cases, which often go undetected, the pollen of the same flower merely germinates more slowly than that of another flower.

5. *Special mechanisms*

In the Laburnum, *Cytisus laburnum*, which is normally cross-pollinated, self-pollination is effective if the stigma is experimentally wounded. Such wounding, by rubbing, is normal when a visiting bee brings about cross-pollination.

Other mechanisms exist but are beyond the scope of this book.

Advantages of Self-pollination

The advantages of allogamy over autogamy have been discussed above but it must not be thought that self-pollination is without advantages. It has the advantage that a genotype which is successfully adapted to its environment will be less likely to be altered than if cross-fertilization occurred. A second advantage is that self-pollination, where it does not rely on external agents, is less vulnerable to failure than cross-pollination. Thus many plants are partly, if not wholly, self-pollinated and some have evolved distinct mechanisms which ensure self-pollination. One of the most remarkable of these mechanisms is cleistogamy in which pollination occurs in the unopened flower. Darwin counted 67 genera in which cleistogamy is either facultative or obligate.

Even in autogamy considerable genetic variation is possible owing to reassortment of genes and genetical crossing over and also to mutation. But variation cannot be as extreme as in allogamy and deterioration due to homozygosity for harmful recessive mutants is more likely to occur. That reduction of variability may be useful where successful adaptation to the environment has been attained is, however, indicated by the adoption of parthenogenesis and vegetative propagation by many plants as the main mode of reproduction.

The Microspore

We have seen that microspores are formed, usually as tetrads (groups of four), by reduction division of each pollen mother cell in the archesporium. The pollen grain may have a single cell wall only, but in most families there are two walls, an outer extine (or exine) and an inner intine, and only the intine participates in forming the pollen tube. The extine becomes differentiated into two layers: the exo-extine, which is a thin layer continuous over the whole surface of the grain, and in zoophilous species typically provided with spines or other protuberances, and the endo-extine which is a thick cutinized layer which is interrupted by pores. In the extine there is a polymerized cyclic alcohol, sporopollenin, which is very resistant to decay and penetration by water. The intine varies in thickness, being thickest under the pores; its superficial layers are of pectin and its innermost layer is of cellulose. In rare cases only one of the four potential microspore nuclei survives and the wall of the pollen mother cell persists as the wall of the pollen grain.

Each pollen grain has a single haploid nucleus when first formed, and is then a true spore, but mitotic division of this results in two nuclei. In tropical plants mitosis is usually immediate on formation of the tetrad but in colder regions there may be a resting period before mitosis. Of the two nuclei produced, one is the generative nucleus which will later divide to form the two male nuclei; the other is the vegetative nucleus, later the tube nucleus. A cross wall cuts off the generative nucleus from the rest of the contents of the grain as a generative cell and this cell later comes to lie free in the cytoplasm of the vegetative cell. By maturity all vacuoles in the cytoplasm of the grain disappear and starch grains or oil droplets accumulate.

FERTILIZATION

The generative cell and the vegetative cell represent a very reduced male gametophyte and it is therefore a gametophyte which is transferred in the old microspore wall to a stigmatic surface in pollination. The term microspore should strictly be applied to the pollen grain only when it is uninucleate.

The vegetative nucleus does not normally divide but the generative nucleus divides to form two male nuclei at any period from maturation of the pollen grain in the pollen sac to entry of the pollen tube into the embryo sac of the ovule, according to the species.

Although pollen will germinate in a wide range of conditions, including contact with a stigmatic surface of another species, the conditions necessary for the normal growth of the pollen tube are often very particular, and stigmatic tissue may positively inhibit growth in a way which resembles an antigen–antibody reaction in animals (see self-sterility and incompatibility, p. 232). The ease of germination of pollen in moist conditions may result in a great wastage of pollen and pollen survives much longer in a dry atmosphere than in a humid one. For instance, the pollen of *Viola odorata*, the sweet violet, remains viable for 235 days if perfectly dry (an unusually long period) but only 35 days in normal air. The shortest-lived pollen seems to be that of *Secale cereale*, rye, which is not viable for more than 12 hr under any conditions.

Germination on the stigma is usually stated to be in response to sugary nutritive secretions of the cells of the stigma, but it appears that in most cases this is an unwarranted deduction from methods of *in vitro* culture. There are few proven cases of nourishment of the germinating pollen grains by the stigma; secretions of mucilage and oils which may bathe the pollen grains probably serve mainly to prevent desiccation. Continued growth of the pollen tube (in contrast to germination) is almost certainly reliant on nourishment from the stigma, however.

In germination the intine absorbs water readily and swells greatly, especially below the pores, where it is thickest. The extine overlying the pores is ruptured and the pollen tube, which is an extension of the intine, grows out. There may be several tubes but only one reaches the ovule. The whole of the contents of the pollen grain pass into the pollen tube, the vegetative nucleus leading the way as the "tube nucleus". The protoplasm is restricted to the distal end of the tube and is cut off by transverse walls of callose from the grain as the tube elongates. The cytoplasm contains starch grains and other reserves of food but it is believed that the pollen tube is formed partly from nourishment derived from the cells of the style; some tubes form apparently absorptive branches or haustoria.

When the tube reaches the ovule the latter may or may not be fully developed. In the Orchidaceae the ovule will not commence development unless pollination has been achieved. It will be clear that delay in the development of the ovule until pollination ensures that materials will not be wasted in the formation of ovules where pollination has failed. What directs the path of the pollen tube to the ovule is not clear. Chemotropism is suspected but the exact stimuli involved are not known. In many plants the direction of growth of the tube, at least as far as the base of the style, is determined mechanically: there is a special conducting tissue enclosing an open stylar canal which may contain a jelly-like substance. Other styles are, however, solid and have no conducting tissue. In some species the ovule sends filaments from the region of the micropyle up into the style, and in extreme cases the stylar canal is filled by these filaments.

The pollen tube enters the ovule by the micropyle, or, much less commonly, by another path, conditions known respectively as porogamy and aporogamy. Aporogamy is divisible into chalazogamy, where the tube enters through the funicle and chalaza; acrogamy, where it enters at the micropylar end but not through the micropyle itself; and mesogamy, where the side of the ovule is penetrated. Whatever the mode of entry, the tube must penetrate the nucellus before entering the embryo sac.

Division of the generative cell to give the two male gametes occurs in the pollen grain or in the pollen tube. The mode of release of the male gametes into the embryo sac varies but generally they are released by dissolution of the tip of the pollen tube, after the latter has penetrated the thin embryo sac membrane and passed between the synergidae. One gamete, together usually with its cytoplasmic sheath, then unites with the oosphere while the other unites with the two polar nuclei or with the product of their previous union. This second male nucleus usually loses its cytoplasm on the journey from the region of the oosphere to the polar nuclei. The result of the fusion of the male nucleus and the oosphere is a zygote, division of which will produce the embryo of the seed. The triple fusion nucleus or primary endosperm nucleus divides to form the endosperm.

CHAPTER 13

Seeds and Fruits and their Dispersal

THE SEED

The double fertilization, in which one male nucleus unites with the oosphere to give a zygote and the other male nucleus unites with the two polar nuclei (or the product of their previous union) to give the primary endosperm nucleus, converts the ovule into a seed. The seed consists of an embryo (including one or more cotyledons) and a food reserve which are invested by a seed coat (testa) or seed coats (testa and tegmen) through which passes an apical pore, the micropyle. If the seed is shed from the ripened carpel, the pericarp, its testa bears a scar, the hilum, which marks the points of attachment of the funicle. Additional structures, e.g. trichomes, wings and arils, may be present on the seed (see below). By maturity, the food reserve has been absorbed into the embryo in non-endospermic (exalbuminous) seeds, or is stored also in a distinct, persistent endosperm in endospermic (albuminous) seeds, or, rarely, resides in the persistent nucellus (perisperm).

Endosperm

Endosperm is formed in all angiosperms with the exception of the two families Orchidaceae and Podostemaceae and the latter family is alone in failing to form a triple fusion nucleus. Apart from these two families, therefore, a non-endospermic seed is not a seed in which no endosperm develops but one which lacks endosperm when mature, usually because this has been utilized directly by the embryo. Endosperm is normally absorbed into the embryo through the cotyledon(s) and in endospermic seeds endosperm remains to be absorbed after the seed has become mature.

Types of endosperm

Three main types of endosperm are recognized. In the nuclear-type division of the endosperm nucleus produces many nuclei embedded in cytoplasm but, at least initially, no cell walls are formed, a phenomenon known as free nuclear division, e.g. *Asclepias*, milkweeds of Africa and America. In the cellular type, which is well exemplified by the Anonaceae, e.g. *Annona muricata*, soursop, cell walls are laid down from the first. In the rarer helobial type, typical of the monocotyledon order Helobiales, the first division of the endosperm cell divides the endosperm into a large micropylar portion and a smaller antipodal portion which later is usually crushed. Recognition of these types requires detailed examination of the tissue and in simpler studies it is convenient merely to recognize classes of endosperm which are based on its consistency or other gross characters. Thus we may recognize fleshy endosperm in many seeds; oily endosperm as in *Ranunculus*; bony endosperm composed of greatly thickened hemicellulose cell walls as in the seeds of *Phoenix dactylifera*, the date palm and *Phytelephas*, the tropical American palm, which has an aggregate fruit consisting of six or more berries united together, each berry having several seeds, the hard white endosperm of which is used as "vegetable ivory" for making billiard balls, collar studs, etc.; horny endosperm as in *Coffea*, coffee, where the endosperm is merely a horny sheath which surrounds the hard perisperm of the bean; mealy endosperm, which is typical of the temperate family Frankeniaceae, in which the endosperm appears powdery owing to the large size and separation of its starch grains; flinty endosperm as occurs in *Zea mays*, maize, where closely packed starch grains fill the cells and give the endosperm an opalescent appearance; and ruminate endosperm as in the Annonaceae, in which the integuments send folds into the endosperm, and *Myristica*, e.g. *M. fragrans*, the nutmeg, in which the nucellus is similarly infolded. Numerous other classes are recognized and many integrate but the examples given serve to illustrate the wide variety of form and consistency of the endosperm.

Food reserves in endosperm

Endosperm contains sugar (rarely), starch, oils and proteins, but one of these is usually predominant. Hemicellulose laid down in the cell walls may be the most important reserve, as in the palms mentioned above, and its presence usually excludes starch.

Oil is very important in various "nuts", for instance, the endosperm of the coconut contains over 65 per cent of oil by dry weight. The oil content of cottonseed, linseed, sunflower and groundnuts ranges from 33 to 47 per cent. Starchy endosperm has a very low percentage of oil; for instance, wheat and barley have only about 2 per cent of oil and peas and beans less than 1·5 per cent. Protein is not usually the reserve in endosperm though it is high in legumes and reaches 39 per cent of dry weight in cottonseed. It also occurs in the aleurone layer of the grains of Gramineae, e.g. maize, and as aleurone "crystals" in castor oil seeds.

Perisperm

The infolded and persistent nucellus in the ruminate endosperm of *Myristica* does not constitute a food reserve but in some seeds the nucellus is an important reserve and it is then known as perisperm. It is the chief reserve in the Zingiberaceae, e.g. *Zingiber officinale*, ginger; in *Coffea*, coffee, where it constitutes the part of the bean which produces the beverage; in the cosmopolitan family Caryophyllaceae; in the Chenopodiaceae, e.g. *Beta*, beet, and *Chenopodium anthelminticum*, worm seed or Mexican tea, the oil of which is used as a vermifuge; in the Amarantaceae, e.g. *Amarantus*, which includes the striking purple-flowered love-lies-bleeding, and *Celosia cristata*, cock's comb; and in the Nyctaginaceae, e.g. *Bougainvillaea* and *Mirabilis*, both ornamental garden plants.

Arils

Bulky outgrowths of the seed are termed arils; the term is not usually extended to flimsy outgrowths such as floss on the testa of the seeds of *Gossypium* (cotton) and wings in *Tecoma*. The term aril is sometimes restricted to outgrowths of the funicle which are persistent on the seed and sometimes only to those funicular outgrowths which embrace the seed so as to give an extra coat; other outgrowths are then termed false arils. A wart-like aril growing out from the region of the micropyle is termed a caruncle. A familiar example of a caruncle or elaiosome is that of the seed of *Ricinus communis*, castor oil (Fig. 171).

True arils (funicular outgrowths) occur in *Byophytum* (Oxalidaceae), a genus of some 60 tropical species with pinnate leaves which, like those of *Mimosa*, are sensitive to touch, in which the aril is explosive; *Dillenia* (Dilleniaceae), a genus of some 20 species in India, Malaya and the Pacific Islands, including *D. cauliflora*, the large yellow flowers of which are typical of Pacific forests; *Durio* (Bombaceae) with about 12 species in

India and Malaya, of which *D. zibethinus* which bears the durian fruit is a member, the fleshy aril forming part of the edible flesh of this delicately flavoured but disagreeably smelling fruit; *Myristica* (Myristicaceae) with about 85 species in the tropics of the Old World of which *M. fragrans* has a spicy seed—the nutmeg—enveloped in a branched, anastomosing, reddish-orange, oil-filled aril which yields the spice called mace (Fig. 138); *Maranta* (Marantaceae), a genus of 30 tropical American species (including *M. arundinacea*, West Indian arrow-root), in some species of which, as in *Myristica*, the aril forces the pericarp to dehisce and then forms a highly coloured attractant for birds; *Nymphaea* (Nymphaceae), the water lilies, found throughout the tropics, in which the seeds have perisperm and endosperm and a spongy aril, which aids in dispersal by water; and lastly, although numerous other examples, exist *Passiflora* (Passifloraceae), mainly American, of which the widely cultivated species with edible fruits have fleshy arils which are eaten with the fruit.

FIG. 138. Seed of nutmeg, *Myristica fragrans*. The spicy seed (nutmeg) is enveloped in a reddish-orange, oily aril (mace), actual size.

FRUITS

A fruit is the result of growth induced in the ovary, and often in neighbouring parts of the flower, by the stimulus of fertilization. It usually consists of the ripened ovary only, when it is called a "true fruit", but frequently other parts of the flower contribute, for instance, the receptacle or the perianth, when it is called a "false fruit". The terms "true" and "false" are misleading, however, and will be avoided in the present work. The wall of the ovary becomes the pericarp or fruit wall and is soft and fleshy or dry and hard, or a combination of these, and may rupture on the parent plant to release the seed, when the fruit is said to be dehiscent, or may fall with the fruit, which is then said to be indehiscent.

Fruits may be simple, aggregate or composite.

Simple fruits are formed from a single flower in which the gynaecium is monocarpellary or is syncarpous, e.g. the capsule of *Aristolochia*.

Aggregate fruits are formed from a single flower with an apocarpous gynaecium, e.g. the "aeterio" of *Ranunculus*.

Composite fruits are formed from an inflorescence. Here fruitlets are grouped together to form a single mass, e.g. *Ananas*, the pine-apple, which is also a "false fruit" because the whole inflorescence forms the fruit and is swollen and fleshy; and *Rubus*, the blackberry, which is made up of many small "drupes" (druplets).

Simple and Aggregate Fruits

A classification of simple and aggregate fruits now follows. For convenience they are divided into dry fruits and succulent fruits, but it will be realized that it is not always easy to decide into which category a fruit should be placed.

Simple Fruits

1. *Dry fruits*

One-seeded fruits. If a seed is dry, indehiscent and one-seeded, it is said to be an achenial fruit. There are a number of types of achenial fruits.

1. The achene: pericarp membranous or leathery; derived from a superior ovary, e.g. each fruitlet of the aggregate fruit (aeterio) of *Ranunculus* (Fig. 130A).

2. The cypsela: as above, but developed from an inferior ovary, e.g. *Helianthus* (Fig. 183), *Zinnia*, *Cosmos* and other Compositae.

3. The caryopsis: an achene in which the testa of the enclosed seed and the pericarp have fused, e.g. *Zea mays* (Fig. 172A). Characteristic of the Gramineae and known as a "grain".

4. The samara: an achene in which the pericarp is winged. We will include here "multiple samaras" which have the appearance of united winged achenes which later separate. An example is the double or triple samara of *Dodonaea*, East African privet (Sapindaceae) (Fig. 139). These multiple samaras are not strictly achenial as they are derived from bi- or trilocular ovaries; the constituent carpels are not true achenes but are mericarps of a winged carcerulus (see below).

5. The nut: an achene with a hard and woody pericarp, e.g. cashew nut, *Anacardium occidentale* (Fig. 140).

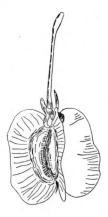

FIG. 139. Triple samara of *Dodonaea*, East African privet, produced
from a trilocular superior ovary. The remains of the perianth are visible
above the wings and a lobe of the stigma below, × 2.

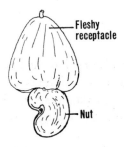

FIG. 140. *Anacardium occidentale*, cashew nut. The woody achene (nut)
is borne on a fleshy receptacle.

Fruits with two or more seeds

A. *Capsular fruits.* If a fruit is dry, dehiscent and has two or more
seeds, it is a capsular fruit. The following are different types of capsular
fruits.

1. The follicle: derived from a monocarpellary ovary; typically it
splits along one side (suture) only, e.g. *Grevillea* and the double follicle of
frangipani, *Plumeria acutifolia* (Fig. 161) and of *Strophanthus eminii*.

2. The legume: derived from a monocarpellary ovary; it splits along
both sutures. These are typical of the Leguminosae, e.g. *Cassia, Bauhinia*

(Fig. 142), *Crotalaria*, *Pisum* (Fig. 180D–F) and *Phaseolus*. Modifications of the legume exist. Examples of these are the one-seeded winged
legumes of the African forest tree mninga, *Pterocarpus* (Fig. 143), a tree
which yields a splendid reddish-brown timber; and of *Dalbergia*, which
includes *D. melanoxylon*, from which Kenya ebony is obtained—these are
structurally samaras; the indehiscent pods of the chick pea or Bengal gram,
Cicer arietinum; purging cassia, *Cassia fistula*, which has an indehiscent

FIG. 141. Follicle of *Nerium oleander*, the oleander, which is atypical
in dehiscing along both sutures, × ⅓. Note the plumed seeds of which
one is shown natural size on the right.

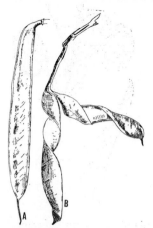

FIG. 142. Legume of *Bauhinia* sp. A, before; B, after, dehiscence, × ¼.

pod in which the seeds are embedded in a laxative pulp (Fig. 144); and "lomentose" pods which break up into one-seeded indehiscent portions (see lomentum under schizocarpic fruits, below).

3. The siliqua: derived from a bicarpellary ovary with two parietal placentas and a false septum. It dehisces from the receptacle upwards and the two valves remain attached to the tip of the septum. Characteristic of the Cruciferae, e.g. cabbage, *Brassica*; wall flower, *Cheiranthus* (Fig. 145).

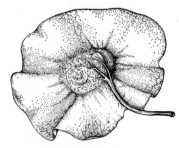

FIG. 143. One-seeded winged legume of *Pterocarpus* sp., × ½.

FIG. 144. Indehiscent legume of *Cassia fistula*, bisected longitudinally, showing the seeds embedded in a laxative pulp.

FIG. 145. Above, silicula of *Coronopus didymus*, × 5. Below, siliqua of *Cheiranthus*, × ½.

4. The silicula: a short, flat siliqua, e.g. cress, *Lepidium*; also shepherd's purse, *Capsella*; *Senebiera*, and *Coronopus* (Fig. 145).

5. The capsule: includes all other kinds of capsular fruits and may be unilocular or multilocular. Various types of dehiscence are met with: by pores; by a lid; by splitting into valves. Dehiscence into valves may be along septa, i.e. septicidal, or between the septa and through the walls of the loculi, i.e. loculicidal. An example of septicidal dehiscence is Dutchman's pipe, *Aristolochia elegans* (Fig. 146), and of loculicidal dehiscence, cotton, *Gossypium* (Fig. 164). Capsules are sometimes succulent as in the case of balsam, *Impatiens*.

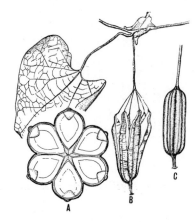

FIG. 146. *Aristolochia elegans*. A, cross-section of a ripe capsule showing hexalocular form, each loculus containing a vertical row of flattened seeds. B, a capsule which has dehisced septicidally, × ¼. C, capsule formed from an inferior ovary with the persistent receptacle at the lower end.

B. *Schizocarpic fruits*. If a seed is dry and has two or more seeds but when ripe splits into one-seeded, and usually indehiscent, parts resembling achenes and called mericarps, it is said to be a schizocarpic fruit. The best known are:

1. The lomentum: a special type of legume or of siliqua, in which the fruit is constricted between the seeds and breaks into one-seeded parts, e.g. sensitive plant, *Mimosa pudica* (Fig. 147); *Desmodium* (Fig. 167D); and *Acacia arabica*, a small tree of arid plains from India to Africa.

2. The cremocarp: a bilocular capsule which splits down the septum, the two mericarps remaining attached at first to a bifid strand, the carpophore. Characteristic of the Umbelliferae (Fig. 148).

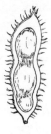

FIG. 147. Lomentum of *Mimosa pudica*, the sensitive plant, enlarged.

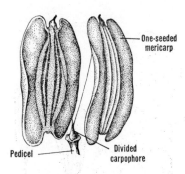

FIG. 148. Cremocarp of *Angelica polycarpa*, from Mexico, × 5.

3. The carcerulus: a capsule derived from a superior ovary which splits into a number of mericarps, e.g. garden nasturtium and other species of *Tropaeolum* (Fig. 149); many Labiatae and some Malvaceae.

4. The regma: a schizocarpic fruit which is unusual in that the one-seeded mericarps into which it splits are dehiscent, e.g. castor oil, *Ricinus communis*, (Fig. 150).

5. The multiple samara: a schizocarpic capsule with wing-like extensions of the pericarp of each carpel, e.g. East African privet, *Dodonaea* (Fig. 139) (see achenial fruits, above).

FIG. 149. Carcerulus of *Tropaeolum* sp. split into three mericarps, actual size.

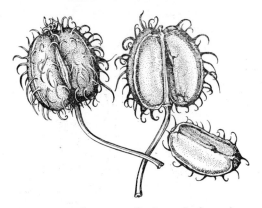

FIG. 150. *Ricinus communis*, castor oil plant. Left, entire regma. Right, a regma with one dehiscent mericarp detached, actual size.

2. Succulent fruits

Succulent fruits are fruits in which the pericarp is fleshy. There are three main types.

1. The drupe: a succulent fruit in which the pericarp has three regions: the epicarp or outer skin; the mesocarp or middle fleshy layer; and the endocarp, which is always hard (contrast the berry) and is popularly called the stone. The stone protects the seed after the succulent part has been eaten or has rotted away. Usually there is only one stone because drupes are usually developed from a monocarpellary ovary, e.g. the mango, *Mangifera indica* (Fig. 151), and some workers restrict the term drupe to such fruits. Sometimes the drupe is developed from a syncarpous ovary as in yellow oleander, *Thevetia peruviana* (Fig. 188F), and in the coconut, *Cocos nucifera* (Fig. 152). In the coconut the mesocarp is fibrous instead of being fleshy; the shell is the endocarp, the edible white part of the endosperm of the seed and the thin layer covering this is the testa.

2. The berry: a succulent fruit in which the three divisions of the pericarp seen in drupes are not usually present and the inner layer of the pericarp is never hard. Examples are the tomato, *Lycopersicum* (Fig. 153A–C); oranges and lemons, *Citrus* spp.; pawpaw, *Carica papaya*— all from superior ovaries; and the cucumbers and gourds, e.g. the guava, *Psidium* and *Fuchsia* (Fig. 153C, D) from inferior ovaries. Some berries have "stones" but the stone is not part of the pericarp; an example of a stony berry is the date, *Phoenix dactylifera*, in which the stone is hard endosperm of the seed and the avocado pear, *Persea gratissima* (Fig. 154), where the testa is hard.

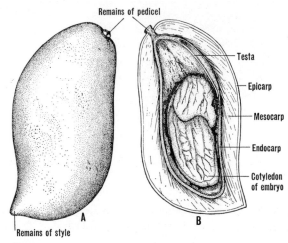

FIG. 151. Drupe of Mango, *Mangifera indica.* A, entire fruit. B, longitudinal section, × ⅓.

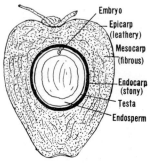

FIG. 152. Drupe of coconut, *Cocos nucifera,* reduced.

3. The pome: derived from an extremely perigynous flower in which the ovary is virtually inferior and the receptacle is fleshy, e.g. apple, *Pyrus malus* (Fig. 155); pear, *P. communis*; quince, *Chaenomeles* (=*Cydonia*); and *Cotoneaster*.

Aggregate Fruits

Aggregate fruits are derived from an apocarpous gynaecium and the individual fruitlets are usually one-seeded. If they are dry as in *Ranunculus*, each is an achene (Fig. 130C, 174J). If they are succulent each may be a small berry, as in the sugar apple, *Annona squamosa* (Fig. 156), or a small drupe (druplet) as in the blackberry, *Rubus* spp. Some species of *Phytolacca* have aggregate fruits made up either of achenes or of druplets.

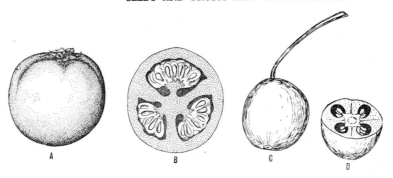

FIG. 153. Berries of A and B, *Lycopersicum*, tomato, developed from a superior ovary; A, whole; B, cross-section. C and D, *Fuchsia*, developed from an inferior ovary; C, whole; D, cross-section. Both have axile placentation.

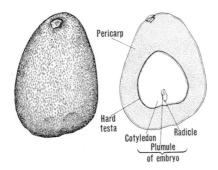

FIG. 154. Berry of avocado pear, *Persea gratissima*. Left, whole; right, in longitudinal section, × ¼.

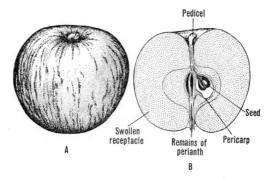

FIG. 155. Pome of apple, *Pyrus malus*. A, entire fruit. B, longitudinal section, × ½.

Some false fruits are aggregate fruits. Examples are the fruit of the rose, *Rosa*, in which many achenes derived from an apocarpous gynaecium are surrounded by a flask-shaped receptacle (Fig. 129B), and the strawberry, *Fragaria*, the flower of which is not markedly perigynous and in which the achenes are therefore exposed on the receptacle which is greatly thickened and fleshy (Fig. 157).

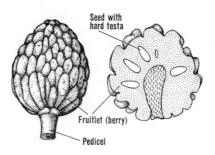

FIG. 156. Succulent aggregate fruit of sugar apple, *Anona squamosa*. Left, entire; right, in longitudinal section, reduced.

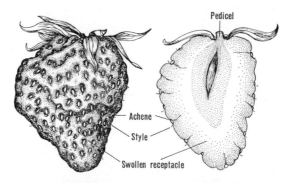

FIG. 157. Succulent aggregate false fruit of strawberry, *Fragaria vesca*. Left, entire fruit showing numerous achenes borne on a swollen fleshy receptacle. Right, longitudinal section, actual size.

Composite Fruits

Composite fruits are formed from more than one flower of an inflorescence. They are very frequently false fruits in that structures in addition to the gynaecium form part of them.

Examples are the pine-apple, *Ananas sativus* (Fig. 158); the bread fruit, *Artocarpus incisa* (Fig. 159); the jak fruit, *Artocarpus integrifolia*; the mulberry, *Morus*; and the figs, *Ficus* spp. (Fig. 160). In the first three,

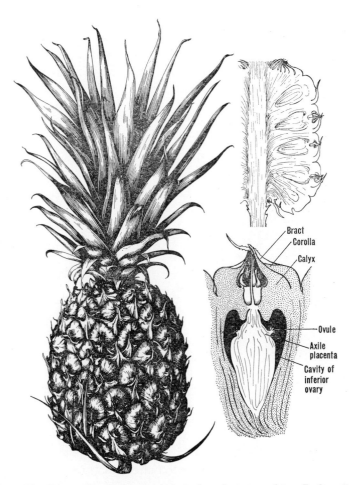

FIG. 158. Composite fruit of pine-apple, *Ananas sativus*. Left, whole fruit consisting of an entire fleshy inflorescence with a terminal crown of leaves, × ⅓. Upper right, longitudinal section showing several fleshy flowers attached to the inflorescence axis, × ¼. Bottom right, a single flower in longitudinal section showing perianth and inferior ovary, both of which are fleshy, actual size. The ovules do not usually develop into viable seeds.

the individual flowers of the inflorescence are joined together from first formation and the unfertilized inflorescence closely resembles the mature fruit, of which the inflorescence axis forms an integral part. In the mulberry, the individual flowers are separate and become crowded together after fertilization by great swelling of the four perianth members of each which constitute the edible flesh of the fruit. In the fig (Fig. 160), the inflorescence is a flask-like capitulum with the numerous flowers on the inside. After fertilization, the inflorescence axis becomes fleshy and encloses the fruits which are drupes.

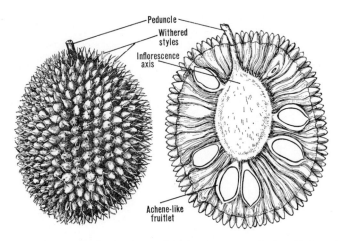

FIG. 159. Composite fruit of bread fruit, *Artocarpus incisa*. Left, whole; right, in longitudinal section, × ½.

FRUIT AND SEED DISPERSAL

We have seen that it is a special characteristic of the angiosperms that their seeds show dormancy, i.e. a period after abscission from the parent plant during which the seed shows no apparent external change. This dormant period allows for dispersal of the seed. Dispersal is important because it minimizes competition between the seedling and the parent plant and with other seedlings for commodities, including light and soil nutrients, necessary for life; reduces the risk of extinction of a species by a natural catastrophe which a limited distribution might entail; and increases the likelihood that some of the seeds will find more favourable conditions for development than those available to the parent. These advantages may be taken to have been responsible for the selection of the adaptations to certain methods of dispersal which we will study below.

The mechanism of dispersal may be part of the seed itself (where the fruit is dehiscent) or may belong to surrounding portions of the fruit (where the fruit is indehiscent, and in some cases where it is dehiscent, as in censer mechanisms).

The principal agencies bringing about dispersal are: Wind, water, animals and explosive devices.

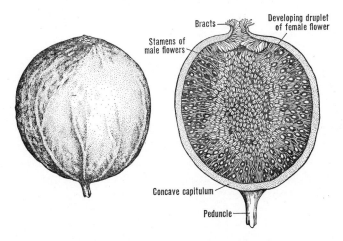

FIG. 160. Composite fruit of a fig, *Ficus megacarpa*, from the Philippines. Right, whole; left, in longitudinal section, actual size.

Dispersal by Wind

The following adaptations facilitate wind dispersal.

1. Minute size.
2. Flattening.
3. Wing-like outgrowths.
4. Feathery appendages.
5. Censer mechanisms.

1. *Minute size*

The seeds of some plants are very minute and because of the large ratio of surface area to weight are easily carried by wind and air currents. The seeds may remain airborne for long periods and, as in wind dispersal of pollen, there is much wastage owing to failure to reach suitable environments for germination. This wastage is compensated for by production of large numbers of seeds which involves no greater use of materials of the parent plant than would production of fewer, larger, seeds. The small size is often associated with incomplete differentiation of the embryo as in the Orchidaceae, a seed of which may weigh only 0·00005 g.

2. *Flattening*

Fruits which are dispersed by wind more readily because they are flattened are exemplified by the cypselas of some Compositae, e.g. *Zinnia*.

3. *Wing-like outgrowths*

There is no sharp distinction between fruits and seeds with wing-like outgrowths and those which are merely flattened. Thus the flattened seeds of *Aristolochia elegans* (Fig. 146) are sometimes said to be winged because there is a peripheral region into which the embryo does not extend. However, distinctly winged fruits occur in East African privet, *Dodonaea* (see p. 241 and Fig. 139), and in the circum-tropical family Combretaceae in which, for instance, *Combretum* and *Terminalia* have double or triple samaras. Wing-like expansions of the testa occur in the seeds of some Apocynaceae, e.g. frangipani, *Plumeria acutifolia* (Fig. 161);

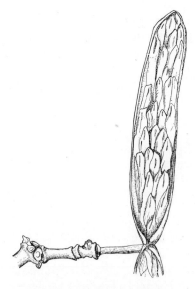

FIG. 161. Fruit of *Plumeria acutifolia*, frangipani. Two follicles, containing winged, wind-dispersed seeds, are produced from a single flower, × ⅓.

and in most Bignoniaceae, including *Tecoma* (Fig. 186), *Bignonia, Catalpa, Newbouldia* and *Jacaranda;* and also in *Casuarina,* the she-oak, of the Casuarinaceae.

4. *Feathery appendages*

Much-divided appendages of fruits and seeds greatly increase their surface area/weight ratio and facilitate wind dispersal. The cypselas of many Compositae, e.g. *Taraxacum,* several tropical weeds, and the cosmopolitan genus *Senecio,* which includes the giant groundsels of East African mountains, bear each a tuft of hairs known as a pappus, which is derived from the calyx. The achenes of the tropical and temperate genus *Clematis* (Ranunculaceae) have persistent, long, feathery styles (Fig. 162).

Seeds with a plumed appendage very similar to the pappus of the composite cypsela are beautifully exemplified by *Strophanthus* spp. (Fig. 163) (Apocynaceae), Asian and African trees or shrubs identifiable by the extremely long tails on the petals and the double follicles and also by *Nerium oleander,* the oleander, of the same family (Fig. 141). *Gossypium,*

FIG. 162. Wind-dispersed, feathery achenes of *Clematis hirsuta,* from Ghana. Above, three heads (aeterios) developed from apocarpous ovaries. Below, one achene, × 3. Redrawn from Gardeman.

cotton (Fig. 164), has hairy outgrowths of the testa which are too familiar to need description. Such floss also occurs on the seeds of *Asclepias* spp., the milkweeds, and the silk cotton or kapok tree, *Eriodendron anfractuosum* (Fig. 165). The floss of the kapok tree is often used for stuffing cushions.

5. *Censer mechanisms*

Fruits which resemble censers in that, like the latter, they distribute their contents when shaken, are common. They are usually capsular fruits which open by pores or by loculicidal or septicidal dehiscence, but must be shaken if the enclosed seeds are to be dispersed. Although wind is probably the most common agent in such dispersal, most "censers" are borne in situations where they may be shaken by passing animals also. The septicidal, hexalocular capsule of *Aristolochia elegans*, which hangs like an inverted parachute by strands of the divided pedicel, is an excellent example (Fig. 146). As shaking of the capitulum of the sunflower, *Helianthus*, causes dispersal of the cypselas, this species may be said to exhibit a censer mechanism which is not of the capsular type.

FIG. 163. Plumed, wind-dispersed seeds of *Strophanthus eminii*, actual size.

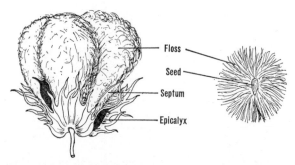

Floss

Seed

Septum

Epicalyx

FIG. 164. Cotton, *Gossypium*. Left, capsule (boll) dehiscing loculicidally to expose the floss of the seeds. Left, a single seed, × *ca.* ¼.

Species of *Begonia* have capsules which bear three wing-like extensions of the pericarp. At first sight it appears that the entire triple samara is wind-dispersed but in fact the minute seeds are dispersed by the wind before the capsule falls, and the wings are adaptations for ensuring that they are shaken out of the capsule, which quivers in the slightest breeze.

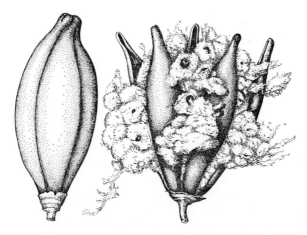

FIG. 165. Capsule of a species of kapok tree, *Eriodendron pentandra*. Left, before; right, after, dehiscence, × ½. As in cotton, the seeds are enveloped in floss and dispersion is by wind or by animals, especially man, which utilize the floss.

Dispersal by Water

Water is the normal agent of dispersal of the fruits and seeds of many aquatic plants and plants which normally grow at the water's edge. It is frequently effective, also, in dispersing seeds which are adapted for dissemination by other agencies; for instance, the winged seeds of *Tecoma stans* are often carried far, with no loss of viability, by rainwater.

It is not sufficient for the water-dispersed seed or fruit to be buoyant; it must be able to withstand the effects of immersion. Resistance to destruction by immersion appears usually to depend on the presence of impervious envelopes, in the pericarp or testa, but in some cases the ability to withstand rotting is probably mainly physiological.

Strand plants, i.e. plants which grow very close to, or in, the sea, afford the most striking examples of dispersal by water as the distances over which the seeds or fruits are dispersed may reach thousands of miles and prolonged immersion in sea water has to be tolerated. Striking evidence of the effectiveness of dispersal by ocean currents is presented by the flora of eastern mangrove communities which contain the same species whether growing on the coasts of East Africa, India or Malaya, the main species being *Rhizophora mangle* (Rhizophoraceae), which is particularly interesting because its seeds germinate before they are shed from the parent tree, *Avicennia nitida* (Verbenaceae), *Laguncularia racemosa* (Combretaceae), *Anona palustris* (Anonaceae), and *Carapa guaianensis* (Meliaceae). Many species of the western mangrove are similarly shared between the coasts of West Africa and eastern tropical America.

Another strand plant, *Cocos nucifera*, the coconut palm, has long been thought to be spread vast distances by the sea, the fibrous pericarp being apparently, admirably adapted to flotation. Some workers have denied the ability of the fruit to survive long immersion, however, and suggest that its strand distribution throughout the tropics, including isolated islands, is due to transportation by man. Its establishment on the island of Krakatoa after the great eruption seems, however, to be a clear case of its spread by water over long distances.

Examples of distribution by freshwater are: *Nelumbium nelumbo*, a lotus, the achenes of which float either singly, or embedded in the large torus, which is made buoyant by numerous air spaces (Fig. 166); by *Nymphaea* spp., water lilies (both genera are Nymphaceae), the seeds of which have spongy arils; and by *Crinum* spp. (Liliaceae), which include white lilies which grow on river banks in tropical African forests, the seeds of which are slightly inflated and are readily dispersed by river currents.

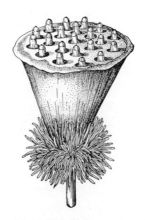

Fig. 166. Water-dispersed fruits of the lotus. *Nelumbium speciosum*, embedded in a buoyant torus, × ½.

Dispersal by Animals

Fruits and seeds are dispersed by animals either by adhering to them or as a consequence of their being used as food. The whole fruit may be dispersed or, where the fruit is dehiscent and the seed is attractive, the seed alone is dispersed. Where eaten, the seed, or the seed and part of the pericarp, may be rejected from the mouth or may be expelled with the faeces.

Adhesive fruits

Adhesive fruits are either sticky or have appendages which engage in hairs or feathers or other parts of the bodies of animals. In *Heteropogon contortus*, spear grass (Fig. 167A), each spikelet is armed with a basal barb which readily clings to hair or clothing or penetrates the skin; the long, twisted awns of separate ears intertwine and the tangled mass thus formed, often joining many grass heads, is an unavoidable obstacle to the passage of animals. If the latter push through they inevitably carry some of the spikelets with them. The pain caused by the barb when penetrating the skin induces the animal to remove and reject the "seed" thus effecting dispersal. Another circum-tropical weed, *Acanthospermum hispidum* (Fig. 167B, C, Compositae), which bears clusters of sessile cypselas, each of which bears two sharp, hooked spines and many stiff bristles; and the African *Tribulus terrestris* (Zygophyllaceae), a creeping weed with paired, stipulate leaves and schizocarpic fruits with viciously spined mericarps, are dispersed as a result of their fruits clinging to or penetrating the skins of passing animals. A carcerulus with hooked mericarps also occurs in *Urena* (Malvaceae) a plant which yields a useful fibre and has been introduced into many parts of the tropics. *Desmodium adscendens* (Fig. 167D) (Leguminosae), a common plant in African forests, has a lomentose pod with sticky hairs; the mericarps are readily carried by passing animals, hence the frequency of this plant along forest paths.

Edible fruits

The most common edible fruits are drupes and berries. Pomes and the composite fruits mentioned above are also dispersed because they are edible. Certain dry fruits are also dispersed for this reason, examples being the cypselas of the sunflower and the grains of many members of the Gramineae, including maize. Certain seeds are carried about by man and other animals because they are edible or are attractive in other ways. A few of the many examples which might be taken will now be mentioned.

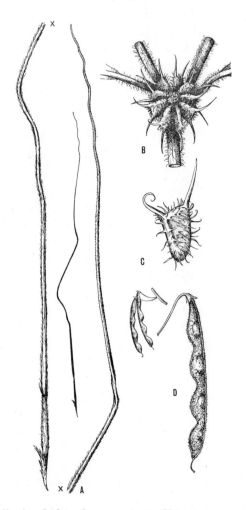

FIG. 167. Adhesive fruits. A, spear grass, *Heteropogon contortus*, actual size and × 3. B, *Acanthospermum hispidum*, cluster of hooked cypselas, actual size. C, *A. hispidum*, a single cypsela, × 3. D, *Desmodium adscendens*, lomentose pod with sticky hairs which breaks up into adhesive mericarps; the single pod, × 1½. All specimens from the Congo.

Edible drupes

Perhaps the most familiar example of an edible drupe is the mango, *Mangifera indica* (Fig. 151). This is much prized by man for its edible fleshy mericarp. The tough skin (epicarp) is stripped off before eating and, after the flesh has been consumed, the stone, consisting of mesocarp and contained seed, is rejected, hence the frequency of mango trees along caravan routes. The drupe of the mango is somewhat unusual in that the endocarp is more fibrous than in most drupes. The coconut is a further example of a drupe which is spread because it is edible but it, too, is unusual, this time because the mesocarp is not succulent or edible and it is the seed which is eaten. Here the seed does not survive eating and it is intentional planting by man, in addition to dispersal by ocean currents, which accounts for the wide distribution of the species.

Edible berries

Edible berries are usually eaten for their fleshy pericarps, and less often for their seeds. If the seeds are large they are usually rejected from the mouth but if they are small they may be swallowed and pass out with the faeces. In the latter case they are specialized to resist destruction by the digestive juices of the animal, usually by the presence of a mucilaginous layer around them or a very thick integument. The pawpaw is an example of a berry which is eaten by man for its fleshy pericarp, the seeds being rejected before eating. Other berries whose seeds are rejected are the date, *Phoenix dactylifera*, the melon, *Cucumis melo*, the orange, *Citrus aurantium*, and the avocado pear, *Persea gratissima*. Examples of berries whose seeds pass through the gut are the tomato, *Lycopersicum*, the cape gooseberry, *Physalis*, and the pepper, *Capsicum*. The seeds of some berries may be swallowed or rejected by man, e.g. passion fruit, *Passiflora* and guava, *Psidium*. The seeds of mistletoe, *Viscum* and *Loranthus*, may also be rejected by birds, which are the main means of their dispersal, when excess of the sticky pulp is rubbed off on a branch.

Plants whose seeds are adapted to surviving passage through the gut have the distinct advantage that the faeces, with which the seeds pass to the exterior, provide a good medium for the early growth of the seedlings.

Cereal grains and the cypselas of the sunflower do not survive eating but are very widely dispersed because they are accidentally dropped by various animals and are sown by man.

Edible seeds

Dry fruits such as the grains of Gramineae and the cypselas of sunflower are eaten for the seed contained within the dry pericarp and therefore they could be included under the headings of edible seeds as well as edible fruits.

Of the many examples of seeds which are dispersed because they are edible or attractive the following may be selected. The seeds of many Leguminosae (e.g. beans, peas, vetches and clover) have been transported throughout the world by man, being planted because they are edible or because they yield fodder for his animals. Where man is the carrier, considerations other than edibility arise; these include cultivation for timber and, of great importance, in dispersal, cultivation to please the highly developed aesthetic sense of man. Many birds show a liking for coloured objects and the seeds of the twining legume *Abrus prectacorius* (Fig. 168) which are bright red with a black region at one end, and are commonly known as "crabs' eyes", are distributed by birds because their appearance, and not their value as a food, is attractive. The same is apparently true of the seeds of *Byrsocarpus*, which are black with a yellow aril which almost covers them. Birds also disperse the seeds of *Momordica* (Fig. 169), which are rendered attractive by the contrast of the scarlet pulp against the orange epicarp of the fleshy capsule which splits on the tree into several valves.

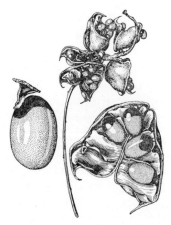

FIG. 168. Bird-dispersed seeds of crabs' eyes, *Abrus prectacorius*. Left, a single red seed with black aril, × 3. Centre, several dehisced pods, × ½. Right, a single dehisced pod, actual size. Specimens from Seychelles.

A very familiar example of a seed which is dispersed by animals is that of the castor oil plant, *Ricinus communis* (Fig. 150). This is dispersed in two ways, first by explosive dehiscence of the regma and secondly by animals, including ants, which eat the oily caruncle, a warty outgrowth in the region of the micropyle. This plant has been widely dispersed by man who extracts a useful oil from the seeds and therefore cultivates it widely.

Explosive Devices

Some fruits eject their seeds very rapidly as a result of sudden changes in the pericarp. These may be termed explosive fruits. Many legumes belong to this class, a fine example being *Bauhinia* (Fig. 142) in which

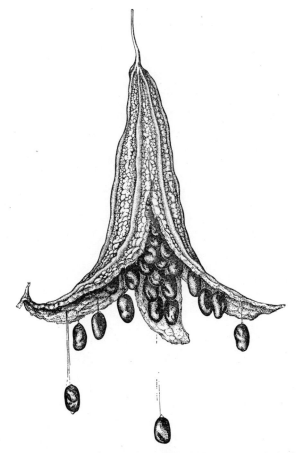

FIG. 169. Bird-dispersed seeds of *Momordica* suspended from the dehisced fleshy capsule, × ⅓.

unequal contraction of fibres in the wall of the pod on drying causes a sudden splitting along the sutures and spiralling of the two halves, with the result that the large seeds are forcibly ejected for many yards. The pods of the West African shrub *Bandeiraea simplicifolia* explode with a small report and scatter the seeds in a similar way. It is said that West African farmers find the explosion a useful indication of the time to plant crops. The cultivated flower, balsam, *Impatiens* spp., has a capsule which dehisces owing to the development of high turgidity, to eject the seeds.

Another example of an explosive fruit is the small wild cucumber, which is widely distributed in warm regions, *Ecballium*. The berry of this plant develops a high hydrostatic pressure which suddenly ejects a "cork" at one end and causes the seeds to be squirted out in a jet of liquid (Fig. 170).

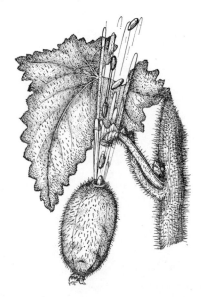

FIG. 170. The squirting cucumber, *Ecballium elaterium*, × ½.

TYPES OF GERMINATION

Two types of germination are recognized: epigeal germination, in which the cotyledons appear above the soil, and hypogeal germination, in which they remain beneath the surface.

In epigeal germination, the cotyledons are raised above the soil because the region of the embryo between the node bearing the cotyledons (the cotyledonary node) and the radicle elongates. This region is termed the hypocotyl. Epigeal germination occurs in the castor oil plant, *Ricinus communis*, the sunflower, *Helianthus annuus*, and the onion, *Allium cepa*, which have endospermic seeds, and in the French bean, *Phaseolus vulgaris*, which has non-endospermic seeds. The student should observe newly germinated seedlings of many species and determine whether germination has been epigeal or hypogeal.

In hypogeal germination, the cotyledons remain below the surface of the soil because the hypocotyl does not elongate. It occurs in *Zea mays* (Fig. 172), which like other grasses has endospermic grains, and in the broad bean, *Vicia faba*, which has non-endospermic seeds (Fig. 173).

Epigeal Germination

The micropyle and hilum (funicular scar) of the seed of *Ricinus communis* are obscured by a warty outgrowth, the caruncle (Fig. 171A). The testa of the seed is a hard, polished envelope with characteristic surface markings. The tegmen is a thin, brownish, papery layer. The bulk of the contents of the seed consists of a massive whitish endosperm, the two whitish cotyledons being very thin. If the seed is split lengthwise in the plane of flattening (B) the surface of a cotyledon may be examined and its palmate venation noted. Still joined to one of the cotyledons will be seen the plumule and radicle. If a seed is divided longitudinally at right-angles to the broadest surface (C), the great thickness of the endosperm relative to the cotyledons will be seen. If the seed is covered with moist soil, the endosperm swells and the seed coats burst. The radicle then grows down into the soil and soon develops lateral roots. Growth of the hypocotyl while the seed is held in the soil causes the former to appear above the soil as a loop. Subsequently the hypocotyl beings to straighten and pulls the cotyledons, often still embedded in the endosperm, and the remains of the seed coats, above the soil (D). The endosperm then shrinks as it is absorbed by the cotyledons (E). By the time it has all been absorbed, the cotyledons have developed distinct petioles and have become green expanded photosynthetic organs (F). Later the foliage leaves of the plumule become functional and the shrivelled remains of the cotyledons fall off.

The looping of the hypocotyl as it pushes through the soil protects the delicate rudimentary foliage leaves and the apical meristem from damage. Most plants have some device for protecting these parts from abrasion in their passage through the soil. In the onion, *Allium cepa*, after its radicle has become anchored, the cylindrical cotyledon, which encloses the plumule, grows out and becomes arched. The end of the cotyledon remains firmly embedded in the endosperm of the seed and further growth of the cotyledon draws the seed above ground, the bend of the cotyledon pushing through the soil and protecting the delicate enclosed plumule. The plumule emerges from a slit in the cotyledon when the latter is fully aerial. In some species of *Allium*, the bend of the cotyledon bears a sharp boring process. In maize (hypogeal, endospermic) the coleoptile protects the plumule. In most dicotyledons, whether epigeal or hypogeal, the plumule is bent over during its passage through the soil and the delicate parts are protected by this posture and by the fact that the leaves do not expand in darkness.

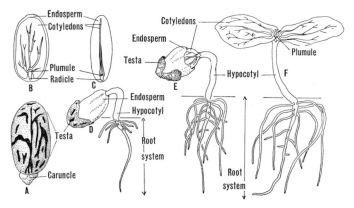

FIG. 171. Epigeal germination of castor oil plant, *Ricinus communis.* Approximately natural size. For explanation see text.

Hypogeal Germination

In taking maize as an example of hypogeal germination, it must be remembered that the maize grain is a fruit and not merely a seed.

The maize grain is a fruit known as a caryopsis, i.e. a one-seeded, indehiscent fruit in which the pericarp, which is membranous, woody or leathery, and the testa are united. It is therefore a type of achene. The fruits are borne in several closely adpressed longitudinal rows on the female inflorescence axis and each caryopsis is compressed, particularly above and below, relative to its position on the cob. The fruits are grouped in pairs around the circumference of the axis.

If a single caryopsis (Fig. 172A) is removed from the cob, it may be seen that it tapers to its attachment and that the upper flattened face bears an opaque whitish area which contrasts with the rest of the grain which is darker and more translucent. This whitish area marks the site of the embryo. Just above this there is commonly a small projection which represents the place of attachment of the style or "silk". If the grain is soaked in water, it can easily be sectioned longitudinally in such a way that the cutting edge passes down the centre of the embryonic area. The internal structure is thus clearly displayed (Fig. 172B).

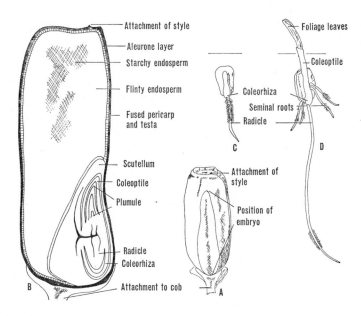

FIG. 172. Hypogeal germination of maize, *Zea mays*. A, whole grain, ×
ca. 2½. B, longitudinal section of grain, × *ca.* 7. C and D, germination,
× ½.

The embryo corresponds in position with the externally visible whitish area. It is in close contact with the fused pericarp and testa and occupies a relatively small portion of the grain and it appears wedge-shaped in section (Fig. 172B). It consists of a plumule with an ensheathing membrane, the coleoptile, and below this, nearer to the attachment to the cob, a radicle which is similarly ensheathed in a coleorhiza. A large structure, the scutellum, arises from the region of the embryo between the coleoptile and coleorhiza. It is sufficiently extensive to intervene between the coleoptile and the coleorhiza and the wall of the caryopsis as a thin, continuous sheath. It is believed to form part or the whole of the single cotyledon (see below).

The rest of the contents of the grain comprise the endosperm. This is of the cellular type and is mainly starchy, although the outer layer of cells contains proteinaceous granules (aleurone grains) and is called the aleurone layer. The starchy endosperm is of two types: flinty endosperm, in which the starch grains are so closely packed that the endosperm has a translucent appearance, and mealy endosperm, which is softer in texture. The proportion of flinty to starchy endosperm varies with the variety of maize. The endosperm also contains up to 6 per cent of a useful oil.

Germination of maize (Fig. 172C, D) is hypogeal and the grain remains below ground. The radicle first emerges from the grain and the coleoptile later emerges and becomes aerial by its own growth and by elongation of the region between its base and the attachment of the scutellum. This region is called the epicotyl, if it be considered that the scutellum is the cotyledon and the coleoptile the first plumular leaf, or the mesocotyl if the alternative view, that the scutellum and coleoptile together constitute the cotyledon, be accepted. The scutellum remains below ground. The typical foliage leaves (see p. 296) break through the coleoptile which remains relatively small. The coleoptile grows to about 5 cm in length and does not, therefore, unless the grain is buried deeper than this, release the foliage leaves below ground. If they are released they remain rolled up while in darkness, a mechanism which prevents exposure of the delicate leaves to abrasion by soil particles by premature opening below ground.

The coleorhiza undergoes little growth and the radicle soon penetrates it. Although the radicle may produce some lateral roots, it does not give rise to the main root system. A small number of adventitious seminal roots, usually four, grows out from the base of the coleoptile and is augmented by a large number of adventitious roots from the subterranean nodes of the shoot which form a vigorous fibrous root system. Prop roots (Fig. 84), which are capable of photosynthesis, may later develop from the lower aerial nodes.

The seed of the broad bean, *Vicia faba* (Fig. 173A) is approximately kidney-shaped with an encircling groove which marks the boundary between the two cotyledons. In this groove, at the lower end of the seed, is a dark scar, the hilum, near the upper end of which is the micropyle.

Immediately above the micropyle is a V-shaped swelling of the testa which marks the position of the radicle. Removal of the tough testa (B) displays two large whitish fleshy cotyledons, and the radicle. The embryo completely occupies the testa, there being no endosperm. If one of the cotyledons be detached the plumule is revealed. It is hook-shaped and consists of a growing point invested by two rudimentary foliage leaves surmounting a stalk. The part of the plumule above the cotyledons is termed the epicotyl. On germination, the radicle ruptures the testa and begins to grow down into the soil. Shortly after the epicotyl elongates and pushes upwards, still arched, through the soil (E), straightening out only when the foliage leaves have been brought above the soil surface (F). Because it is the epicotyl and not the hypocotyl which elongates, the cotyledons are left beneath the soil, where they wither as their food reserves pass to the seedling.

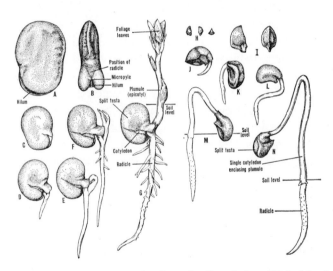

Fig. 173. A–G, hypogeal germination of a dicotyledon, *Vicia faba*, broad bean. A, side view of seed. B, front view of seed, actual size. C and D, emergence of radicle. E, emergence of plumule. F, plumule freed from testa. G, young plant with the plumule, here consisting entirely of the epicotyl, emergent above the soil, × ½. H–N, epigeal germination of a monocotyledon, *Allium cepa*, onion. H, seeds, actual size. I, side and front views of seed, × 3. J, emergence of radicle. K and L, elongation of cotyledon which encloses the plumule. M, cotyledon protruding arched through the soil and drawing the testa with it. N, testa freed from the soil by the enlarging cotyledon. Shortly after this the foliage leaves of the plumule burst the ensheathing cotyledon, × 3.

CHAPTER 14

Selected Floral Types

IN THIS chapter a few of the many families of tropical flowers will be briefly discussed and some of their more important genera and species listed. Species of some of the families will be described in detail. The species selected are cultivated throughout the tropics and should be available to the student. If they are not, the brief description of the families and of the selected species will enable the student to draw up descriptions, at a similar level, of flowers available locally. The mechanism of pollination can usually be deduced by observation of the form of the perianth, whether there are insect or other visitors, whether the stamens ripen before, after or with the pistil, and by experiments such as placing muslin bags over the flowers to see if self-pollination can occur, and removing stamens, before they are ripe, from the young flowers to see if cross-pollination occurs. By such observations the student may in some cases be the first to discover the mechanism of pollination in a chosen flower.

RANUNCULACEAE

The Ranunculaceae are very widespread but are less common in the tropics than in the temperate regions. They include the buttercup, *Ranunculus*, in which the floral organs are in a primitive and little modified condition and which consequently is a useful starting point in a study of floral morphology. In the tropics *Ranunculus* is limited to high ground and will rarely be available to the student, but because of its particular interest it is described below.

The family also includes *Aquilegia*, *Delphinium* and *Paeonia* and other garden flowers. These display a great variety of floral form.

Ranunculus

Distribution and morphology

The genus *Ranunculus* occurs chiefly in temperate regions but several species occur in Africa, India and other tropical countries.

The following description (see also Figs. 174, 175) refers to those species of the genus which have typical "buttercup" flowers, particularly to *R. multifidus*, which occurs on high ground from Arabia to Cape Province and west to Angola and Nigeria, including the three East African territories.

The members of the genus are herbs with simple, or compound, spirally arranged leaves. The flowers are actinomorphic and are borne singly or in inflorescences and the floral organs are borne in spirals.

Calyx

The calyx is polysepalous, consisting of five green sepals which in *R. multifidus* are bent back on themselves abruptly (reflexed).

Corolla

The corolla is polysepalous and consists of five free, yellow, shiny petals each of which typically has a pocket-like nectary at its base.

Androecium

The stamens are indefinite in number and are free (androecium polysteminous). Each stamen is innate, i.e. the filament is attached to the base of the connective. The anther is bilobed and extrorse and dehisces longitudinally. In the young flower the stamens hide the carpels.

Gynaecium

The gynaecium is apocarpous and the number of carpels is indefinite. The short style is persistent and in *R. multifidus*, as in some other species, is hooked. Each carpel contains a single ovule which is erect and anatropous and has a single integument.

The floral formula is $\oplus$ K5 C5 A∞ G$\underline{\infty}$.

The fruit

The fruit is an aeterio of achenes. An aeterio is a group of fruitlets derived from a single gynaecium and therefore borne on a single pedicel; each fruitlet is separate from the others. An achene is the product of a single uniovulate carpel the pericarp of which is membranous or woody and is indehiscent.

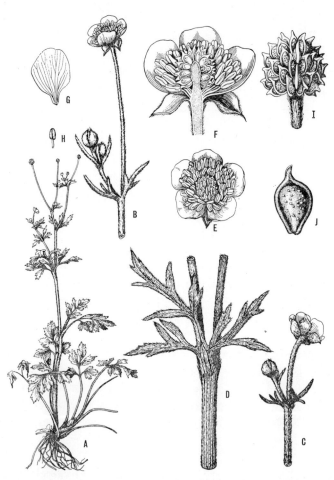

FIG. 174. *Ranunculus multifidus*, a buttercup. A, habit of plant, showing simple, much divided (pinnatisect) leaves, × ¼. B and C, parts of inflorescences, actual size. D, a leaf, actual size. E, whole flower, × 2. F, half flower, × 3. G, a petal, × 2. H, a stamen, × 2. I, the aggregate fruit, an aeterio of achenes derived from an apocarpous gynaecium, × 3. J, a single achene.

The fruits of some species of *Ranunculus* are dispersed by birds and this is probably the case in *R. multifidus,* as frequently each achene has a persistent hooked style. The seed possesses copious oily endosperm and the embryo is minute.

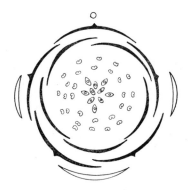

Fig. 175. Floral diagram of *Ranunculus.*

Pollination

Ranunculus is effectively protandrous because the stigmas are not exposed for pollination until the stamens have shed their pollen. The stamens are extrorse and are outwardly inclined and therefore pollen falls not onto the stigmas but onto the petals. A visiting insect (usually a small bee or a hover fly) seeking nectar at the base of a petal therefore receives pollen on both sides: from the anthers and from the petals. If it probes other nectaries of the same flower, it is unlikely to cause self-pollination because the stigmas are hidden by the stamens. If, however, it visits an older flower in which the stigmas are exposed owing to enlargement of the carpels, and sometimes loss of the stamens, it will bring about cross-pollination. A flower with the stigmas exposed may also be self-pollinated by a visiting insect if some of its stamens are still shedding pollen. Self-pollination is impossible in some species of *Ranunculus* owing to self-sterility.

Whether *Ranunculus* is truly protandrous or merely simulates protandry by the initial concealment of the ovaries is not certainly established.

LEGUMINOSAE

The Leguminosae is one of the largest families of flowering plants but is now usually divided into three families. These are the Caesalpiniaceae, including pride of Barbados, *Caesalpinia pulcherrima;* flamboyante,

Poinciana regia (Fig. 176); *Cassia* and *Bauhinia*; the Mimosaceae, including *Mimosa* and *Acacia*; and the Papilionaceae, including the garden pea, *Pisum sativum* (Fig. 180), the sweet pea, *Lathyrus odoratus*; the runner bean, *Phaseolus multiflorus*; broad bean, *Vicia faba*; *Abrus* and *Crotalaria*.

There is a great variety of floral and vegetative morphology in the Leguminosae but a unifying feature is the fruit which is almost always a legume, i.e. a dry several-seeded fruit derived from a superior monocarpellary ovary which is usually dehiscent (see p. 242).

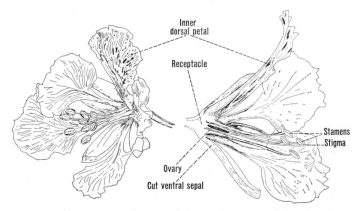

FIG. 176. *Poinciana regia*, flamboyante, showing typical features of the Caesalpiniaceae. Left, whole flower. Right, half flower, × *ca.* ⅓.

CAESALPINIACEAE

Some characters of the family are: leaves usually compound, pinnate or bipinnate; stipules present or absent; flowers usually in showy racemes and zygomorphic or less commonly almost actinomorphic (subactinomorphic); calyx of five, usually free, sepals; corolla of five or less (to 0) free petals; the upper (adaxial) petal always inside the others; stamens usually ten, often free; ovary superior and monocarpellary. *Cassia siamea* is selected for description below because it is planted throughout the tropics as a firewood tree and decorative hedge, and flowers most of the year. Other species of *Cassia* differ in the relative development of the stamens and in the asymmetry of the corolla.

Cassia siamea

Distribution and morphology

Cassia siamea (Figs. 177–179) is a native of the East Indies and Malaya but is grown as an ornamental and firewood tree throughout the tropics.

It grows to about 15 m in height and has a much branched crown. The leaves are compound and pinnate and the leaflets, of which there are four to fourteen pairs, are elliptic to elliptic oblong, or obtuse.

The flowers are slightly zygomorphic (subactinomorphic) owing to asymmetry of the calyx, the smaller size of the single dorsal petal relative to the other petals and the unequal development of the stamens. They are borne in terminal inflorescences each of which consists in a few to many corymbs arranged in a panicle. At the base of each long slender pedicel, there is a bract which is about 4 mm long. Only some of the bracts persist until the flower is open.

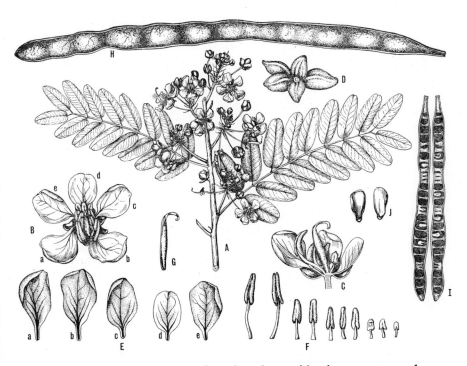

FIG. 177. *Cassia siamea.* A, flowering shoot with pinnate compound leaves and corymbs of flowers arranged in a panicle, × ¼. B, whole flower; C, half flower; D, calyx; E, petals lettered in the same order as in B; F, the ten stamens; G, the pistil; all actual size. H, pod, × ½. I, pod opened to show seeds, × ¼. J, two seeds, actual size.

Calyx

The calyx is composed of five sepals. The arrangement of these is imbricate. The ventral sepal is connate (fused) with a dorsal sepal; both form tough, inflexible shells which are wholly outside and enclose almost the whole of the flower in bud. A third petal which is partly sclerotized, and is usually fused with them, completes the envelope. The other two sepals are wholly inside and are larger. They are yellow and somewhat resemble the petals though smaller than, and lacking the claw of the latter.

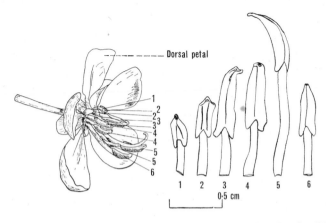

FIG. 178. *Cassia siamea*. Left, side view of flower with the six different types of stamens numbered; 1, unpaired dorsalmost antepetalous; 2, paired dorsal antesepalous; 3, paired dorsal antepetalous; 4, paired ventral antesepalous; 5, paired ventral antepetalous; 6, unpaired ventralmost antesepalous. Right, the stamens numbered in the same order, to a larger scale.

Corolla

The corolla is polypetalous. The petals are yellow and each possesses a distinct claw. They do not overlap in the open flower but their arrangement in the bud (aestivation) is imbricate with the single somewhat oblong dorsal petal wholly inside and one of the other petals (of which one is variable) wholly outside. The corolla is almost regular but the dorsal petal is somewhat smaller than the others. Zygomorphy of the corolla in other members of the family is usually greater and may be extreme, as in *Cassia spectabilis*, the flowers of which are not only irregular but are also asymmetrical.

Androecium

The stamens are free. There are ten, five opposite and five alternating with the petals, i.e. five antepetalous and five antesepalous. There is a marked disparity in their size (Fig. 178), filaments and anthers increasing in size from the dorsalmost antepetalous stamen to the ventral pair of antepetalous stamens. The single ventralmost antesepalous stamen is smaller than the latter pair, being intermediate in size between the two most dorsal pairs. The anthers are bilobed and open by apical pores.

FIG. 179. *Cassia siamea.* Floral diagram.

Gynaecium

The gynaecium is monocarpellary and superior (flower hypogynous). The pistil is about 1·5 mm long. The distal quarter, which is much thinner than the rest, comprises the style. The tip of the style curves dorsally to form a simple stigma.

The floral formula is ↑ K (3) + 2 C5 A10 G1.

Pollination

Flowers of the genus *Cassia* have a wide circle of visitors of which the most important pollinators are bees. They lack nectar and therefore butterflies and moths, with mouth parts specialized for sucking only, do not bring about pollination. Their attraction to bees and other visitors is pollen, and some of the stamens are set aside for production of pollen which is edible but apparently does not effect pollination. The two large ventral stamens seem to be the most important in supplying pollen for fertilization and are so situated that they readily touch the sides of a bee gathering pollen from the dorsal stamens. Insects are guided to the flowers by their yellow colour and sweet scent.

PAPILIONACEAE

The Mimosaceae, though an exceedingly important part of the flora of the tropics, will not be considered in this book as their flowers are not suitable for elementary studies. Some important characters of the Papilionaceae are: leaves simple or compound; flowers zygomorphic and usually hermaphrodite; sepals usually five, more or less united as a tube; petals five, imbricate, free; the upper (adaxial) petal outside the others and forming a conspicuous standard, the two lateral petals forming "wings" (alae), the lower two petals inside and united to form a "keel" (carina); stamens usually ten with nine united and one free (the diadelphous condition) or all united (the monadelphous condition); anthers usually opening lengthwise; gynaecium as Caesalpiniaceae.

Pisum sativum

Distribution and morphology

Pisum sativum, the garden pea (Figs. 180, 181), is grown throughout the world although in the tropics, it only fruits well, on fairly high ground. It is a climbing herb which attains a few feet in height. The leaves are compound and pinnate with paired leaflets (paripinnate) and have very well developed photosynthetic stipules. The large size of the stipules perhaps compensates for the transformation of terminal leaflets of the leaves into tendrils (Fig. 180A).

Calyx. The five sepals are united.

Corolla. The corolla is as described for the family.

Androecium. The androecium is diadelphous (see family).

Gynaecium. The ovary is superior and monocarpellary. The style is clothed in hairs and it and the stigma are hidden within the keel. Nectar is secreted between the tube formed by the fused filaments of nine of the stamens and the ovary.

The floral formula is ↑ K(5) C (2) + 3 A (9) + 1 G $\underline{1}$.

Pollination

The anthers dehisce before the flower opens, and pollen collects within the keel on the hairs of the style which may be termed the stylar brush. The pollen is prevented from reaching the stigma by protective bristles and the stigma is not receptive until it is damaged by an insect rubbing

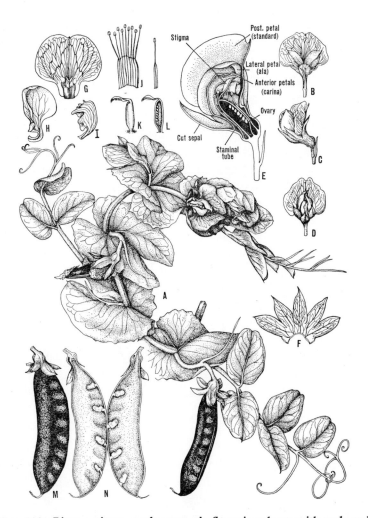

FIG. 180. *Pisum sativum*, garden pea. A, flowering shoot, with pods and bipinnate compound leaves with terminal tendrils, × ½. B, adaxial view of flower. C, lateral view of flower. D, abaxial view of flower; all × ½. E, half flower, actual size. F, calyx opened; G, standard; H, lateral petal (wing or ala); I, anterior petals (keel or carina); all × ¾. J, diadelphous stamens, actual size. K, L, pistil whole and in longitudinal section, × ¾. M, pod whole; N, pod opened to show young seeds with marginal placentation, × ½.

against it. As the nectar is at the base of a long staminal tube, only long-tongued insects can reach it and of these, only a heavy insect, usually a humble bee can open the flower. The keel of the flower is roughly horizontal and, with the wings, forms a platform on which the bee can alight. In order to reach the nectar, the wings are forced apart and the keel depressed. When the keel is depressed, the pistil remains in its normal position and therefore the style protrudes from the keel and brushes out pollen onto the body of the bee. If the bee has previously visited a pea flower, pollen will be transferred from its body to the stigma which becomes receptive shortly after rubbing. The floral organs return to their former position after being visited and further pollen is ejected on each successive visits until it is exhausted. The stigma remains receptive long after the anthers have withered so that even if pollination failed on the first visit it is likely to occur on later visits, producing a legume (pp. 242, 274).

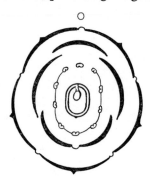

FIG. 181. Floral diagram of *Pisum sativum*.

COMPOSITAE

The Compositae comprise the largest family of angiosperms, with more than 10 per cent of known species, and are found throughout the world. Familiar examples are *Zinnia*, *Dahlia*, and *Cosmos* which are cultivated for their decorative flowers; *Helianthus annuus*, the sunflower, from the cypselas of which a useful oil is extracted; and *Lactuca scariola*, the lettuce.

What is popularly referred to as the "flower" of the Compositae is a compressed racemose inflorescence, the capitulum or head. Each head is surrounded by bracts which are usually green and perform the functions, for the whole head, which in other plants are performed by the calyx, i.e. protection of the bud and young fruit. The individual flowers are known as florets and are arranged on a common receptacle which is the expanded end of the inflorescence axis. Between the florets are small scaly bracteoles.

In most Compositae there are two types of florets: zygomorphic ray florets, on the circumference of the capitulum, which have the attractive function of petals in other families and have the corolla tube drawn out into a coloured and attractive "petal"; and disc florets, which are actinomorphic in most species, and which comprise the great majority of the florets and are inconspicuous. The disc florets are usually hermaphrodite but the ray florets are often sterile, as in the sunflower (Fig. 184), or pistilate only, as in *Zinnia*.

Helianthus annuus

Distribution and morphology

Although the sunflower, *Helianthus annuus* (Figs. 182–4), is grown in all but the colder parts of the world it is native in America. It is a very tall herb with considerable secondary thickening and has spirally arranged, serrate, ovate leaves.

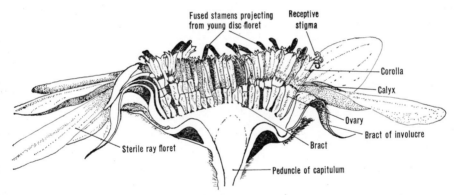

FIG. 182. Vertical section of a capitulum of *Helianthus annuus*, sunflower, × ½.

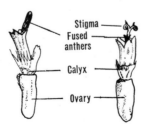

FIG. 183. Disc florets of *Helianthus annuus*. Left, a young floret; right, an older floret in which the stigma has protruded through the tube of fused anthers, × *ca*. 1½.

K

Disc florets

The disc florets of the sunflower (Fig. 183) are fairly representative of those of the Compositae. The flower is epigynous and the inferior ovary is bicarpellary and one-celled with a single erect, basal ovule. The calyx is very reduced and does not develop into the hairy pappus which is the characteristic dispersive mechanism of the fruits of Compositae. The corolla is yellow, gamopetalous and actinomorphic, with five pointed lobes. The five stamens are epipetalous on the base of the corolla tube; their filaments are separate but their anthers are united in a ring around the style (the syngenesious condition). Dehiscence of the anthers is introrse. The style is single and the stigma bilobed. The disc florets of *Zinnia* are very similar. The floral formula is ⊕ K vestigial C(5) A(5) G($\overline{2}$).

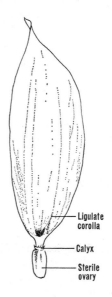

FIG. 184. Sterile ray floret of *Helianthus annuus* with strap-shaped (ligulate) corolla, × *ca.* ⅔.

Ray florets

These are sterile in this species (Fig. 184).

The fruit

The fruit is a cypsela and is discussed on p. 256.

Pollination

The disc florets are protandrous and mature centripetally, a wave of blooming progressing from the circumference to the centre. When the disc floret first opens the anthers project as a cylinder beyond the corolla. Pollen is shed into the cavity of this cylinder and is forced out of the open end by growth of the style. The two lobes of the immature stigma are close together and hairs on their outer surfaces help to brush the pollen out of the androecium. The centrewards wave of pollen shedding is followed by a wave of maturation of the stigmas; in each flower when the anthers have lost almost all of their pollen the long stigma lobes separate widely above the anthers and are susceptible to pollination. Normally cross-pollination occurs (geitonogamy) by moderately long-tongued insect such as male tabanid flies. An insect taking nectar from the base of the corolla receives pollen on the head and thorax and if it moves outward to probe a floret with a receptive, open stigma, brings about cross-pollination. If a floret does not receive pollen from another, its stigma lobes curl and receive pollen from its own anthers; self-pollination is thus assured if cross-pollination from the same or another capitulum fails. The pistilate ray florets of *Zinnia*, can, of course, only be cross-pollinated.

The effectiveness of this mechanism of pollination in florets massed in a capitulum is obvious if an old sunflower head is examined: it will be seen that almost all the florets have set seed.

The fruit

The fruit of all Compositae is a cypsela, that is, an achene (one-seeded dry indehiscent fruit) developed from an inferior ovary. In many Compositae the calyx serves for dispersal, being a hairy parachute or pappus in most, e.g. *Taraxacum*, the dandelion, or hooked as in *Bidens*. In sunflower and *Zinnia* it remains undeveloped and the fruits are merely shaken off the capitulum.

Reasons for the Success of the Compositae

The great success of the Compositae has been related to:

1. The massing of flowers in heads surrounded by an involucre of bracts which results in:

(a) Greater conspicuousness, particularly when ray florets are developed.
(b) A saving of materials because the corollas of the disc florets are small.

(c) The likelihood that many florets will be pollinated by a single insect visitor.

2. The very simple and effective floral mechanism which:

(a) Ensures self-pollination if cross-pollination fails.
(b) Because the corolla tube is not so long and slender as to permit only very long-tongued insects to get nectar, ensures that there will be a wide circle of visitors.

3. The use of the calyx for dispersal of the fruits in most members.

BIGNONIACEAE

The Bignoniaceae occur throughout the tropics and subtropics and are most abundant in tropical America. Well known genera are *Bignonia* (Figs. 121, 185), *Catalpa*, *Tecoma*, *Jacaranda* and *Spathodea* (the latter is the Uganda flame tree). Of these *Tecoma* has been selected for description below because it is commonly grown for its yellow flowers, and as a hedge, in most tropical countries and has a longer flowering season than the others.

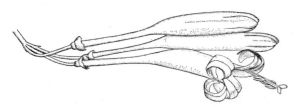

FIG. 185. *Pyrostegia* (= *Bignonia*) *venusta*, golden shower. Flowers actual size.

The flowers of all these genera are fairly, or very, similar. The most common differences being in colour, length of the corolla, and relative sizes of stamens. The flowers of *Jacaranda* and of *Bignonia unguis-cati* (also called *B. tweediana*) (Fig. 121) especially, fit the description of *Tecoma stans* very closely. All the genera mentioned have winged seeds and bilocular capsules as fruits. Some other genera of the family bear berries or dry indehiscent fruits.

Tecoma stans

Distribution and morphology

Tecoma stans (Figs. 186, 187) is popularly known as trumpet flower or yellow elder. It is a native of tropical America and the West Indies but is cultivated as an ornamental plant throughout the tropics. It is a much branched shrub or small tree with a height of about 3–25 ft. The leaves are compound, pinnate, opposite and decussate and lack stipules. The leaflets are usually serrate.

The flowers are zygomorphic owing to slight irregularity of the corolla and modification of the androecium. They are borne either in simple racemes or in panicles. At the base of each pedicel there are three sharply pointed bracts. One of these is small and ventral and overlaps the bases of the other two, which are larger and more lateral.

Calyx

The calyx is gamosepalous and campanulate (bell-shaped) and encloses only the very young flowers. It has five pointed lobes, one of which is dorsal, which represent the fused sepals. It is pale green and glabrous (smooth and lacking hairs) and persists until it ruptures and withers on the fruit.

Corolla

The corolla is gamopetalous. The petals are free only for one-third of their lengths where they form five lobes which overlap in a characteristic manner, one (variable in position) being wholly outside and another, the ventral, being wholly inside. This arrangement is said to be imbricate. The lobes form two lips: an upper of two and a lower of three lobes. The corolla is bright yellow with red honey guides in the mouth. It is shed before the fruit appreciably develops.

Androecium

The stamens are epipetalous and alternate with the corolla lobes. There are five but the dorsal one is greatly reduced and is represented only by a staminode and is occasionally absent. The filaments of the ventral pair are longer than those of the dorsal pair. Those of each pair bend upwards and inwards so that the anthers of each pair are connivent, that is, lie together. Each anther consists of two elongated cells at right-angles to the filament with their long axes parallel to the long axis of the corolla. These cells dehisce lengthwise to shed their pollen.

FIG. 186. *Tecoma stans* (*Stenolobium stans*). A, habit of flowering branch showing simple racemose inflorescence and pinnate compound leaves, × ½. B, whole flower; C, half flower, × ½. D, campanulate calyx viewed ventrally, × 2. E, corolla opened dorsally to expose four epipetalous stamens and (left) a minute staminode, × ½. F, a single stamen, × 2. G, calyx cut open, and corolla removed, to show pistil, × 2. H, two fruits dehisced and revealing the septum which bears winged seeds, × ½. I, a winged seed, actual size.

Gynaecium

The gynaecium is syncarpous, consisting of two fused carpels, and is superior (flower hypogynous). In cross-section it is seen to be two-celled (bilocular) but there are two placentas in each cell, each placenta being situated on the septum where it meets the ovary wall. Ovules are numerous, in a single row, on each placenta. It seems probable to the writer that the ovary is not truly bilocular and that the septum is a "false septum" developed from parietal placentas which have intruded into the single cavity of a bicarpellary ovary. The stigma has two leaf-like lobes, one dorsal, the other ventral. It lies on a level with and often touches the anthers of the longer stamens. Nectaries are situated around the base of the ovary.

The floral formula is ↑ K(5) $\widehat{C(5)}$ A5 G(2).

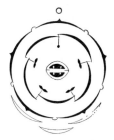

FIG. 187. Floral diagram of *Tecoma stans*.

The fruit

The fruit is a dehiscent capsule which resembles a siliqua in that it consists in a pod divided into two cells by a septum which bears the seeds when the walls or valves have opened. The valves remain attached to the receptacle, however, and not, as in the siliqua of the Cruciferae, to the apex of the septum. The seeds are winged. They lack endosperm and have a straight embryo.

Pollination

Ants seen visiting *Tecoma* flowers are probably stealing nectar without bringing about pollination. Humble bees frequently visit the flowers but after their visits the flowers are usually found to have been bitten through at the base of the corolla, the nectar having been removed from the outside without any pollen being brought to the stigma. The fact that the stamens shed pollen before the two stigma lobes separate suggests that a flower exposed to the visits of the appropriate insects would be cross-pollinated before self-pollination became possible. That self-pollination ever occurs is doubtful as flowers enclosed in muslin bags while in bud have not so far been found to set seed and normally very little or no pollen remains on the anthers to be transferred by insects to the stigma by the time the stigma lobes open. The actual pollinators are probably long-tongued butterflies and moths, and small bees which are able to push their bodies in between corolla and stigma.

APOCYNACEAE

This is a mainly tropical and subtropical family with representatives native to the Old and New Worlds. Perhaps the lovely frangipani, *Plumeria acutifolia*, and the oleander, *Nerium oleander*, are the best known. *Allamanda* and *Thevetia* are also grown throughout the tropics as ornamental plants. *Carissa carandas*, of India, bears edible berries, known as karanda; *Acokanthera schimperi*, of East Africa, yields an arrow poison; the root of *Strophanthus eminii* of the same region is used as a cure for snake bite and its relative *Strophanthus kombe* bears kombe seeds; and various species of *Landolphia* are used throughout tropical Africa as sources of rubber.

Usually the flowers of the Apocynaceae have five united imbricate sepals, and petals; five epipetalous stamens with sagittate (arrow-shaped) anthers grouped together round the stigma, and a one- or two-celled superior ovary with two carpels.

In frangipani (Fig. 161), oleander (Fig. 141), *Allamanda* and *Strophanthus* the fruit is a double follicle with winged or plumed seeds, those of *Strophanthus eminii* being probably the finest example in the flowering plants of plumed seeds (Fig. 163). *Thevetia* has a one- or two-celled drupe. A description of *Thevetia peruviana* follows.

Thevetia peruviana

Distribution and morphology

Thevetia peruviana, yellow oleander (Fig. 188), is a tree or shrub up to 10 m high, native to tropical America but cultivated throughout the tropics. The glossy, smooth leaves are linear (strap-shaped) and are borne densely on the branches. The lateral veins are not apparent. The bark is grey and smooth. All parts of the plant exude a white latex if cut.

The flowers are actinomorphic and are borne in few-flowered terminal racemes. The pedicels are about 3 cm long; the flowers about twice this. Each flower is borne in the axil of a conspicuous lanceolate bract. The internodes between successive bracts are very short.

Calyx

The calyx is composed of five lanceolate sepals which are united basally. It is small and protects only the youngest flowers when its aestivation is imbricate (p. 276). One sepal is posterior (dorsal).

Corolla

The corolla is gamopetalous but each petal is free for half its length. It is yellow with the exception of the corolla tube and the section of each lobe which is exposed in bud which are green. The aestivation of the corolla lobes is contorted, i.e. each lobe overlaps the adjacent lobe. They alternate with the sepals.

Androecium

The androecium consists in five epipetalous stamens which alternate with the corolla lobes. The arrow-shaped (sagittate) anthers are sessile in the mouth of the corolla tube. Above each anther is a shelf-like out-growth of the corolla about the size of the anther. Collectively these outgrowths may be considered to constitute a corona (Fig. 188). Each is fringed with a thick pad of hairs. The effect of the corona is to restrict the opening of the corolla tube to five radial hair-lined slits, convergent to a central pore, each opposite a petal lobe. The tips of the anthers face inwards so that the anthers form a cone lying over, and in close contact with, the stigma. The stigma is supported below by five hard outgrowths of the corolla tube each of which lies vertically below an anther. Each of the lower outgrowths bears below a tuft of long white hairs. The inside of the corolla tube is also lined by more delicate hairs.

Gynaecium

The ovary is superior and is composed of two carpels. It is divided into four cells by two septa mutually at right-angles, one of which does not actually connect with the walls of the ovary. The ovules, of which there is one to a cell, are borne on axile placentas. Normally only two persist after fertilization. Occasionally only one persists. In the fruit one

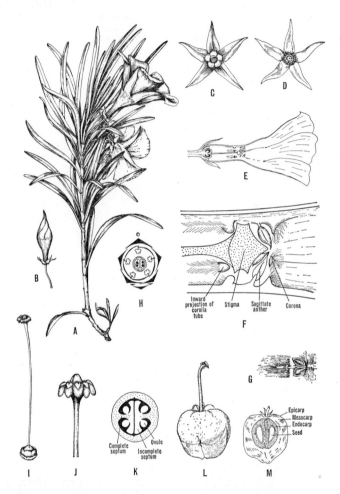

FIG. 188. *Thevetia peruviana*, yellow oleander. A, flowering shoot, × ⅛.
B, bud showing contorted corolla, × ⅓. C, calyx from below. D, calyx
from above. E, half flower. F, details of internal structure of flower.
G, a single sagittate stamen, *in situ*. H, floral diagram. I, pistil. J,
stigma and part of style. K, cross-section of ovary. L, fruit. M, longitudinal section of fruit.

septum becomes papery, though still thick. The other septum forms a thick rigid, though often distorted, partition of the hardened endocarp.

The stigma is borne on a long slender style which is divided almost into two by longitudinal furrows near the ovary. The summit of the stigma is conical and is deeply cleft. Its base is divided into almost horizontal lobes which roof over corresponding vertical lobes of its lower border. It lies in the space between the anthers and the lower series of outgrowths of the corolla. The floral formula is $\oplus$ K(5) $\widehat{C(5)}$ A5 G(2).

Pollination

Pollination is probably by long-tongued insects, e.g. moths, in which the tongue is sufficiently strong to be pushed between the corona-lobes and is long enough to reach the nectaries at the base of the corolla tube.

Fruit

The fruit is a drupe. The epicarp forms a glossy green skin, the mesocarp constitutes a white fleshy covering of the stony endocarp and is rich in latex which exudes as a white viscous liquid if the fruit is cut. The endocarp is very hard and thick but is almost perforated near the placentas at each end. A fission line joins these two weak points and extends less conspicuously to the apex of the stone.

The fruit falls with the persistent calyx and in moist conditions, after the epicarp and mesocarp have withered and turned black, the endocarp opens along the fission line. Each seed is enveloped in a papery testa which bears a small pointed outgrowth which represents the funicle (stalk) of the ovule and the position of the radicle of the embryo. The tegmen is a tough white membrane. No micropyle is visible. The embryo is straight. Its cotyledons are large and the endosperm is represented only by a small gelatinous sticky mass between them. Germination is epigeal.

CARICACEAE

This family has only two genera and a single well known species, *Carica papaya*, the papaya or pawpaw. This is the only flowering plant which we will study in which the male (staminate) and female (pistillate) flowers are on separate plants.

FIG. 189. *Carica papaya*, pawpaw. A, habit of tree. B, a deeply lobed (palmatifid) leaf, × ¼. C, a male inflorescence, × ½. D–I, a male flower: D, half flower showing rudimentary ovary, actual size; E and F, calyx, × 2; G, corolla cut open showing long and short epipetalous stamens, actual size; H, rudimentary ovary, × 2; I, stamens, × 2. J, female flower, × ½. K, vertical section of ovary, actual size.

Carica papaya

Distribution and morphology

The pawpaw (Figs. 189, 190) is native to tropical America but is cultivated for its edible fruits throughout the warmer parts of the world. It is a small tree with few or no branches and an apical crown of very large alternate leaves with palmate venation, which are usually so deeply lobed (palmatifid) that they give the false impression of being compound palmate (Fig. 189B). The grey trunk bears a spiral pattern of old leaf scars.

The plant is either male or female, i.e. dioecious. The male flowers (Fig. 189C–I) are small and numerous on racemose inflorescences in the axils of the leaves; the female inflorescences (Fig. 189J) are also axillary to the foliage leaves but bear few, large flowers and only one of these is in bloom at a time. The flowers are white and, as is often true of white flowers, are very sweetly and powerfully scented.

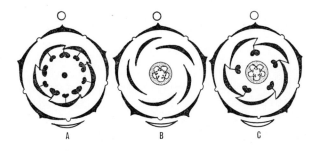

Fig. 190. *Carica papaya*, pawpaw. Floral diagram of A, male; B, female; and C, bisexual flowers.

Male flower

Calyx. The calyx is small, green and gamosepalous with five pointed lobes.

Corolla. The five petals are united for about two-thirds of their length as a slender tube.

Androecium. The androecium (Fig. 189H, I) consists of ten stamens which are united at the base and are borne on the corolla near its mouth. Five of the anthers are almost sessile and the alternate five protrude beyond them, having longer, but still small filaments. Dehiscence of the anthers is lengthwise and introrse.

Gynaecium. The gynaecium is present in the male flower though rudimentary. If the plant is damaged or the roots disturbed the plant may change its sex owing to the development of the rudimentary ovaries. Male trees are sometimes found to bear small fruits. Hermaphrodite flowers are not uncommon.

Female flower

The calyx resembles that of the male flower but the sepals are larger. The petals are very much larger than those of the male flower and are united only at their bases or may be free. The corolla is cup-shaped rather than tubular (Fig. 189J). Reduced stamens (staminodes) are rarely present. The ovary is superior and is large and ovoid, and bears three to five lobed stigmas, corresponding with an equal number of carpels. It is one-celled, with parietal placentas which bear many ovules (Fig. 189K).

The floral formulae are:

Male flower: ⊕ K(5) C͡(5) A(5 + 5) G (vestigial)

Female flower: ⊕ K(5) C(5) A(0 or vestigial) G (3̲–5̲)

Fruit

The ovary after fertilization rapidly develops to a very large, smooth, hollow berry with a fleshy orange mesocarp and endocarp which are edible, and numerous black seeds, each about the size of a small pea, arranged along the three or five parietal placentas. The stigmas fall early. When the fruit is ripe its green colour usually changes to yellow and it falls from the tree. The seeds are chiefly dispersed by man and other animals, which transport the fruit and, while eating it, reject the seeds.

The immature fruit exudes a milky juice, as does the tree if wounded. This juice contains a protease which is termed papain and is extracted for medicinal and other uses. Its addition to beer prevents cloudiness when chilled. The wrapping of meat in pawpaw leaves to make it tender relies on exudation of papain. The juice is also used as a base for chewing gum.

Pollination

The dioecious condition ensures cross-pollination (xenogamy). The slender, long tubes of the male flowers are adapted to long-tongued insects which, while obtaining nectar from the nectaries at the base of the corolla, receive pollen on the head and body from the anthers near the mouth of

the tube. The very strong, sweet scent of the flowers is especially noticeable at dusk when many moths are active. The female flowers attract
nectar-seeking insects by a similar scent and, if the insect has received
pollen from a male flower, the pollen is brushed off on the stigma lobes
as the insect seeks nectar at the base of the ovary. In pawpaw plantations
it is usually found that one male tree suffices to pollinate ten female trees
in its vicinity.

GRAMINAEAE

The Graminaeae (grasses) comprise the largest family of the monocotyledons and are probably the most important group of plants economically. There are about 4500 species, in all parts of the world. Most are
herbs with fibrous roots but some bamboos are tree-like, attaining a height
of 100 ft. Grasses may be annual or perennial and many propagate vegetatively by runners or by rhizomes. The stem has well marked nodes
above each of which is a soft intercalary growth zone. A leaf with a
sheathing base arises at each node and a ligule is usually present internally
at the junction of leaf blade and base. If the shoot is laid horizontally, a
basal node grows more rapidly below than above, with the result that the
stem above the node returns to the vertical position. Upright rooted branches known as "tillers" are produced at prostrate nodes in some species.
Wheat and some other cereal grasses are deliberately flattened or "laid" to
encourage such vegetative propagation. Examples of grasses are rice,
Oryza; maize, *Zea*; millet, *Sorghum*; and pasture grasses and bamboos.

The inflorescence is exceedingly complex, its units being not flowers
but "spikelets", each of which is a small spike of flowers. The spikelet of
maize is described below and no account of grass spikelets in general is
necessary here. It must, however, be pointed out that maize is somewhat
unusual in having separate male and female inflorescences whereas most
grasses have hermaphrodite flowers. A floral diagram of a generalized
grass flower is given for comparison in Fig. 192.

The fruit of grasses is a caryopsis or grain. That of *Zea* is characteristic
of the family and has already been discussed (pp. 241, 266).

Zea mays

Distribution and morphology

Zea mays, maize (Figs., 191, 192), is cultivated throughout the world
where the mean temperature and rainfall are sufficiently high. It is believed

to have originated in Central America as a hybrid between the grass *Euchlaena* or *Tripsacum* and an unknown species.

Maize is a monoecious annual monocotyledon with unisexual flowers. It may reach a height of 15 ft. There is usually a single shoot and tillers are only rarely produced. As is typical of grasses, the radicle of the young plant is soon replaced by large adventitious seminal roots (seed roots) and in addition a fibrous adventitious root system develops from the lower, subterranean, nodes of the stem. Prop roots which are partly photosynthetic grow out from the nodes nearest the ground and help to support the shoot (Fig. 84). The leaves, which are very long and strap-like, are borne alternately. Each has a conspicuous midrib, is hairy above, and has a sheathing base which surrounds the stem completely at the node where it arises but splits further up. At the junction of blade and

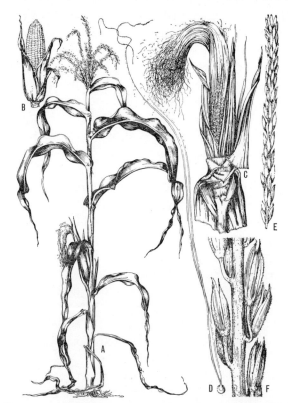

FIG. 191. *Zea mays*, maize. A, plant, × $\frac{1}{10}$. B, cob. C, female inflorescence shortly after fertilization, × $\frac{1}{4}$. D, pistil of a female flower, × $\frac{1}{2}$. E, male inflorescence, × $\frac{1}{2}$.

sheathing base there is a broad ligule. The internal anatomy of the stem and root is discussed on p. 175.

Male inflorescence (*Fig.* 191)

The male flowers are borne in pairs, each pair within two tough purplish scales called glumes. The two glumes and the two flowers they contain constitute a spikelet. The spikelets are borne on a many-branched panicle which terminates the shoot and is elevated above the leaves. Each raceme of the panicle bears two alternate rows of tiny branches and each of these

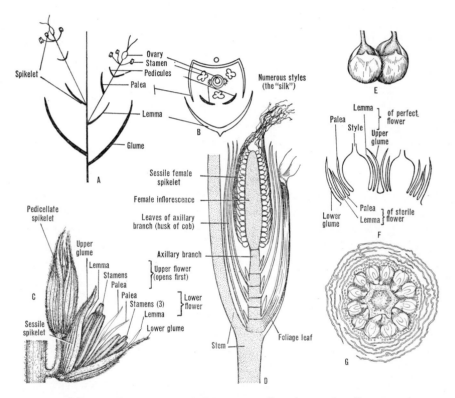

FIG. 192. A, diagram of an inflorescence of an hermaphrodite grass to show the structure of two spikelets. B, floral diagram of hermaphrodite grass flower. C–G, *Zea mays*, maize. C, pedicellate and sessile spikelets, enlarged. D, diagram of a longitudinal section through the female inflorescence. E, two ovaries. F, diagram of a pair of female spikelets, each spikelet containing one sterile and one fertile flower. G, diagrammatic cross-section of female inflorescence (newly fertilized), showing pairs of spikelets.

bears two spikelets, one sessile at its base and the other terminal. Each spikelet is itself an inflorescence bearing two flowers. The two glumes may be regarded as sterile bracts at its base which enclose the rest of the inflorescence to form the spikelet. Above the glumes on the axis, though in close proximity to them because the internodes are much reduced, are two transparent scales, the lemmas, or fertile glumes, in the axil of each of which arises the pedicel of a male flower. On the pedicel but close to the lemma owing to shortening of the internodes arises a similar scale, the palea, which is morphologically a bracteole; finally, each pedicel bears two four-sided blunt fleshy lodicules which perhaps represent the perianth, and above these, three pendulous anthers. The filaments are long and exceedingly slender and the anthers of a mature flower hang below the glumes and are easily shaken by a slight breeze; they are pendulous and not versatile as is sometimes stated. Both flowers in a spikelet do not mature simultaneously and the anthers of the upper flower may have shed all their pollen before the stamens of the lower flower emerge. The pairs of spikelets on the terminal axis of the panicle are approximately opposite and decussate, being borne in four rows.

Female inflorescence

The female inflorescence or cob is borne low down on the same plant. It terminates a short axillary branch and is completely enclosed by sheathing leaf bases which arise close together on the same axis and form a husk. These leaf bases bear no laminae. The axis of the inflorescence is greatly thickened and bears many rows of paired sessile spikelets on its circumference. There are two flowers in each spikelet: the lower flower is reduced to a lemma and palea and is therefore non-functional, while the upper is functional and consists of a lemma and palea surrounding a rounded ovary from the walls of which arises a very long hairy style which is bifid at its tip and which projects from the tip of the husk with the other styles as the "silks". There are no lodicules. The function of lodicules is to cause the flowers of Graminaeae to open by separating the palea and lemma, a function which is no longer necessary in the flowers of maize with their long, exposed styles. The two glumes of each spikelet are reduced to small membranous scales which do not enclose the flowers, their protective function having been taken over by the husk. The ovary is superior and contains a single, erect, anatropous ovule. It is usually considered to be monocarpellary but there is some evidence that it is tricarpellary and that the style is a prolongation of two of the carpels.

The fruit

The fruit or grain is a caryopsis (Fig. 172), that is to say, an achene (see p. 241) in which the pericarp has fused with the testa. The seed has copious endosperm and a straight embryo; its structure is discussed on p. 266. The grains are very tightly packed on the axis of the infructescence.

Pollination

There are two waves of liberation of pollen from the male inflorescence because of the different times of maturation of the two flowers of each spikelet. These waves of anthesis spread down the inflorescence as the spikelets ripen from above downwards. Pollen shedding may thus be spread over as many as 14 days. The silks of the female inflorescence are receptive throughout their lengths from the time that they emerge at the apex of the husk. The low position of the female inflorescence and the apical position of the male inflorescence on the plant are well suited to pollination by gravity or wind. Self-pollination is common in *Zea* although cross-pollination occurs readily. After fertilization the styles wither and the grains develop and swell out the husk.

CHAPTER 15

Organs of Perennation

A PERENNIAL is a flowering plant which lives for more than 2 years. This plant may consist of a single individual or of a number of individuals produced from a single plant by vegetative means. However many individuals there are, all are ultimately derived from a single seed. The products of this seed may persist for many years and some plants which propagate mainly if not solely by vegetative means (e.g. banana) may be the products of seeds produced hundreds of years ago.

In ephemeral and annual plants sexual reproduction marks the end of the life of the individual after a few weeks or months. In the biennial, reproduction in the second year by seed production shortly precedes death. In perennial plants, however, the accomplishment of sexual reproduction only rarely is related to decline of the plant and death. The century plant, *Agave americana* (Fig. 193), (Agavaceae) is commonly cited as an example of a perennial which flowers once and then dies. The plant takes many years to reach maturity when the immense inflorescence is produced at the apex of the single stem. Death of the stem and of its large, sword-shaped, leaves follows rapidly. However, the organism as a whole does not normally cease to exist as a result of flowering as suckers and bulbils are usually produced by the plant. These grow into new plants and thus perennate the plant beyond the first phase of flowering.

Death in perennials appears normally to be the result of senility (ageing) or of inability, which usually increases with age, to resist unfavourable conditions of the environment. This inability may be in itself an expression of senility but it is often due to increasing invasion by micro-organisms from the environment. Often the activity of disease organisms results in the premature death of healthy plants.

Trees and shrubs which survive from year to year are termed woody perennials. In these the aerial parts of the plant do not usually die back with the seasonal onset of unfavourable conditions, for instance, the coming of winter or of a marked dry season. Their woody nature is the result of intermittent or continuous secondary thickening from year to year according as the region has a seasonal climate, or a relatively unvarying climate as in equatorial rain forest, respectively.

Stem Tubers

Stem tubers are portions of stems, above or below ground, which are swollen by stored food. Stem tubers differ from rhizomes in that, whereas in a rhizome each new season's growth is an extension of the old rhizome by means of an axillary bud (sympodial growth) or a terminal bud (monopodial growth), development of a new tuber does not proceed directly

FIG. 193. Century plant, *Agave sisalana*, much reduced. A bulbil is shown, on a larger scale, on the right.

from a tuber of the previous season but from a shoot developed at the expense of the old tuber. The latter has usually disappeared before the new tuber begins to develop.

Stem tubers usually form in the axil of a scale leaf or basal foliage leaf of the plant and therefore the mode of branching of the plant through successive seasons is fundamentally similar to that of a rhizome with the difference, noted above, that there is no direct continuity of tubers of successive seasons. The tubers of some plants are perennial, however, e.g. that of the elephant's foot, *Testudinaria elephantipes* (Dioscoreaceae), which grows in South Africa. Its tuber is a very large, gnarled, cork-covered swelling of the first internode and from it arise the annual climbing stems. Stem tubers developed by thickening of the main axis of the plant, as in *Testudinaria*, form a distinct category from those developed from axillary buds. They are seen also in the yams, *Dioscorea sinuata* and *D. batatas*, being derived in the former from internodes above the cotyledon and in the latter from the hypocotyl. Aerial tubers developed as round swellings of the nodes occur in *Ceropegia woodii* (Asclepiadaceae); they do not detach but develop adventitious roots which anchor the climbing stems.

Gradations exist between stem tubers and rhizomes and caution is required in using the following criteria which are commonly held to distinguish stem tubers from rhizomes: they do not form part of the main stem (obviously non-axillary tubers of the sort seen in *Testudinaria* do), they do not show continuous growth and shrink when they give rise to aerial shoots (not so in *Testudinaria*), they consist only in localized swellings (generally true) and they lack adventitious roots (not true of the tuber of Jerusalem artichoke, *Helianthus tuberosus*).

Typical stem tubers are to be seen in the Chinese or lesser yam, *Dioscorea esculenta*, and other yams; the Chinese artichoke, *Stachys tubifera;* the frafra potato, *Coleus rotundifolius*, and the Irish potato, *Solanum tuberosum* (Fig. 194), in all of which the tubers are subterranean and are cultivated by man for food.

The tuber of the Irish potato conforms well to the criteria of stem tubers given above. Each tuber develops as an oval underground swelling of a branch which has arisen as a bud in the axil of a basal foliage leaf or of an

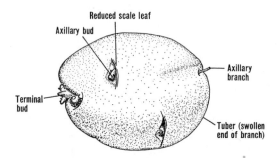

Fig. 194. Stem tuber of potato, *Solanum tuberosum*.

underground scale leaf. Sometimes the tubers are formed well above ground as swellings of axillary buds. The young tuber bears small spirally arranged scale leaves in the axils of which are buds. Each axillary bud and the associated scale or scales constitutes an "eye" of the potato. One end of the tuber bears the scar of the branch which gave rise to it while the other end bears a large terminal bud. This bud and the others give rise to aerial shoots or "haulms" under favourable conditions.

Root Tubers

Root tubers are roots which have become greatly swollen owing to the development of thick food-storing tissues. They develop from tap roots in the biennial "root crop" plants such as carrot and turnip (p. 155) or from adventitious roots as in *Dahlia* (Fig. 195), the sweet potato, *Ipomoea batatas* (Fig. 204), jalap, *Ipomoea purga*, cassava, *Manihot utilissima* (Fig. 196) and many orchids. It is in some ways preferable to restrict the term root tuber to those developed from adventitious roots and to refer to the type seen in carrot, etc., as fleshy or swollen taps.

Root tubers cannot usually be used by themselves to propagate the plant; a portion of the stem must be attached. In the case of sweet potato and cassava, stem cuttings are commonly used for propagation.

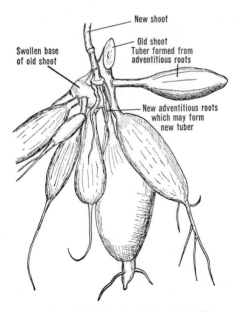

FIG. 195. Root tubers of *Dahlia*.

Corms

Corms are stem bases swollen by storage of food materials. The internodes are compressed and the nodes are distinguishable only by the presence of thin scale leaves, which if removed leave encircling lines around the corm. The absence of stored food from these leaves distinguishes corms from bulbs. Corms frequently have the form of spheres flattened dorsoventrally; adventitious roots are borne ventrally. Axillary buds are

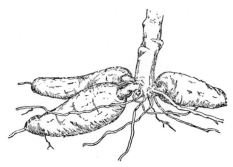

FIG. 196. Root tubers of cassava, *Manihot utilissima*. From Irvine.

borne in the axils of some of the scale leaves. These may be basal, as in the autumn crocus, *Colchicum autumnale*, or apical, as in *Crocus* and *Gladiolus* spp. (Fig. 197), and each is capable of giving rise to a flowering shoot at the base of which a new corm will develop after flowering. Thus the corm multiplies by sympodial branching. In *Tritonia* (Iridaceae), of which many species are found in South and tropical Africa and are widely cultivated (often under the name of *Montbretia*), the axillary buds produce rhizomes which give rise to aerial shoots which in turn form corms at their bases.

There is no sharp distinction between corms, stem tubers and rhizomes. Thus the "corms" of certain Araceae, e.g. the cocoyam, *Colocasia antiquorum* (also known as eddo, dasheen and taro) (Fig. 198) are often referred to as rhizomes because the growths of previous years persist longer than is typical of corms and the perennial storage organs of *Testudinaria elephantipes* and *Cyclamen* spp. may be referred to as stem tubers, corms or even root stocks.

The corms of *Crocus*, *Colchicum* and *Gladiolus* (monocotyledons) and of certain Ranunculaceae represent a single season's growth, however, remnants of the growth of previous seasons being insignificant, and they form a category easily distinguished from other types of storage organs.

The corm of *Gladiolus* (Fig. 197), a tropical genus, resembles that of *Crocus* and is equally useful for study. Gladioli are cultivated throughout the temperate and tropical regions and some species grow wild on high ground in the tropics. The corm consists of a cushion-like subterranean stem the greater part of which is composed of cortical tissue which surrounds a distinct central stele. Basally it bears adventitious roots and a vestige of the previous season's corm. Apically there is an axillary bud

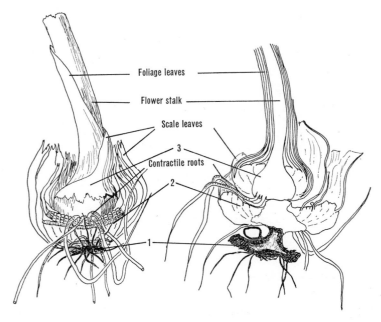

Fig. 197. Corm of *Gladiolus*. Left, whole; right, in vertical section. Corm 2, from the previous year, has produced foliage leaves and an inflorescence (now withered). Food materials from the foliage leaves are giving rise to a new corm (3) which will produce leaves and inflorescences in the following year. The withered remains of the corm (1) which produced the previous year's inflorescence are also present.

composed of leaves ensheathing a rudimentary inflorescence. Other, similar, axillary buds are often present. Near the apical bud is the shrivelled remains of the previous season's aerial shoot, the subterranean base of which, by swelling, formed the present corm.

On return of favourable conditions the apical bud develops into an aerial shoot terminated by an inflorescence. Other axillary buds develop in a similar way. During this growth the corm becomes depleted in food reserves and begins to shrink. The shrinkage is hastened by the development of a new corm at the base of the aerial shoot. The foliage leaves continue to function for some time after flowering and food assimilated in them is transferred to the new corm. Adventitious roots grow out from the base of the new corm where it is demarcated from the vestige of the old corm. Some of these roots are contractile and gradually pull the corm into the space left by depletion of the old corm.

Fig. 198. Corm of *Colocasia.*

Rhizomes and Root Stocks

Rhizomes are stems which grow, usually horizontally, beneath the surface of the soil. Like stem tubers, they are distinguished from roots by the presence of scale leaves in the axils of which axillary buds may occur, by the absence of a root cap and by the internal structure. All gradations exist between rhizomes and stem tubers so that the two are not really distinct. However, a true rhizome differs from a stem tuber in being generally of fairly uniform thickness throughout its length and in usually bearing adventitious roots, which are often absent from stem tubers, at the nodes. A further difference is that rhizomes form the main shoot of the plant and exhibit continuous growth whereas stem tubers are usually lateral branches, formed by the main shoot which is aerial, and last only for one season, shrinking with the growth of new aerial shoots which in turn give rise to new tubers.

Rhizomes function as food storage organs and for rapid propagation and spreading of the plant, but one function is usually of greater importance than the other. Thus in elephant grass, *Pennisetum benthami*, and other creeping grasses the rhizomes are long and wiry and, although serving for food storage, serve primarily to spread the plant rapidly and far whereas those of ginger, *Zingiber officinale* (Zingiberaceae), arrowroot, *Maranta arundinacea* (Marantaceae), canna lily, *Canna indica* (Fig. 199) (Cannaceae), some arum lilies (Araceae), some irises (Iridaceae) and Solomon's seal (Liliaceae) are fleshy and serve mainly for food storage although effective in spreading the plant.

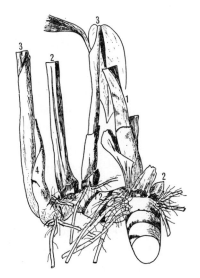

FIG. 199. Rhizome of *Canna indica*, canna lily. The branches are numbered in order of development.

Some plants have erect rhizomes which are known as root stocks. These are seen in certain *Dioscorea* species, a genus which includes the yams, and in rhubarb, *Rheum* (Polygonaceae) and some primulas (Primulaceae).

In most rhizomes the aerial leaves and the flowers develop from a terminal bud. The growing axis is thus terminated and further growth of the rhizome takes place by extension underground of a bud or buds in the axils of leaves which may be scale leaves or foliage leaves at the base of the aerial shoot. Growth of the rhizome is thus continued by a side branch formed from an axillary bud and is therefore sympodial, branching being cymose. The bud is protected from damage when it finally grows up through the soil by preserving either a pointed form protected by hard scale leaves or the form of a crook which unfolds only when it reaches the light.

The rhizomes of some plants, e.g. *Oxalis*, are racemose and exhibit monopodial growth. In these growth of the rhizome is not terminated by an aerial shoot as the latter arises directly from an axillary bud and the terminal bud continues horizontal growth.

The form of a sympodial rhizome is well shown by the canna lily, *Canna indica* (Fig. 199). The older part of the rhizome is from half to an inch or more thick. It is whitish in colour and bears periodically a small number of brown or pinkish scale leaves, the bases of which form a complete ring round the rhizome. Each ring of scale leaves marks a node and the short distance between two successive rings an internode. The tip of the rhizome turns up as an aerial shoot with sheathing foliage leaves and a central inflorescence axis. Arising from the axil of a scale leaf just behind the aerial shoot is a bud, the tip of which forms a long whitish point. This tip is protected by young, hard, tightly packed scale leaves. Frequently further buds arise from the axils of basal scale leaves of this bud or of the main rhizome. They give rise to branches of the rhizome and serve to multiply the plant. All the buds are pointed in form, this form enabling the bud to push through the soil without injury.

In the younger parts of the rhizome adventitious roots grow out from the nodes and penetrate the bases of the scale leaves. They are more numerous and thicker at the base of the aerial shoot than elsewhere. The tips of these adventitious roots are frequently conspicuously swollen, forming root tubers. The food materials stored in the latter serve with those in the older parts of the rhizome to nourish the axillary buds before they become aerial. When an aerial shoot dies down it leaves a scar behind the growing tip.

Bulbs

Bulbs are subterranean upright shoots which differ from corms in that the stem is reduced and stored food is situated in the bulb scales. The bulb scales may be the swollen bases of foliage leaves as in *Narcissus* (Fig. 200) (*Amaryllidaceae*) or swollen underground scale leaves as in *Tulipa* (Liliaceae), or may be of both types as in the onion, *Allium* (Fig. 201) (Amaryllidaceae). The outer bulb scales are usually papery and are sometimes highly coloured. The bulbs of the above species are said to be tunicate because the outermost bulb scales completely enclose and obscure the inner. Some bulbs are said to be scaley bulbs, however, e.g. those of *Lilium*. In these the bulb scales are less closely packed and only the base of each is covered by the adjacent more peripheral scale so that the bulb is composed of overlapping scales. The bulb of *Oxalis* (Fig. 202) is intermediate between tunicate and scaley bulbs.

Growth of bulbs may be sympodial as in *Tulipa* and *Allium*, or monopodial as in *Narcissus* and *Hippeastrum*, an amaryllid lily commonly cultivated in tropical countries. In sympodial growth the flowering axis

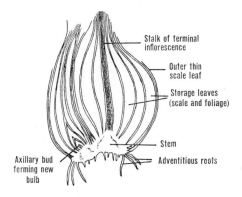

FIG. 200. Vertical section of a bulb of the daffodil, *Narcissus*. The inflorescence is axillary and the bulb continues growth from year to year. Daughter bulbs are also formed from axillary buds and serve for multiplication.

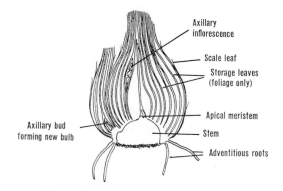

FIG. 201. Vertical section of a bulb of the onion, *Allium*. The inflorescence is terminal and prevents further growth of the bulb which is replaced by one or more axillary buds.

terminates growth and the next season's bulb, which encloses a rudimentary flowering shoot, develops as an axillary bud. In monopodial growth the new bulb develops from the stem tip of the old bulb and flowering stems are always produced from buds axillary to the bulb scales so that flowering does not terminate growth of the main axis. In some species, e.g. *Narcissus*, such bulbs represent more than one season's growth. Both monopodial and sympodial bulbs may produce daughter bulbs as axillary buds and in some, e.g. *Tulipa* and *Oxalis* (Fig. 202), "dropper bulbs" may be produced at the tips of downwardly growing, axillary, rhizomatous branches.

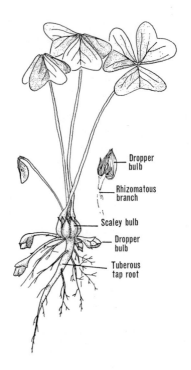

FIG. 202. Plant of *Oxalis* sp., showing how dropper bulbs are produced at the ends of rhizomatous branches.

Bulbils

These are axillary buds which become fleshy owing to storage of food materials and which fall with the plant, root, and give rise to new plants. Plants which produce bulbils and those which propagate by means of detached adventitious buds are said to be adventitious.

Bulbils occur in the axils of the leaves in the orange lily, *Lilium bulbiferum*, and in *Remusatia vivipara*, an epiphytic member of the Araceae which rarely flowers. They are formed in place of flowers in some species of onion, *Allium*, in *Globba* (Zingiberaceae) and in members of the American and Australian family Agavaceae (Fig. 193). Several European alpine species, e.g. the grasses *Festuca ovina* v. *vivipara* and *Poa alpina* and the alpine *Polygonum*, *Polygonum viviparum*, reproduce by bulbils, the production of which is probably correlated with the short growing season.

In sisal, *Agave sisalana*, *A. americana* (Fig. 193) and Mauritius hemp, *Furcraea gigantea*, a single inflorescence may be replaced by hundreds of bulbils which closely resemble bulbs but are distinguishable from the latter by their green colour and the absence, when on the plant, of adventitious roots.

Pseudobulbs

Pseudobulbs are green tuberous growths involving part or the whole of stems or branches in Orchidaceae e.g. *Bulbophyllum* (Fig. 203). New shoots arise as branches in the axils of scales at the base of the pseudobulbs and may themselves form pseudobulbs so that a chain of green tubers connected by segments of stem is produced.

Suckers and Off-sets (Off-shoots)

Suckers and off-sets constitute an unsatisfactory and arbitrary class of organs of perennation. They may be defined as branches or stems which develop one or more nodes before the terminal bud forms a new, though not immediately independent, plant with adventitious roots. Suckers originate below ground and develop only a few nodes, if more than one, before emerging above ground, whereas off-sets originate at or above ground level. In a single plant, e.g. sisal, every intergrade between the two structures may exist.

Suckers usually arise in the axils of scale leaves on subterranean stem bases or rhizomes but sometimes originate from adventitious buds on roots. Suckers occur in banana and plantain, *Musa* spp., and in bamboos, *Bambusa* spp., in all of which they arise from a short rhizome; in sisal and other Agavaceae both suckers and off-sets occur; in pine-apple, *Ananas comosa*, off-sets develop in the axils of the lower leaves and if covered by soil may be termed suckers; in the date palm, *Phoenix dactylifera*, clumps of suckers or off-sets develop if the tree is untended. Finally the floating water cabbage, *Pistia stratiotes* (Fig. 89) affords an example of organs which are not readily classified because of the habitat of the plant: short propagative side branches which might be termed suckers or off-sets.

Runners and Stolons

The terms runner and stolon are often used as synonyms. The term stolon is, however, sometimes used for an underground runner. In other usage stolon is used for a branch arising at some distance above the ground but touching ground and rooting at its tip as in the blackberry, *Rubus*, whereas runner is used for the appropriate structure running on the soil surface. This confusion of terminology seems irresolvable and it is here suggested that, if the term stolon is retained at all, it should be used as a synonym of runner.

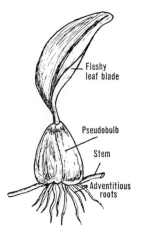

FIG. 203. *Bulbophyllum* sp. An epiphytic orchid in which the nodes are swollen for food storage (pseudobulbs).

Runners are axillary buds which arise at or above ground level and have many nodes. At certain of the nodes a new plant is formed by the growth of an axillary bud and of adventitious roots. This becomes independent on the death of the runner on each side.

The distinction between runners and off-sets is not sharp. Off-sets are in fact short runners, with few nodes, the terminal bud of which gives rise to a single new plant.

Good examples of runners are afforded by the purple leguminous plant, *Desmodium triflorum*; the sweet potato, *Ipomoea batatas* (Fig. 204); many species of *Lamium* and several grasses.

Creeping Stems

Unbranched creeping stems can be regarded as a means of vegetative propagation only in cases where they root at the nodes and become severed from the plant. Where branching occurs at a node and the normal habit of the plant is prostrate, there is no true distinction between a creeping stem and a runner. Thus the common blue-flowered weeds *Commelina benghalensis* and *C. nudiflora*, both natives of East Africa, and the similar purple-flowered, American spiderwort, *Tradescantia virginica*, which is cultivated throughout the world, are, except for the inflorescence stalks, prostrate and root frequently at the nodes where branching occurs.

FIG. 204. Runner and root tubers of sweet potato, *Ipomoea batatas*.
From Irvine.

If a branch, together with the adventitious roots at the node of origin, is considered to constitute a new plant (and it can give rise to a new plant if severed) the creeping stem should be called a runner. Another example is thus afforded of the arbitrary and unsatisfactory nature of the commonly used terminology.

The sea-side goat's foot convolvulus, *Ipomoea biloba*, is a common species on tropical shores which has creeping stems.

Hibernacula (Turions)

Hibernacula or turions are apical buds which become detached and effect vegetative propagation. These occur in the pond weed *Elodea canadensis* and account for the extraordinarily rapid increase of this plant, which bears usually only female flowers, when introduced into Britain. They occur also in *Hydrocharis* (Old World) and *Stratiotes* (Europe and N.W. Asia), water weeds which, with *Elodea*, belong to the Hydrocharitaceae.

L

The turion of *Hydrocharis* is made up of scale leaves which are morphologically stipules and it possesses rudimentary adventitious roots. The turion sinks to the bottom in winter owing to the weight of starch accumulated in the tissues. There it hibernates and on the return of favourable conditions it floats to the surface because of the formation of gas bubbles as a result of the renewal of photosynthesis and increased respiration. It then develops into a normal plant.

Adventitious Buds

Buds which develop in positions other than the stem apices and in the axils of leaves are said to be adventitious.

Adventitious buds arising on the margins or damaged surfaces of leaves in some plants are effective means of vegetative propagation. They are numerous on the tubular leaves of the succulent *Kalanchoe* (Crassulaceae) (Fig. 205). In this species they are easily detached when mature

Fig. 205. Tubular leaf of *Kalanchoe* bearing adventitious buds with adventitious roots.

and bear long, fine adventitious roots while still attached. In the crenate-leaved *Bryophyllum pinnatum* (Crassulaceae) (Fig. 206), there is a region of persistent meristematic tissue in each notch of the leaf margins and each is capable of giving rise, when the leaf falls, to a small plant. The petioles have a special abscission zone and the leaf is easily detached by a small pressure while still fresh and succulent. The young plants are nourished by the leaf until they are well established. The leaves of some *Begonia* spp. act similarly.

Propagation by adventitious buds is found in other Crassulaceae and in those species in which it occurs is, perhaps, the most effective mode of reproduction. Nevertheless, these species produce viable seeds and the reddish inflorescences of the species mentioned are a common sight in gardens in the tropics. Flowering terminates the life of an individual plant.

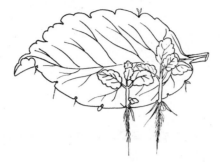

FIG. 206. Fallen leaf of *Bryophyllum pinnatum* producing small plants on the margin.

CHAPTER 16

Vegetation Types and Plant Communities

VEGETATION TYPES

Individual species of flowering plants are usually adapted to a fairly narrow range of habitats, particularly with regard to water supply. Later we will deal with the four chief vegetation types which are distinguishable on the basis of their water requirements. These are xerophytes, mesophytes, hydrophytes and halophytes. Vegetation types can also be distinguished in relation to their nutrition, there being in flowering plants both autotrophes and heterotrophes. The latter include saprophytes and parasites. A further class of plants is recognized in terms of their situation, those growing on other plants but not parasitizing them being termed epiphytes.

Xerophytes

Xerophytes are terrestrial plants which live in regions where they are normally subject to prolonged and severe drought. Typically they are plants of deserts or semi-deserts but plants of other regions where water is difficult to obtain should be included. Examples of the latter are alpine plants, which live in mountainous places where water in the soil, though abundant, may be frozen and therefore unavailable.

James (1936) has divided xerophytes into three classes, each with its own peculiar way of surviving drought. These classes are: (1) drought evaders, which pass through the drought as seeds and grow only during the short period when rain is sufficient; (2) succulents, which store large quantities of water and transpire very slowly; and (3) drought endurers, which are divisible into: (a) deep-rooted forms which transpire rapidly but are able to tap the water which usually occurs, even in arid regions, at great depths; and (b) shallow-rooted forms, which survive by virtue

316

of the ability of their protoplasm to recover from almost complete drying. Of these classes it will be seen that the only ones which are capable of surviving as mature plants in conditions where water is not available to the roots over long periods are succulents and shallow-rooted drought endurers.

The most familiar succulents to students living in Africa and India are succulent members of the great genus *Euphorbia*. In America the dominant succulents are the cacti. Both groups have evolved many points of similarity, although the flowers in particular remain, of course, very different. In both groups the leaves are transient and the body of the plant consists of a thick succulent cladode covered with spines (Figs. 103, 116). In *Euphorbia* the spines are in pairs and are derived from stipules, while in cacti they are possibly derived from leaves and are borne on rounded prominences termed areoles. The succulence of *Euphorbia* is associated with the presence of a milky, viscous sap or "latex" (it has been said that a *Euphorbia* is like a cow—it has two horns and exudes milk!) while the sap of a cactus, although viscous, is colourless. Evaporation of water from these succulents is greatly reduced because colloids in the sap hold water by imbibition. Other features which retard evaporation of water are the bulkiness of the cladode, in other words its small surface area/volume or weight ratio and structural modifications such as the location of the stomata at the bases of pits and the development of a thick external cuticle. The rate of transpiration of an *Opuntia* cactus was found experimentally to be only one-thirtieth of that from an equal area of a thin leaf and a cactus kept in a laboratory, without once being watered, lost only one-third of its original moisture in 6 years. Cacti are shallow-rooted and in the dry season uptake of water ceases.

We may now list those characteristics which are commonly possessed by xerophytes. They are:

1. Reduction or early loss of the leaves and development of cladodes which have a small surface area/bulk ratio and hence lower the rate of transpiration relative to leafy plants. Cladodes occur in succulents such as *Euphorbia*, cacti, *Stapelia*, *Haworthia*, *Edithcolea*, *Colletia* (Fig. 105) and in some non-succulent types, e.g. *Casuarina* and *Ruscus*.

2. Development of mucilaginous cell sap (e.g. cacti) and also a milky latex (*Euphorbia* and *Colletia*).

3. Thick cutinization of the epidermis and even of underlying cells. This restricts transpiration to the stomata and therefore makes it controllable. This adaptation occurs in most xerophytes.

4. Sunken stomata. The stomata of xerophytes are usually located at the bases of pits, or of grooves, which may be over-arched by the cuticle or by hairs. A higher humidity will develop in the sunken chamber than in the surrounding air and transpiration will therefore be reduced. The drying effects of the wind will also be lessened. Mechanisms for bringing about curling of the leaf, as occur in many grasses, have a similar effect in permitting the development of a higher humidity over the stomata than in the outside air and may be combined with sinking of the stomata. In some plants the stomata are not sunken but transpiration is reduced by extreme hairiness of the leaf.

5. Lignification. The ratio of lignified to photosynthetic cells in the leaves is usually higher in xerophytes than in other plants. Lignification may occur in the epidermis, in cells around the sub-stomatal cavity, in hypodermal cells and in cells, comprising a sclerenchyma, around the vascular bundles. The development of a hypodermis, i.e. one or more layers of cells between the epidermis and the mesophyll, is itself a xerophytic adaptation as it reduces loss of water from the thin-walled mesophyll cells via the epidermis, especially where the hypodermal cells have thickened walls. The development of sclerenchyma around the vessels prevents undue wilting of the leaves.

6. Reduction of leaf area. Even when photosynthesis is not taken over by cladodes, the area for transpiration may be reduced by the development of needle-like leaves which are relatively bulky and have a smaller surface area/weight ratio than flattened, expanded leaves.

The "dry-sclerophyll" vegetation of Australia (p. 323), which includes the genus *Hakea*, demonstrates very well the development of thick cuticle, sunken stomata, lignification and needle-like leaves.

Some plants show many or all of these xerophytic characters and yet are unable to survive drought. To avoid applying the term xerophyte to a plant which possesses the morphological characters of a xerophyte but is not certainly known to be drought-resistant, the term xeromorph has been coined. A xeromorph is thus any plant which possesses the morphological characteristics of a xerophyte. It seems likely, however, that wherever xeromorphic characters occur, they are adaptations to reducing water loss although the plant as a whole may not resist drought.

Halophytes

Halophytes are vascular plants which grow in a medium of high salt content. They usually have their roots in mud which is periodically covered by brackish water or the sea, and the bulk of the shoot system in the air. They are regarded by some workers as true xerophytes. It has been suggested that halophytes have difficulty in obtaining water because of the high osmotic pressure of the medium in which they live. It is clear, however, that this difficulty has been overemphasized as the osmotic pressure of their cell sap is correspondingly high. The latter fact has led to their being regarded as xeromorphs but not xerophytes. Nevertheless, the combination of many characteristics seen in xerophytes in these plants can hardly be accidental and there are some reasons for considering that water may not be readily available despite the high internal osmotic pressure. One reason is that, owing to the fact that the soil in which they grow is often waterlogged, the supply of oxygen to the roots is poor, a condition which might reduce water uptake. Furthermore, the poor oxygenation of the medium is associated with a weak development of the root system in most cases.

Where aerating roots or pneumatophores are developed, as in the mangroves (Fig. 87), the root system is well developed. The thick cuticularization of the leaves in the latter case might conceivably be to prevent removal of water from the leaves by salt deposited on their outer surfaces.

Examples of halophytes are the cosmopolitan genera *Salicornia* and *Suaeda*.

Hydrophytes

Hydrophytes are vascular plants which grow partly or wholly submerged in fresh water. They typically show the following adaptations which are not characteristic of other plants.

1. A cuticle, and stomata, are limited to those parts of the plant which are exposed to the air. Frequently, however, the whole of the plant is submerged so that these structures are completely absent.

2. The epidermis is composed of thin-walled cells which may contain chloroplasts. Through it dissolved gases diffuse.

3. Hydrophytes frequently have aerenchyma, a parenchyma in which there are large interconnected air spaces. These chambers may form a continuous system throughout the plant from leaves to roots. In the stem and leaves the cells between the chambers are photosynthetic (i.e. chlorenchyma). In the leaves of the water lily, *Nymphaea*, the chambers are prevented from collapsing by branched fibres (sclereids). The aerenchyma serves for storage and diffusion of gases and gives buoyancy to the plant, rendering a skeletal system unnecessary.

Carbon dioxide diffuses into the plant in solution through the epidermis and through stomata, if these are present, in gaseous form. Where there are no stomata, depletion of dissolved carbon dioxide in the water in the immediate vicinity of the plant would soon occur and the speed of diffusion of the gas through water would become a limiting factor in photosynthesis. However, except in very soft waters, the bulk of the plant's carbon dioxide is produced by decomposition of bicarbonates in solution in the water in response to removal of carbon dioxide by the plant:

$$Ca(HCO_3)_2 \rightarrow CaCO_3 + H_2O + \boxed{CO_2 \text{ Removed by the plant.}}$$

The calcium carbonate so produced is sometimes visible as a chalky deposit on the outside of the plant. Carbon dioxide produced in respiration is stored in the aerenchyma, particularly at night, and used in photosynthesis during daylight.

4. Reduction of vascular tissue. Since gases and water can diffuse across the epidermis, the root system is reduced, serving mainly for anchorage, there being in many cases no root hairs. With the reduced importance of the xylem elements for conduction of water and solutes, these elements are less numerous or have disappeared. Phloem remains well developed, however, though usually the sieve tubes are less in number and are smaller than in terrestrial plants. Those parts of the shoot system above the water, if there are any, have fairly normal vascular tissue.

5. Lignification is reduced or absent as the skeletal function of xylem and sclerenchyma is assumed by buoyancy of the tissues. Aerial parts of the plant, if present, may possess well developed sclerenchyma and other supporting tissues, however.

Mesophytes

Mesophytes are plants which require a moderate water supply throughout the year. They do not normally show any of the adaptations which are characteristic of xerophytes and hydrophytes. Their leaves typically have broad, thin laminae. A cuticle, though present, is typically thin. The stomata are not normally sunken. The leaves therefore wilt easily and the wilting is enhanced by the poor development of sclerenchymatous and other supporting tissues relative to those of xeromorphic leaves. The cytoplasm of mesophytes lacks the ability to recover from severe drying and they usually lack other physiological adaptations for withstanding drought, such as the secretion of latex. They lack aerenchyma and the roots, and other parts, are usually killed, mainly as a result of oxygen-lack, if submerged for long periods in water.

PLANT COMMUNITIES

The species of plants which are adapted to the conditions of a given region make up a plant community. The prevailing conditions vary with latitude and altitude, which in turn affect the climate; with the type of soil; and with regard to the activities of man and other animals. The plant community may be referred to as a climatic formation when its nature is determined primarily by climate; an edaphic formation where the type of soil causes significant modification of the type of vegetation (as happens on limestone soils in Europe); and an anthropogenic formation where it owes its particular make-up to the activities of man. Climate is the major factor in determining the type of community as it directly affects the metabolic processes of the plant and modifies the soil-type and influences human activities. The type of community which develops in a given climate if undisturbed by man is known as the climatic climax, e.g. tropical rain forest. The same type of community in different parts of the world may, of course, contain wholly different species.

Because climate changes with latitude, it is understandable that the climatic climaxes form fairly distinct vegetation belts passing latitudinally around the world, with their borders coinciding with major discontinuities of climate. The uniformity of climate and therefore of a vegetation belt is, however, modified by ocean currents, the presence of mountains, and other geographical features and these, with variations in edaphic and anthropogenic and other factors, account for the blurring of the boundaries and mixed nature of the belts which in fact exists. We will deal in the following account only with some of the major types of plant communities of the tropics.

Tropical Rain Forest

Tropical rain forest occurs in the lowlands of the tropics where the annual rainfall is high and there is no distinct dry season. Among the countries in which it occurs are South America, tropical Africa and India, Malaysia, Indonesia, New Guinea and Queensland. Near the equator, where temperature and rainfall are high throughout the year, dense forest may develop on poor soil, but nearer the limits of the tropics it develops only where the soil is fertile. Tropical rain forest is characteristically evergreen. The number of species of trees is very much greater than in temperate-zone woodland and, whereas in the latter one or two species are usually dominant, in tropical rain forest no one tree species is dominant by itself. The trees usually have straight, columnar trunks, frequently with buttress roots, and their branches and foliage are typically borne near the upper part where the light is more intense. The foliage of the different species form several tiers or stories, frequently three. The trees of the upper, dominant, tier are sufficiently close together for their crowns of foliage to touch so that a closed canopy is formed; the same is true of the second tier but the lower tier forms an open canopy, in which the trees are not in contact. Because the sun is overhead at midday, more light penetrates through the canopies than would be possible in temperate regions. Nevertheless, the amount of light reaching the ground is often sufficient only for a few specialized plants including colourless saprophytic angiosperms. Many plants are adapted to raising their leaves to the light by climbing and their thick, woody twisted stems and branches loop and trail between the trees. These are lianas or vines and they include aroids, climbing palms (of which the rattans of the Malayan region, which belong chiefly to the genus *Calamus*, are well known examples), climbing bamboos and, in South America, members of the Bignoniaceae, including *Bignonia unguis-cati* which is illustrated in Fig. 121. The trunks and branches of the trees bear and are often almost completely concealed by epiphytes, chiefly ferns, such as *Platycerium*, the staghorn or elephant's ear fern, orchids, and, in South America, members of the pine-apple family, Bromeliaceae. Parasitic plants are also more common than in temperate-zone forests, but are much less common than epiphytes. Flowers are not a conspicuous feature of tropical rain forest. This is not because they are not abundant but because flowering is spread over the year, there are few herbs or low plants to bear flowers, and the flowers of the epiphytes and trees are commonly hidden by the dense foliage.

Monsoon Forest

We have seen that true tropical rain forest develops in regions where the rainfall and temperature are high and fairly uniform throughout the year. Greater areas of the tropics experience one or two dry seasons, however. Where the rainfall is high (about 40 in.) during the wet season, a tall monsoon forest may develop. It is not, however, as tall or as luxuriant as tropical rain forest, buttress roots are usually absent, and the number of species of trees is less. During the dry season much of the foliage is shed except along river courses; flowering occurs mainly at this time. Because of the seasonal rainfall, the trees have annual rings, as in temperate woods where the ring formation is controlled by temperature.

Vegetation in Drier Regions

In drier regions, with more arid or longer dry seasons, the monsoon forest is replaced by xerophilous ("dry-loving") woodlands which consist predominantly either of evergreen or of deciduous trees, or maybe a mixture of these. The canopy is single-tiered and, if closed, is sparse and may be open. In either case it allows much light through to the ground. A sparse ground covering of herbs may develop in the rainy season or there may be a permanent cover of xerophytic woody herbs or low shrubs. Plants which pass over the dry season as bulbs, tubers or other perennating organs may be common.

Xerophilous and monsoon forest are probably the climatic climax vegetation of vast areas of tropical Africa and India and much savanna (defined below) is probably an anthropogenic formation which replaces them and is conditioned by seasonal burning-off by man. In evidence of this, savanna which is protected from fire, and from erosion by cattle, will often develop into woodland. Savanna intergrades spatially with xerophilous woodland and closely resembles it, but the trees, which are reduced to relatively few species of which thorny members of the Mimosacae, e.g. *Acacia*, predominate, are lower and more widely spaced and their crowns are rarely in contact. During the wet season grasses and other herbs cover the ground. In drier conditions, or where man and his domestic animals have destroyed vegetation and caused erosion, grasses and other ground cover become sparse and the trees may be replaced (in Africa and Asia) by giant, branched, succulent *Euphorbias*, the equivalent of the cacti of arid regions in the Americas. Finally, in extremely dry conditions, only a few xerophytes (e.g. *Stapelia*), at most, survive; such regions are termed deserts.

In tropical Australia in regions with about 10–30 in. of rain per annum, and light soils, savanna occurs in which the dominant trees are relatively tall *Eucalyptus* spp. and *Acacia* spp. Here "grass trees" of the genus *Xanthorrhoea* are frequent. Xerophilous forest in Australia, known as dry sclerophyllous woodland because of the sclerenchymatous nature of the leaves of many of the shrubs, is unusual in supporting very tall trees mainly of the genera *Eucalyptus* and *Angophora*, the leaf blades of which are vertical, an adaptation which reduces exposure to the sun's rays. In this woodland shrubs and woody herbs of a sclerophyllous type are exceedingly abundant, both in numbers of species and of individuals, but true herbs are not common. Dry sclerophyll occurs even in regions with more than 40 in. of rain spread fairly uniformly throughout the year where soils are sandy and consequently have little water-holding capacity and low fertility. In the same areas, rain forest may occur, where the soil is derived from shales or basalt. These soils are more fertile, have better water-holding capacities and, in the case of shales, are often moistened by subterranean seepage. Even in subtropical districts such as the southern part of New South Wales, this rain forest resembles tropical rain forest.

Mountain Vegetation

The vegetation of tropical mountains usually forms a striking contrast with that of the surrounding lowlands. This is particularly the case where high mountains rise abruptly from plains which are arid and bear desert or semi-desert vegetation or savanna. No better examples of these could be found than the mountains of East Africa such as Ruwenzori, Kilimanjaro, Kenya and Elgon. On these mountains a very conspicuous altitudinal zonation is found, a vegetation belt over one range of altitudes giving way remarkably abruptly to quite different types of vegetation above and below it. The vegetation zones differ little on all of these mountains and Ruwenzori will be taken as an example. The savanna of the arid plains, which lie at about 3000 ft, gives way on the lower slopes of the foothills to a narrow band of very dense elephant grass, *Pennisetum*. Above this is a broad zone of mountain forest which at about 8000 ft becomes interspersed with bamboos and gives place to a zone consisting predominantly of bamboo at about 9000 ft. The bamboo continues to about 10,000 ft when a mossy forest of which the dominant flowering plants are giant groundsels (*Senecio*), averaging about 20 ft in height, giant heaths (Ericaceae), forming tall trees, and huge *Lobelias* with flowering spikes about 15 ft high. In this mossy forest, rocks and trees alike are thickly cushioned by mosses and liverworts and the trees are festooned with pendant lichens. Shrubs such as *Hypericum* and the blackberry, *Rubus*, are common. In exposed places *Senecios* predominate and their trunks may be prostrate. Above the mossy forest, a tussocky grassland develops over which are dotted the *Senecios* which give it the superficial appearance of a high altitude savanna. At about 13,000 ft the most conspicuous plant is a woody herb or shrub, the everlasting flower, *Helichrysum*, few other flowering plants being present. This continues to near the snow line at about 14,000 ft.

This altitudinal zonation is due chiefly to the effect of increasing altitude on rainfall and temperature. Temperature decreases fairly uniformly with increasing altitude (about 3°F for every 1000 ft), but the situation with regard to rainfall is more complex. Air from the hot plains rises to the peaks of the mountains as shown by the presence of deposits of ash from bush fires in the glaciers. As it rises it cools and its capacity for holding water vapour therefore decreases. Clouds and rain are consequently formed. The lower and middle heights of the mountain therefore experience a high rainfall which, in the case of the East African mountains, is far higher than that of the surrounding arid plains. The mountain rain forest occurs in this zone. Higher up, mists are prevalent but the air has less moisture to give up and the total precipitation of water on the terrain is less, low temperatures prevent growth of plants of lower regions, and cause the development of a "mor" acid humus. It is here that *Senecio* and *Helichrysum* develop.

The trees of mountain forest are not as high as those of tropical rain forest, the canopy is more open and only two tiers, if tiering is apparent, develop. Fewer different species of trees are present and lianas are less frequent. Tree ferns may occur and a shrubby undergrowth is often present which does not occur in well developed lowland rain forest. The mossy forest of higher altitudes corresponds roughly with the mossy elfin forest which develops above the mountain rain forest in, for instance, the Philippines and which is characterized by the predominance of prostrate, twisted trees.

In West Africa, in the Cameroons, tropical rain forest extends up to about 3300 ft. In this mountain forest occurs the tree fern *Alsophila camerunensis*. Between 6500 and 9900 ft woody plants are absent and the terrain may be described as a grassy prairie. This is followed by an alpine prairie, between 9900 and 11,500 ft, which is rich in genera found at low altitudes and in temperate countries, including scabious, geraniums, violets and clematis. Here, also, a few lobelias occur but groundsels, found on East African mountains, are absent. Above 12,500 ft. few species grow; they include grasses, rushes, mosses and lichens.

A somewhat similar zonation occurs in tropical India where, again, the savannas or rain forest of the plains give way to hill forests. In the latter, the trees are again generally less tall than in the lowland rain forest, tree ferns occur at higher elevations and epiphytic orchids and bryophytes may be abundant. Shrubs of the genus *Strobilanthes* are common in some places.

In the western Himalayas, in the Indian subtropics, altitudinal zonation occurs which resembles the latitudinal zonation which occurs in a northward direction. Thus above a height of 3000 ft the characteristically Indian vegetation gives way to "warm temperate" forest containing oaks, elms, walnut, poplar and horse chestnut trees. Above 7000 ft a "cool temperate" coniferous forest develops. Above 11,500 ft birches, typical of far northern latitudes, occur but a specialized and somewhat xeromorphic alpine vegetation, including junipers and rhododendrons, co-exists with them. The moister, eastern Himalayas support a different vegetation.

Index

(Numbers in *italic* refer to pages which include an illustration of the item listed.)

327